THE BILBURY REVELS

THE
BILBURY
REVELS

Vernon Coleman

Chilton Design Publishers

First published in the United Kingdom, 1994,
by Chilton Designs Publishers,
Preston House, Kentisbury, Barnstaple, Devon EX31 4NH, England.
Copyright Vernon Coleman 1994

A catalogue record for this book is available from the British Library.

ISBN: 1 898146 05 5

Printed in Great Britain at The Bath Press, Avon

Dedicated to

Barrie and Pat Tracey,
honorary Bilburians and ever welcome visitors
to the village.

CHAPTER ONE

The snow in Bilbury was deep and crisp but it definitely wasn't even. The wind had seen to that. The wind that scours the North Devon coast, shaping trees and moulding hedgerows, removing roofs and whipping up the sea, isn't one of those balmy south coast breezes. It's a tough, unwavering, unrelenting, real god of a wind. In my first autumn in Bilbury I had noticed that the moment the leaves on the trees started to turn brown and die the wind whisked them off to the East. Even our walled garden was magically emptied of leaves within days. The wind is so fierce that rain in Bilbury doesn't fall vertically; it comes in from the West, driven horizontally and finding its way through invisible hair line cracks in door and window frames.

It had started snowing late the previous evening, just as Patsy and I were getting ready for bed. I'd gone outside to take Ben, our Welsh collie, out for her customary late night potter around the garden and had seen the first few delicate flakes floating gently down out of the moonlit blackness above.

It had clearly not been snowing for more than a few minutes for there were still no more than a few flakes on the ground, and no sign as yet that this was going to be serious snow. I checked that our four pet sheep were safely tucked up in their stable, laid down extra straw, gave them enough hay to see them through the night and then shut the bottom half of their stable door and dropped the kick bolt. I left the top half of the door open. They hated being shut in the dark and the moon was their nightlight. They had grown good, thick fleeces since the summer and snuggled down in the straw, protected from the wind and the wet, they looked warm and content.

*   *   *

1

The snow must have fallen heavily all night for when we awoke the following morning the whole world had turned white. I tied the cord around my dressing gown, pulled back the bedroom curtains and stared in amazement at the view. It had been a long time since I'd seen such a heavy snow fall. It was impossible to see where the lawn ended and the driveway began and the small stone sundial we'd bought at an auction in Hatherleigh was now just a snowy white lump. Tree boughs, laden with snow, were bent down with their burdens and I made a mental note to go outside after breakfast and clear as many of them as I could before they broke.

Ben, who had as usual slept at the foot of our bed, came over to the window, jumped up on the window seat, rested her front paws on the window sill and stared for a moment at the curious world outside. She looked up at me, looked outside again and barked twice, clearly asking me what on earth had happened. One of our two cats, Sophie, ears pricked at the sudden noise, looked up from where she was curled at Patsy's feet, contented herself that she wasn't missing anything and yawned lazily before burying her nose back underneath her tail and going straight back to sleep.

I stroked Ben's head to reassure her that there was nothing for her to worry about and then lit the fire I'd laid the previous evening in the bedroom fireplace. Although we had an AGA in the kitchen which kept us supplied with endless quantities of hot water and which produced so much heat that it kept the whole house above freezing, we didn't have any central heating at Bilbury Grange, and certainly couldn't afford to have any installed, so we kept ourselves warm by lighting wood fires in the rooms we used most: the living room, the hall, our bedroom and the bathroom. We were still burning the old wooden laths that Thumper had taken off when he had repaired our roof and they made excellent fire lighters. To supplement this store of wood I had spent much of the autumn collecting, sawing and storing branches that had been blown down in the fields that surrounded our home. The wind that brought the cold, the rain and the snow had also given us much of our firewood. The breath of god which took away warmth and comfort also gave us back those things.

I had grown well accustomed to our idiosyncratic fireplaces

and each has its own peculiar likes and dislikes. Give one too much paper and it will blaze into a moment of glory but give out little or no heat. Put too large a log onto another before it's ready and the promise of heat will disappear in an instant.

The bedroom fireplace was easy to satisfy and so efficient that we could even burn wood with the sap in it if we wanted to, though most of our firewood was well dried. Three or four sheets of crumpled newspaper topped with two layers of roofing laths were the basis of a good fire. I lit the paper with a match in two opposing corners, stood back for two or three minutes and then dropped a small well seasoned ash log onto the flames; just big enough to keep the fire going until we were both washed and dressed. The ash tree had stood in a corner of one of our fields for nigh on sixty years before it had finally succumbed to the executioner wind.

'Why was Ben barking?' asked Patsy, pushing herself up onto one elbow but keeping the quilted counterpane up around her shoulders.

'It's been snowing.'

'Are we snowed in?'

'Yes. At least I think so. It looks pretty thick.'

Patsy's response might have sounded strange to a city dweller. 'Wonderful!' she said, meaning it. We had good stocks of food in the larder and cellar and plenty of logs in the shed. Even if the electricity went off, which it usually did two or three times a week in winter when the wind brought down overhead cables, we could stay warm and well fed. We had plenty of hay and straw for the sheep, a good supply of books to read and Bilbury Grange had a strong roof. We were well prepared for snow or storm.

'I'm going to have to go outside and knock the snow off some of the evergreens,' I told her. 'A couple of the conifers already look as if their branches may have broken under the weight.' The deciduous trees, their branches stark and leafless, were in no danger but the conifers, the rhododendrons, the yew, the laurel, the holly and many others needed help.

'I'll cook us a decent breakfast first,' said Patsy, throwing back the eiderdown, getting out of bed and walking over to the window. She stood for a brief moment or two then shivered. You could feel the cold through the glass. She ran back to warm herself at the now blazing fire, picking up her dressing gown as she did so. Then she knelt down, stared at the flames and rubbed her hands together while I filled the bedroom sink with hot water, stripped off to the waist and washed and shaved. When I'd finished and before I started dressing I filled the bowl with fresh, hot water for Patsy. The steam rose from the sink in great clouds and I blessed the AGA for the umpteenth time. Huge, solid and imperturbable the boiler asked only that we fed it regularly on its twice daily diet of coke. In return it worked quietly and efficiently to protect us from the worst of the cold. Steam condensed on the windows and the beautiful snowy landscape outside gradually disappeared from view.

I pulled on a pair of thick jeans, a woollen work shirt which I'd bought from a farm supply shop in South Molton and a thick jumper which Patsy's mother had made for me with wool she'd spun herself from their own sheep. The wool was still coated with the sheep's natural oils and the sweater was heavy but cosy and waterproof.

Downstairs I pushed my feet into Wellington boots and pulled a floppy, old tweed fishing hat down over my ears. I didn't fish but had found the hat in a cupboard underneath the stairs. It was slightly too large for me but I didn't mind because that meant that it covered more of my head than a more fashionable fitting hat would have done. I then opened the back door and went out to check that the sheep were all right.

*   *   *

A few minutes later, back in the kitchen, I took off my sweater and boots and padded around in my stockinged feet. Sophie and Emily, our two cats, had both finished their breakfasts and were curled up together on the rug in front of the AGA. In the winter they avoided the cold by finding somewhere warm to sleep, curling up together and shutting out whatever horrors the weather might bring. In the summer, if the sun was out, they avoided the heat by finding somewhere cool to sleep. They had a simple but effective way of dealing with whatever problems life threw at them.

'Are the sheep O.K.?'

'They're fine. They want to know why they can't go out but they're fine.' They had baaared at me and playfully butted me when I had refused to open up their stable door to let them out. Their protests hadn't lasted long, however. They had soon tucked into the fresh supply of hay I'd given them.

I fed Ben, who wagged her tail in thanks and then immediately started eating. I had had to bite my tongue not to laugh at her antics in the snow; the first she'd ever encountered. She had rubbed her nose in it, licked it, spat it out, tried again and swallowed some. Then she had run round and round in tiny circles, kicking up great fluffy clouds of snow and finally spluttering to a halt in a small two foot thick drift.

Sophie and Emily had been far more circumspect. Sophie had poked her head through the cat flap which Thumper had fitted for us and had taken a long hard look at the white world on the other side of the door before gingerly poking a front leg through to test the temperature of the outside world. With her three other legs still in the house, and her head and body sheltered by the cat flap from the lightly falling snow, Sophie had paused, frozen in mid movement, before carefully retreating back into the kitchen. She had obviously decided that whatever it was she was planning to do outside could wait until the world had returned to normal.

'I've made us porridge to start with,' said Patsy, putting two huge bowls onto the table and ladling porridge out of an old iron pan which her mother had given her, and which had been warming gently on the AGA top. 'There's syrup on the table.' Two huge mugs of steaming tea were already poured.

I used the handle of a tablespoon to open the syrup tin and then put two huge spoons of syrup into the centre of my bowl of porridge. Whatever the Scots may say I like syrup on my porridge. I can't abide the thought of eating it laced with salt.

'Mushrooms?' asked Patsy, a few minutes later as I tipped a hod of coke into the AGA.

'Yes, please!'

'Eggs?'

'Two.'

'Poached, fried or scrambled?'

'Scrambled, please.'

'Tomatoes?'

'Oh, yes please!'

'How many slices of toast?'

'One with the eggs on, one with the tomatoes on and two to have with marmalade afterwards.'

Patsy had made her own marmalade in the autumn, using a recipe handed down from her grandmother, and it was much thicker, tangier and tastier than any mass-produced competitor I've ever tasted. She had made a minor mistake with the quantities and had made 54 lbs of it but I wasn't complaining, although there had been quite a run on jam jars in the village at a time when every woman in every house and cottage was busy making jam. (In addition to the marmalade Patsy had made 17 lbs of gooseberry jam, 44 lbs of strawberry jam, 38 lbs of blackberry and apple jam, 67 lbs of blackcurrant jam and 45 lbs of rhubarb and tomato chutney plus smaller quantities of other jams! Only the discovery of a large cache of jars in a dark corner of the cellar had solved our jam jar shortage).

I put the empty coke hod down by the back door so that it was ready for refilling after breakfast, picked up the cats' bowls, which were empty, and rinsed them in the sink, and then got two large plates out of the crockery cupboard, two knives and two forks out of the cutlery drawer and a jar of Patsy's rhubarb and tomato chutney out of the larder. Breakfast didn't usually consist of anything much more than toast and marmalade and tea or coffee but I was looking forward to this morning's feast.

Twenty minutes later, I sat back with a sigh and wiped a few remaining crumbs from around my mouth. I glanced out of the kitchen window into the courtyard. It was still snowing. The sky was now as white as everywhere else and the snow was now clearly here to stay for a while. Just then the kitchen light went out. It didn't really matter, it was now light enough to see quite well without it, but we were now really on our own. The electricity had just failed.

*   *   *

It took the two of us an hour and a half to go around the garden using long sticks to knock the worst of the snow off the bushes and the lower branches of all the evergreen trees. There were still a few conkers left clinging to the upper branches of one of our largest horsechestnut trees and periodically the additional weight of the ice with which they were coated brought these

6

crashing down through the snow laden boughs. Sophie and Emily had sensibly stayed indoors but Ben had, of course, come out with us. Nothing would keep Ben indoors if Patsy and I were going out. She danced around barking and snapping at the falling snow, dodging first this way and then that to avoid each fresh mini avalanche.

We checked the vegetable garden, the greenhouse and all the outbuildings and then walked around the house to make sure that the wind had not done any damage. It hadn't, though it was still blowing hard. The snow had been blown into deep drifts on the windward side of every wall and Ben had great fun throwing herself into each fresh, virginal snow-bank.

Using an old pick axe I started to break the ice on the water butts, the pond and the lake. Around the lake I had to help a dozen gulls free themselves from where they had settled down the night before to sleep. The birds' feet had frozen to the ground around the edge of the lake. The ice on the lake was no more than half an inch thick but it still took quite a lot of hammering to break. I used a long handled pick axe to clear an area about ten foot long and three foot wide on the lake and nearly fell in trying to reach out further. In the vegetable garden the water butts seemed to have frozen solid and the ice was impossible to break. The snow there was crisscrossed with animal tracks: the large, five toed track of a badger, the bizarre, jumping track of a squirrel and the tracks of a dozen other animals: moles, rabbits, mice and maybe (I wasn't sure) even a hedgehog.

I had lined two old wooden seed trays with newspaper and was filling them with earth from inside the greenhouse so that the cats could use them as litter trays when Patsy, who was rummaging around at the far end of the greenhouse, suddenly produced two large, old, shallow metal trays.

'What on earth do you want those for?' I asked her. The trays had once been painted green and were too shallow for any practical purpose I could think of.

Patsy grinned at me, rather sheepishly.

'How long is it since you went tobogganing?' she asked.

'Tobogganing? I can't remember. Years and years.'

'Come on then!' cried Patsy. She came up behind me and

pushed me towards the greenhouse door. 'These'll make terrific toboggans.'

We stopped off at the house to leave the two litter trays for Emily and Sophie (both of whom poked their noses through the kitchen doorway, sniffed again at the snow, and then ran back indoors to the rug in front of the AGA) and then carried our tin trays over to the long, steep hill in Tumbrill's Meadow. We spent the next two hours playing in the snow like a couple of carefree children.

We went back to the house as the wind started to blow stronger and the snow came down heavier than before. The sky was heavy and dark and from past experience I knew we were in for a long and bitter night. Before we went in I walked round the house and closed the shutters over all the windows, fastening them tightly against the coming storm.

*   *   *

Our bathroom at Bilbury Grange has two huge, cast iron baths side by side. While water gushed out from the four huge taps I lit a wood fire and threw on some twigs of rosemary. The bathroom fireplace works well and within minutes there was a blaze big enough to take the chill off the room. Patsy and I undressed and, as the fire crackled and roared and the air filled with the fragrant smell of burning rosemary wood, we each climbed into a bath and soaked our aching bodies in water so hot that we could only just bear it. Our wet clothes lay tumbled together in a soggy mass on the bathroom floor while huge bath towels (bought at a sale when a country house hotel went bankrupt and the receivers sold the contents at auction) warmed in front of the fire on a Victorian wooden towel rail.

Outside the wind was beginning to build up again and it was clear that the sky had told the truth. It was going to be another stormy night. The window panes were now opaque with condensed steam.

There was, I felt, something strangely, irresistibly decadent about having a bath in the middle of a Monday afternoon when all decent God fearing men and women should be at work, hunched over desk or machine, brows anxiously furrowed and eyes for ever glancing towards the clock.

A spark shot out from the fire, landed in the puddle of water that had seeped from our clothes and expired with a hiss. Ben, lying a yard or two away from it, lifted her head and pricked up her ears. Satisfied that nothing had happened for her to worry about, or to protect us against, she lay her head back down again between her paws and rested, with one eye half open, half on guard. Sophie and Emily, curled together as usual, didn't move a whisker. I lay back, closed my eyes and floated in my bath.

*　　*　　*

It seemed a lifetime ago since I'd first arrived in North Devon and although, in truth, it was no more than a few years, I could hardly remember the life I'd had before I'd found Bilbury.

I had come to the village, soon after I'd qualified from medical school, to work as an assistant to Dr Brownlow, the ageing and much loved local general practitioner. I had exchanged asphyxiating traffic fumes, endless rules, regulations and restrictions, and a glass and concrete skyline for country air, real responsibility, and a skyline dominated by trees, hills and storm-tossed, white-crested waves.

When Dr Brownlow had unexpectedly decided to retire (after a water diviner had discovered an underground stream on his land and Dr Brownlow had decided to open a bottling plant) I had, with some initial diffidence, taken on the practice myself and by the time bureaucrats and administrators made the decision to close the practice down and amalgamate it with a bigger medical practice in Barnstaple I had met and married Patsy.

By then we had bought and started to renovate Bilbury Grange. Bilbury had become my home and I loved the village and the life we had started to create for ourselves there more than the medical career I'd originally chosen. Without hesitation I had made the decision to stay in Bilbury and to try to earn my living as a writer.

I was nervously waiting to receive the finished copies of my first book. With the books should come the final instalment of my advance royalty. The £250 cheque, a third of the total advance, would be very welcome. The first third had been paid when I signed the contract to write the book. The second instalment, another £250, had been paid when I had delivered the typescript of the book.

Since I had retired from general practice our only regular income had come from the weekly medical column I wrote, which was syndicated to several local newspapers in different towns around the country. We had supplemented this modest income by selling fruit and vegetables from our garden, by renting out the small flat in our courtyard to holiday-makers during the summer months and by going to local house clearance auctions, finding old books and selling them on to a dealer in London. I had hoped to be able to earn a little more money by writing articles, features and stories for other newspapers and magazines but I had found it harder going than I had anticipated. Although I'd written a dozen pieces I'd sold only two: a short story to a local paper in London and an article about infectious diseases to a womens' magazine.

Outside Bilbury Grange the incoming snow was now being hurled against the house by a constantly increasing and ferocious westerly wind. The bathroom, lit only by the flickering flames from the open log fire, was cosily romantic. The wind whistled through the slits in the shutters and through a tiny hole it had found under the eaves and I remembered someone once telling me years before that although they may look soft, large and fluffy snowflakes can find their way through the meanest of gaps. I wondered whether I ought to find a ladder and go and check out the loft. After a moment's thought I decided that I would leave this chore until the next morning.

'What do you want for tea?' asked my wife, lazily lifting her right leg out of the water and soaping it.

I turned my head and could only just see Patsy's eyes and the top of her head, peeping over the top of her bath. Her long blonde hair was wet against the side of her head. 'I don't know,' I confessed. 'I hadn't even thought about tea.'

'I thought we might perhaps have crumpets and jam in front of the fire in the living room,' suggested Patsy. She finished rubbing soap on her leg and lowered it gently back down into the water without so much as a splash.

'Sounds absolutely splendid,' I murmured. I lifted my right foot out of the water, turned on the hot tap with my toes and topped up the bath with more hot water. Exhausted by this simple effort I sank even lower into the water. In the fireplace a flaming log slipped an inch or two, sending a small shower of sparks out over the hearth. Ben, ever vigilant, raised her head and pricked her ears, checked out the noise, reassured herself that all was still well and settled herself back down again. Sophie and Emily, happy to leave all watchdog duties to Ben, didn't even stir.

A log fire. Hot buttered crumpets thickly covered with home-made jam. Bilbury Grange battened down against the storm and all our animals locked up safely. Life seemed good and I felt grateful. I thought that perhaps I might mix a bowlful of hot punch to drink with our crumpets.

*   *   *

CHAPTER TWO

The storm raged for two days and two nights. On the second night I had just managed to get to sleep when I was woken by the telephone. Still at least nine tenths asleep I picked up the receiver and spoke. 'Hello?' I couldn't hear anyone at the other end and assumed that the caller, whoever it was, had given up at the very moment that I'd picked up the receiver. It's amazing how often that seems to happen. I was about to put the telephone down again when I heard a familiar voice. It was Frank, the genial licensed victualler who, with his wife, Gilly, runs the village pub, the Duck and Puddle. He sounded faint, as though he was calling from the other side of the world, and I could hardly hear him. Deciphering what he had to say was made even more difficult by the fact that the wind was rattling the shutters and whistling through the loft above us.

'... lines aren't ... very well ... hear me?'

'Frank?' I sat up in bed and reached out to switch on my bedside light.

'... storm ... school ..!' I heard him say. There was clearly some sort of intermittent fault on the line.

My fingers found the switch on the lamp. Click. Nothing happened. No light. I had forgotten that we had no electricity. Only much later did I find out that a huge old oak tree on the corner of Parsonage Lane and Frog Road had been uprooted by the gale and had brought down all the incoming electricity cables.

'I can't hear you properly,' I told Frank. 'Can you say it again?'

As I spoke the storm grew steadily more powerful. I was glad we had wooden shutters across our windows. When we had restored the house we had thought seriously about having the old, slatted wooden shutters taken off but Thumper Robinson had insisted that the wood was quite sound and simply needed painting.

'... tree ... roof ... cottage,' was all I heard from Frank's next sentence. I sat up straighter, pressed the receiver more firmly against my ear and concentrated hard.

'Sorry, Frank,' I said. 'I can't hear you properly. Can you say it again? Keep on saying it.' I repeated this rather tedious litany three or four times so that Frank, who was, I presumed having as much difficulty in hearing me as I was in hearing him, would stand a chance of hearing what I was saying. Inevitably, Patsy woke up.

'What's the matter?' she asked, sleepily. 'Who is it?'

I put my hand over the mouthpiece. 'It's Frank,' I answered in a whisper. 'From the Duck and Puddle,' I added rather unnecessarily for at the time I don't think either of us knew anyone else called Frank. 'There seems to be some sort of emergency but there is something wrong with the phone line.' Patsy nodded knowingly. She'd lived in Bilbury all her life. She knew from past experience that the telephone and electricity cables were often affected by Bilbury's fierce south westerly gales.

Frank repeated his message several times and each time I managed to hear a few different words.

'I'll be there as soon as I can!' I said the moment I understood what Frank was saying, throwing back the sheets and blankets on my side of the bed as I spoke. I winced as the cold hit me. Downstairs the old AGA must have been furiously pumping out its heat but the weather was so cold that the boiler didn't seem to have made much difference to the temperature in the bedroom. I put the telephone handset down on its rest, opened a drawer in the top of the bedside table and took out a candle, an old fashioned candle holder and a box of matches. Working entirely by feel I put the candle in the holder and then lit the match. The sudden flare of the match lit up the room. I lit the wick and waited for the candle to settle down to a steady flame. Then I put down the candle holder on the bedside table, climbed out of bed and rapidly started to dress. Ben, her ears pricked, jumped down off the bed and sat expectantly on the carpet by my feet. Neither Emily nor Sophie moved.

13

'What's the matter?' asked Patsy, sleepily. 'Where are you going?'

'The storm has blown a tree down onto School Cottage,' I explained, taking a fresh, thick, woollen shirt from a drawer and pulling it over my head. 'Frank says they think Miss Hargreaves is still inside the wreckage. The road from Barnstaple is blocked with snowdrifts so they want me to go over in case they find her and she's injured.' Miss Hargreaves, a formidable looking but kind hearted spinster in her fifties was the village schoolmistress. She had, I knew, come to the school in her early twenties, fresh from teacher training college, and for thirty years had dedicated her life to educating the young people of Bilbury.

Little more than a year earlier I had been Bilbury's general practitioner and had borne the sole responsibility for the health and physical wellbeing of the villagers. Now I no longer had any official responsibilities in the village but the villagers knew that I was a doctor and they still called on me from time to time whenever there were emergencies.

Patsy managed to slide out of bed without disturbing the sheets and blankets on her side of the bed too much. Gently, she lifted Sophie, pulled her dressing gown from where Sophie had been lying on the bed, and then replaced the still sleeping cat. She shivered involuntarily, pulled the dressing gown around her and tied it tightly.

'You don't need to get up,' I told her, rummaging around in the drawer where I kept my socks. The dim light from the candle, barely enough to see by at the best of times, flickered as an extra strong gust of wind found its way through a gap somewhere in a wall or windowframe. Eventually I found what I was looking for: a pair of really thick knitted socks. I put them on. They came up almost to my knees.

'You'll have to walk,' said Patsy. 'You won't be able to drive in this. I'm going to put up some food for you.' She took her own candle out of her bedside drawer, lit it and used it to light her way around the bedroom and to the door.

I took my black Gladstone bag out of the bottom of the wardrobe, followed her out onto the landing and down the stairs to the kitchen. Ben padded down behind me. The Gladstone bag contained my medical equipment. I always kept it ready packed and handy for emergencies.

The kitchen was much warmer than anywhere else in the house and I pulled my jeans and sweater down from the line above the AGA where I had left them to dry the night before and put them on. They were as warm as fresh toast. Patsy put a saucepan of home-made tomato soup on top of the cooking plate. Then she opened the white enamelled metal breadbin which stood by the side of the oven and took out half a loaf of bread. She cut eight thick slices of bread and made me a huge pile of sandwiches: two with egg, cress and home-made rhubarb and tomato chutney and two with home-made strawberry jam. By the time she had finished the soup pan was boiling. She carefully poured the contents of the pan into a vacuum flask. Then she wrapped the sandwiches in greaseproof paper. While she was doing this I took a small, sturdy knapsack from a hook just behind the cellar door and put it down on the kitchen table. Then I opened my Gladstone bag and carefully tipped out the contents onto the table alongside it. I wanted to have both hands free so needed to put everything I wanted to take with me into my knapsack. I packed my stethoscope, small sphygmomanometer, thermometer, suture kit, scalpel, syringes, needles and a small supply of essential medicines including pain killers. When I had finished Patsy took the knapsack from me and packed the wrapped sandwiches into one side pocket and the flask into the other. Before she fastened the haversack she filled a brown paper bag with dog biscuits and popped the bag into the knapsack.

'I'm not taking Ben,' I told her.

'I don't think you'll be able to stop her,' said Patsy quietly, nodding in Ben's direction, The collie was sitting patiently by the back door, ears pricked and obviously ready to go. 'Take her with you,' said Patsy. 'I don't know why but I'll be happier if you do.'

Half reluctantly I said I would. I was only half reluctant because, selfishly, I knew that I would welcome her company.

'Take care,' said Patsy.

I said I would.

'I hope she's all right,' said Patsy.

'Ben?' I asked, puzzled.

'Miss Hargreaves,' said Patsy. 'She taught me to read and write. When I was a kid we all loved her. She used to be very pretty you know when she was young.' I sometimes forgot that Patsy had grown up in the village.

I gave Patsy a big hug and told her that I would do whatever I could. Then I pulled on a pair of waterproof leggings and my green, oiled coat and stuffed a large rubber torch into one of the pockets. I pulled a thick woolly hat firmly onto my head (my usual hat would have been blown off within seconds and would, in any case, have done nothing to keep my ears warm), slipped my feet into my boots, put my arms through the straps of my haversack, pulled on a pair of woollen gloves and then added a pair of thick thornproof gardening gloves that were slightly too large for me and would, therefore, allow me to wear the woollen gloves as well, kissed Patsy goodbye, chose a five foot long hickory stick from the stand by the back door and grinned at Ben. These preparations may sound a little 'over the top' but if you have ever experienced a snowstorm on Exmoor you will know that they were not. Finally, I unbolted the back door, and cautiously peered outside.

I knew it had been snowing hard for a long time and I knew that the wind was fierce but I had not expected the conditions to be quite as dramatic as they were. The snow in the courtyard had drifted up against the back door and was nearly four feet high and the wind sent clouds of thick snow whirling into the kitchen. I shut the door with far more difficulty than I had opened it. I hadn't even stepped outside and yet my eyes were already smarting from the wind and the icy sharp flakes of snow.

'I need some goggles,' I told Patsy, pulling off my thick gloves and rubbing at my sore eyes. It seemed an impossible hope. Where on earth could I find goggles?

Suddenly I had a brainwave. I opened the cellar door, took the torch out of my pocket and went down the stairs. There, hanging on a rusty nail, I found the light plastic goggles Thumper Robinson had used when he had sprayed the loft with a chemical mixture designed to kill woodworm and dry rot. When he had finished with them I'd washed them and kept them, convinced that they looked too useful to throw away. I dusted them off and put them on.

16

With virtually every inch of me now protected against the wind and the blizzard I half walked and half fell out into the drift which had accumulated against the back door. Ben, doing an undignified but effective variation on the dog paddle, half walked and half swam though the snow.

A yard or two away from the back door I turned round and peered through the thick white curtain of snow which surrounded me. I could just make out the kitchen door and the faint, yellow light of the candle I knew that Patsy was holding. Doubting whether Patsy could see me I hesitated for a moment, waved my stick and then turned to head for the gateway out of the courtyard.

* * *

The village school in Bilbury is situated about half a mile along the road from the Village Green and the Duck and Puddle. It is about two, maybe two and a half miles away from Bilbury Grange if you follow the road round; though as the crow flies the distance between Bilbury Grange and the school is no more than a mile and a half at the most.

The Bilbury village school was built in the 1930s by a millionaire from the north of England who had made a considerable fortune out of exploiting hordes of poorly paid women and children in textile factories all over the world. When he retired he bought a house and came to live in Bilbury and was clearly determined to purge his soul of the evil he had done. Driven, I suspect, by guilt his final two decades were spent performing what are usually referred to as 'good works'. He was never shy about his generosity and both the school and the village hall (a much repaired, weather scarred, wonderful neo-gothic creation which must be the only building in England to have four stained glass windows and a corrugated iron roof) which was also built with his money, have his name carved into the brickwork. The School Cottage, much photographed by visitors to the district, and traditionally occupied by Bilbury's resident schoolteacher, had a thatched roof and its walls were totally covered with a fine mixture of ivy, rambling roses and clematis.

There is a little known footpath between the Grange and the village which Patsy and I often used in the summer when we

17

needed something from the village shop but weren't in too much of a hurry and wanted to walk rather than drive. I didn't intend to waste time following the road for I was pretty sure that the road itself would be blocked with snow and that the route that way would certainly be no less impeded than the path.

The path runs across three of our fields, down the valley to the small stream which runs along one of our boundaries, through the small wood which provides Elijah Huttlecombe with wood for charcoal burning and thin stakes for wattle fencing, and up the long hill that is a sort of small, unofficial local nature reserve to rejoin the main road through the village. The path comes out onto the main road alongside the school playground.

It was my simple plan to follow this path.

I turned right out of the Bilbury Grange courtyard, walked along the track and climbed the wooden post and rail fence into the field where we keep our four sheep. The torch I had brought with me was a good one but the snow was falling so thickly and the night was so black that I very nearly walked into the gate. I could see no more than a yard, maybe a yard and a half, in front of me. The sheep, tucked up in their stable, must have heard me walking by for they all started to baa very loudly. One of them, probably Lizzie, started to bang one of her front feet against the closed, lower half of the stable door.

Our four sheep all had quite distinct personalities. Lizzie was brash, domineering and demanding. She always wanted to be fed first if there were any treats to be had. She was the undoubted leader of our small flock and it was invariably she who seemed to decide when it was time to lie down and rest and when it was time to get up and start eating again. She took her leadership responsibilities seriously and if one of the other sheep was not well Lizzie would always stay with her and keep her company. Cynthia was the prettiest of the bunch and she knew it. She had a naturally haughty air which sometimes led casual observers to suspect that she felt that she was really rather too good, rather too special, to be living in a field and sleeping in a stable. If anyone ever went into the field with a camera Cynthia would always pose willingly to have her picture taken. The other three would back away rather nervously but Cynthia would present her best profile and hold it until the shutter had clicked. Petula was always in trouble. It was Petula who got foot rot first when there was a wet spell. It was Petula who caught orf when half a dozen infected sheep from a neighbouring farm got through a thick hawthorn hedge and into our field. It was Petula who always knocked over the water bucket. It was Petula who got locked in the tack room and knocked over six bales of straw. And it was Petula who wandered into the kitchen garden and ate a whole row of foot high runner bean plants when a gate was accidentally left open. (The other sheep had stayed behind in the field and when I returned Petula to the fold in disgrace I just knew that the moment my back was turned she would have to put up with the other three telling her that they knew she would get into trouble).

Sarah-Louise was the worrier of the four. She worried about anything and everything. She had huge, sad, brown eyes and loved nothing more than having her neck massaged. She was quiet and polite and always last to be fed. If one of the other three tried to push in front of her she would always back out of the way. She was, without a doubt, the most loving of the four. Whenever I left the stable at night she would always come after me, her big brown eyes looking up at me, pleading with me to stay and stroke her neck for just a little while longer.

I shouted to the four of them and couldn't help wondering how many sheep and other animals there were seeking shelter out on the moors, huddling together for warmth behind small, inadequate stone walls and underneath wind blown gorse bushes. I thought for a moment about going over to the stable to close the upper half of their door but decided against it for they always hated being shut in completely. The wind was blowing from the west and the stable door was on the east side of the building. This was no coincidence, of course. The farmer who had originally built the stable knew very well that the prevailing winds always came from the west. The only door on either Bilbury Grange itself or any of the numerous outbuildings which surrounded it that faced due West was the kitchen door, which was normally protected from the wind and the rain by the fact that it opened into the courtyard.

*   *   *

Neither time nor distance are the constants we usually think they are. Both vary according to circumstances. An hour of pleasure always passes far more speedily than an hour in the dentist's chair. In summer, a mile and a half, walked along a grassy path, is a pleasant half an hour stroll. But given different circumstances that same mile and a half walk can become a difficult and even life threatening journey.

Of course, it didn't help that once I started to walk across our first field and head down towards the stream I had no way of knowing exactly where I was nor in which direction I should go. The path, normally so easy to follow even in the dark, was completely buried under several feet of snow. I could see no more than three or four feet in front of me: there were no landmarks by which I could set my course. And above me the sky was so full of falling snow that I could see neither moon nor stars. I could have done with a compass. All I knew was that in order to reach the stream I had to keep on heading downhill.

I quickly realised that I had made an important mistake: although it would have entailed a longer journey I should have followed the road instead of trying to take a short cut across the fields. On the road the presence of the hedges on either side would have meant that I would have not have been able to get lost.

Every step I took was a tremendous effort and although I thought of myself as reasonably fit I soon felt exhausted. I tried to walk with my face turned away from the wind but it didn't help much. Within a few minutes my face was burning with the cold and stinging with what felt like an endless barrage of driven needles of ice. Even though I was wearing two pairs of gloves both my hands felt like blocks of ice. The cold had seeped through my boots and my thick woollen socks and I couldn't feel my feet. Every step was a real effort and the further I went down the hill the deeper the snow seemed to get. Soon I found myself struggling to get through snow that came up past my knees, snow that crept in through every opening and then, melted by the warmth of my body, soaked into my clothes. Never straying more than a foot or so away from me Ben continued bravely and silently to battle on alongside me. Half of me wished she had stayed behind, safe and warm in the house; but half of me was glad to have her company. She never flagged and never complained though I could tell by the way her head drooped that she was cold and weary.

At the bottom of the field the path goes across a small wooden bridge before climbing upwards again. Each end of the bridge is guarded with an old fashioned wooden stile. A thick, layered hedge marks the boundary on each side of the stile. Because I hadn't been able to follow the path when I reached the bottom of the field I found myself face to face with the top few feet of the hedge instead of the stile. The stile and the bridge were, I guessed, buried deep beneath the snow. I lay still and listened hard; trying to tell whether or not the stream was still running or if it had frozen up completely. I couldn't hear anything except for the wind whistling through the nearby treetops.

I somehow managed to drag myself through the hedge and up the hill into the small wood. Here there was some slight shelter from the wind and the blizzard. I took off my haversack and sat down with my back against a huge oak tree. Ben, totally exhausted, lay down close by my side. I sat in such a way that I was protected from the worst of the wind by the tree trunk. The trunk was at least two feet thick but when the wind reached its peak I could feel the whole tree shudder.

Gingerly I parted the cuff of my glove and the sleeve of my coat and used the torch to look at my watch. It had taken me an hour and a half to travel little more than half a mile, though to be honest I was so exhausted that if I had had to guess I would have said that I had been walking for four or five times as long. I desperately wanted to rest, even to sleep, but knew that if I did it could well be fatal for us both. I knew that Ben wouldn't leave me and if I went to sleep and didn't wake up there was a real chance that we would both freeze to death. We both had to keep moving.

But first I needed to eat. I took off my thickest pair of outer gloves and opened the haversack. I fed Ben first, giving her a handful of biscuits to eat. Then I poured myself a cup of warm soup and ate a sandwich. I felt so much better with the warm, thick, liquid inside me that I poured a cupful for Ben too, holding the cup while she licked up the soup. Then I screwed the cup back on the thermos flask, put everything back into the haversack and scrambled wearily up onto my feet.

21

Walking through the wood seemed to be the easiest part of that terrible journey, for the snow there was no more than two feet thick. Because the branches of the trees acted as a filter, thinning out the falling snow, I could see quite a lot further than I had been able to see out in the field. Once I had found my way back to where I thought the path ought to be I managed to keep to it simply by walking along the narrow passageway which ran between the trees. I found the going so easy that I picked Ben up and carried her; holding the torch in my left hand so that I could look out for the many branches which had been brought down by the snow and the wind.

Suddenly, I went crashing down. The torch flew one way, Ben flew the other and my long hickory stick snapped as it took my weight. Ben yelped as she landed in thick snow. I had tripped over an unseen tree stump and the moment I tried to get up again I knew that I was in trouble. I had badly twisted my ankle. It was all I needed to make my night complete. I limped onwards, using what was left of my stick as a support and for the first time in my life I think I was seriously afraid.

The wind had blown the snow into drifts and forcing a way through the snow was a tremendous struggle. I had never before felt so cold. My whole body ached with it. My joints seemed to have seized up. My leg, back, chest and arm muscles were sore and aching from fighting through the snow drifts and my cheeks, nose and mouth were all raw from the biting, burning cold wind and the endless, searing of the icy blizzard. My ankle was swelling and though it was frozen with cold it hurt like hell to walk on it. I knew I couldn't be far from the road or the school but I could neither hear nor see anything. I might as well have been a million miles away.

In the end I could go no further. In desperation I looked around but there was no shelter to be seen anywhere. I collapsed where I stood and curled myself into a tight ball. Dimly I could hear Ben barking furiously. I reached out to comfort her but before my frozen fingers could find her I blacked out.

*   *   *

CHAPTER THREE

Frank and Thumper told me that Ben had almost certainly
saved my life.

'She wouldn't leave you,' said Frank. 'You were curled up in
the snow and she was standing beside you, ears pricked, barking away as loudly as she could.'

I sipped again at the cupful of hot, sweet tea that Frank had
forced into my hands and looked around. I was sitting in a chair
in the sole classroom at the village school. There was no electric
light but two hurricane lamps had been lit and in the soft yellow
light I could see that the walls around the classroom had been
decorated with paintings of kings and crusaders and colourful,
carefully drawn plans of castles, keeps, moats and draw-
bridges. There was hardly an inch of wall that wasn't decorated
in some way with these childish paintings. It wasn't difficult to
see which period of history Miss Hargreaves had been teaching
the children in her class.

The hot tea almost burned my mouth but I could feel the
warmth from it circulating through my body as I drank. The
rescuer had become the rescuee. I had, they told me, been less
than a quarter of a mile from the school and the schoolteacher's
damaged cottage when Frank, Thumper and the others had
heard Ben's insistent barking and had come out to look for me.
They had found me semi-conscious in the snow and had carried
me back to the village school.

'I wouldn't have given you much of a chance if you hadn't
had Ben with you,' said Thumper. 'We could have searched all
night and not found you.' He nodded down, somewhere in the
direction of my feet. I looked down. Someone had removed my
clothes, presumably because they were soaking wet, and had
wrapped me in a blanket. Ben, ever faithful, was lying by my

feet looking up at me. I bent down and stroked her head. She reached up, touched my leg gently with one paw and held her head on one side. She looked exhausted and bedraggled. Her coat was still soaked.

'Have you got a towel?' I asked. 'She's wet through!'

Frank nodded, disappeared for a moment and reappeared a few seconds later clutching a large, freshly laundered towel. I put down my cup, took the towel from him, bent down, and wrapped Ben in it. She let me dry her.

'Could you get her some warm milk?' I asked.

Frank nodded again and disappeared. When I'd finished drying Ben I stood up, opened the blanket for a moment and looked inside. I was wearing my thick woollen shirt, socks and underpants. 'Where are the rest of my clothes?' I asked Thumper. My ankle still hurt likes blazes.

'Behind you,' he said. I turned round. My jeans and sheeps' wool jumper were draped over two huge old iron radiators. My oiled jacket and waterproof trousers were hanging up on a peg. A large puddle lay on the floor beneath them. 'We managed to get the boiler going,' explained Thumper. 'Thank heavens it's an old fashioned one that doesn't rely on an electric motor.'

Frank returned with a bowl full of warm milk. He put it down on the floor in front of Ben. She looked up at me. I nodded and she hungrily started to drink. Outside I could hear the wind battering at the windows and I suddenly remembered why I was there.

'Miss Hargreaves...,' I began. 'How is she?'

'She's still trapped,' said Thumper quietly. 'We've been working all night to get to her. The storm brought her chimney crashing down on her cottage roof. The timbers under the thatch smashed under the weight and she's stuck in her bedroom.'

'Has anyone managed to get a message through to Barnstaple? To the fire brigade? The ambulance?'

Thumper shook his head. 'All the phone lines are down now and the roads out of the village are totally impassable. I tried to come in by tractor but I had to abandon it and walk.' He shook his head. 'I've never known anything like it before.'

'I'll go and see if I can do anything,' I said, looking round. 'I brought some drugs with me.' I paused and looked around. 'In my haversack,' I added. 'You don't know where it is, do you?' Thumper walked across the room, picked up my haversack and brought it across to me. 'I'll see if I can find you some dry trousers,' said Thumper. 'Your jeans are still soaking. Wait there for a few minutes.'

I still felt weak and shivery. I wrapped the blanket around me, although it really wasn't cold in the classroom, and sat down. Ben, who had finished her warm milk, edged a little closer to me and rested her head on my foot. I wondered how Patsy was and wished that I could telephone her. I was glad that Bilbury Grange had a good, strong roof. I picked up my still unfinished cup of tea and emptied it. It tasted as though it had at least half a dozen spoons of sugar dissolved in it. I thought how odd it was that although I never normally have sugar in tea or coffee the sweet tea tasted good. My body, exhausted by the efforts of the last few hours, clearly needed a quick boost of instant energy.

*   *   *

Fifteen minutes later, dressed in a pair of Frank's old suit trousers and my own jumper (the oil in the wool meant that a quick shake got rid of most of the water that had found its way through my oiled jacket) I pulled on my waterproofs and followed Frank and Thumper outside. Frank's trousers (heaven knows where they'd come from) were several inches short in the leg but considerably larger than I needed around the waist and I had to tie them up with a length of orange baler twine taken from my jacket pocket. My ever faithful companion, and now saviour, Ben, dry, rested and full of warm milk and dog biscuits, trotted along behind me.

To my astonishment I discovered that the snow still hadn't stopped and nor had the wind, though the sky was lighter now and dawn had started to break. I had forgotten to put on my hat and the bitter cold wind sparked off sharp pains in both my ears. I pulled my coat collar up as high as I could and hobbled along behind Thumper. He, Frank and the others had walked along the footpath between the village school and Miss Hargreaves' cottage so often that they had left a trail of footprints into which I could tread. I picked up Ben and carried her.

In front of me Thumper stopped so suddenly that I almost

bumped into his back. He said something to me but I couldn't hear him because of the wind. Instead of repeating himself he just pointed upwards. I shaded my eyes against the blizzard and looked up into the sky. The whole of the roof of Miss Hargreaves cottage seemed to have disappeared. Where once there had been a neat thatch and a high chimney stack (chimneys are always built tall on thatched cottages to keep sparks from the fire away from the highly inflammable thatch) there was now nothing but a mess of broken rafters, pieces of stone and tufts of thatch sticking out at crazy angles. The whole chaotic mess was covered with a thick layer of snow. A downstairs window had been flung open and underneath, half buried in a snow drift, lay bits and pieces of debris which had been jettisoned through the window. A large, triangular chunk of plaster stuck out of the drifted snow like a massive pink sail. Miss Hargreaves' neat, picture book cottage, over the years the target of a thousand tourist cameras, had become a ruin overnight. Thumper pulled a face. I grimaced back. Thumper opened the front door to Miss Hargreaves' cottage and walked in, automatically but pointlessly wiping his feet on the doormat. I entered behind him, put Ben down onto the carpet and told her to stay where she was and shut the door firmly behind me. I too wiped my feet on the doormat. Miss Hargreaves was a very particular woman. It was almost as cold inside the cottage as it was outside but at least inside we were protected from the wind.

There were five people working inside the cottage and judging by the amount of rubble and thatch and snow they had moved they had been at it for a long time. I recognised Gilly Parsons, the landlady from the Duck and Puddle, Peter Marshall, the village shopkeeper and Jack and Ollie two farm labourers who lived in adjoining cottages two hundred yards along the road into the village. It was Jack who had heard the crash of Miss Hargreaves' chimney and who had alerted Frank at the Duck and Puddle. The only light came from three hurricane lamps: one on the mantlepiece, one hanging from the picture rail and one dangling from the top of the door frame.

When the chimney had gone through Miss Hargreaves' roof it had landed directly on top of her bed and the weight of the chimney, the rafters, the thatch, the snow and the ceiling plaster had then taken the bed, the chimney and Miss Hargreaves herself crashing down into the living room. The result was that Miss Hargreaves' living room was filled to where the ceiling would have been with rubble, thatch and, somewhere in the middle of it all, Miss Hargreaves and her bed. I looked up and found that I was staring out through a massive hole in the cottage roof at the early morning sky. Thick snow fell steadily onto the wreckage and onto Miss Hargreaves' rescuers.

'How's it going?' Thumper asked no one in particular. A tall figure in a yellow oilskin, who was tugging on a long piece of wood, half turned. For a moment I couldn't see who it was.

'She's alive,' whispered the man in the oilskin. He gently freed the wood from the wreckage and turned a little further. It was Patchy Fogg, the antique dealer. Patchy doesn't normally live in Bilbury but I guessed that he had probably been stuck at the Duck and Puddle when the snow had started. 'We reached her about half an hour ago.'

'Do you mind not talking about me as though I wasn't here?' demanded a voice I recognised immediately. It was Miss Hargreaves. Although I did not have much experience of talking to people who were trapped in house wreckage she sounded far brighter than I had expected. I had to strain a little to make out what she was saying but even through several feet of assorted rubble there was no mistaking her voice.

'The doctor's come to see you, Miss Hargreaves,' said Patchy.

'About time too!' replied the school mistress, with a slight snap in her voice. 'When are you boys going to get me out of here?'

Patchy turned to me and smiled.

'How are you, Miss Hargreaves?' I called down into the debris.

'How do you think I am?' demanded Miss Hargreaves testily.

'Are you in any pain?' I asked her.

There was a long silence.

'Are you in any pain?' I asked her, again.

'Don't hurry me!' she said sharply. 'I'm thinking about it.'

Patchy, who was busy filling a bucket with small pieces of plaster, turned and winked at me.

I waited, bent down and started to help Patchy fill his bucket with bits of plaster and broken wood. When the bucket was full Patchy walked over to the window and emptied the rubbish out into the snow, throwing it as far out onto the snow covered lawn as he could. I couldn't help remembering that Miss Hargreaves had been extraordinarily proud of her garden. It had been full of traditional 'cottage' flowers and had always been a blaze of colour in the summer months. It was going to take a long time to restore the cottage and its garden to their former glory.

'No! I don't think so,' said a disembodied voice which belonged to the buried Miss Hargreaves. 'Everything seems to work.'

'That's great!' I said.

'I seem to be lying on my sofa,' said the invisible Miss Hargreaves. 'What am I doing on my sofa?'

I looked across at Patchy. He shrugged, making it clear that it was up to me to decide how much to tell her.

'There's a storm,' I explained. 'Your roof was brought down. But you're going to be all right. That's the important thing.'

'Well just you people make sure you don't make a mess,' said Miss Hargreaves. 'I cleaned my carpets yesterday.'

I looked around at the mess in Miss Hargreaves' cottage.

'Have you wiped your feet?' she demanded.

'Yes,' I shouted back. I looked around. The others all nodded. 'We've all wiped our feet.'

'Good!' said Miss Hargreaves firmly. 'Well, just you remember that if there's any mess I'll hold you personally responsible.'

'Yes, Miss Hargreaves,' I said. 'We'll clean up any mess for you,' I promised. There was a half reluctant grunt of acknowledgement from somewhere in the middle of the debris.

We carried on digging away at the debris, throwing rafters, bits of stone, chunks of thatch, bits and pieces of plaster and broken pieces of furniture out through the window into the garden in our battle to free Miss Hargreaves. We talked steadily to her; offering encouragement, telling her bits of gossip (which she claimed very loudly that she was not the slightest bit interested in) and asking her advice on just about every subject under the sun. I didn't know much about how to care for patients buried deep under debris. It wasn't something they had taught us at medical school. But common sense told me that we should do our best to keep Miss Hargreaves awake, alert and distracted from her predicament. Every twenty minutes or so two of us would go outside to move some of the debris away from the area directly underneath the window. And every half an hour or so we took it in turns to pop into the school house for a few minutes to get warm, drink more sweet tea and eat cheese and pickle sandwiches made by Frank. Once Frank came into the cottage to help with the digging but I made him go back into the school house. Frank is desperately overweight, suffers from high blood pressure and is a prime candidate for a heart attack. Cold weather made the risk much greater and I didn't want any more dramas. Besides we needed someone in the school house to make sure the boiler didn't go out, to keep the kettle boiling and to make a constant supply of cheese and pickle sandwiches. Frank made a good cheese and pickle sandwich.

* * *

The sun had risen and the snowstorm was showing signs of having started to blow itself out when Gilly cried out, with unmistakeable excitement in her voice, that she could see Miss Hargreaves' leg!

'Goodness me!' called Miss Hargreaves. 'Has someone left the door open? My leg is freezing cold.'

We all looked at one another.

'The heating isn't working,' I told the schoolteacher, quite truthfully. I didn't want to tell her what had happened to her cottage, and that her leg was cold because her cottage had no roof, until I could be with her. The shock wouldn't do any her good at all and I didn't want her to faint into unconsciousness while she was still buried under the rubble of her cottage.

Gilly disappeared and came back a moment or two later with a large white bath towel that she'd brought from the kitchen, the only room in the cottage that had not been destroyed. I assumed that Miss Hargreaves must have had an airing cupboard in the kitchen. Gilly carefully reached into the rubble and covered Miss Hargreaves' leg with the towel. Then we carried on, carefully digging away at the rubble.

Gradually, it became clear that when Miss Hargreaves and

her bed had fallen through the floor the bed had tipped over and was now lying on the top of its former occupant. I could only assume that the falling chimney stack must have landed on a corner of the bed and flipped it over. Whatever the truth was about the way it had happened there was little doubt that the bed springs and the mattress had saved Miss Hargreaves' life. When we eventually found her she was lying in a small space between her living room sofa and her bed.

Peter, the shopkeeper, Patchy, the antique dealer and Jack and Ollie, the two farm labourers, and I took hold of one side of the bed and pulled and pushed upwards with all the power we could muster between us. Slowly, we managed to lift the bed up into the air. Gilly Parsons peered in under the bed.

'Who's there?' demanded Miss Hargreaves, warily.

'It's Gilly, Miss Hargreaves!' said Gilly. 'Can you move?'

'Who else is there?' demanded the schoolteacher.

'The young doctor, Patchy Fogg, Peter Marshall and...,' began Gilly. The villagers still referred to me as the 'young doctor' even though I had been living there for a while, and was no longer practising medicine. The 'old doctor' was Dr Brownlow, my predecessor, who still lived in his huge old house in the village. 'Can you move?' she asked.

'Get me my dressing gown!' demanded Miss Hargreaves sharply. 'I've only got my nightie on.'

'It's a bit difficult, Miss Hargreaves,' apologised Gilly. She knelt down and started to crawl underneath the bed. There was still quite a lot of rubble on top of it and even though the two farm labourers were very strong it was quite a strain holding it up.

'Where has all that snow come from?' demanded Miss Hargreaves. 'Is my front door still open?'

'Can you move?' Gilly asked again.

'Of course I can move!' insisted Miss Hargreaves. 'But I'm not moving out of here until you've got me my dressing gown. Not with all those men in the house.'

Gilly crawled back out from underneath the bed and shrugged her shoulders. 'What shall I do?' she asked me in a whisper. 'I don't have the faintest idea where her dressing gown is!'

'It's hanging up behind the bedroom door!' said Miss Hargreaves, though I don't know whether she had heard what Gilly had said.

I looked upwards. The snow fell lightly on my face now. The wind seemed almost to have stopped. Through the shattered floor of Miss Hargreaves' bedroom I could see her bedroom door. Sure enough her dressing gown was hanging up behind the door.

'Go on,' I said to Gilly. I looked at Patchy, standing next to me. There were beads of sweat on his forehead. Peter Marshall, the shop keeper, was looking very red faced. The two farm labourers nodded to indicate that they could hold on for a little longer. 'But be quick!' I told her.

Gilly clambered over some broken rafters and started to climb up the staircase.

'Be careful!' I called to her.

'Yes!' cried Miss Hargreaves, misunderstanding my warning to Gilly. 'You be careful! I don't want dirt and snow treading into my carpets.

I looked upwards and watched Gilly open the bedroom door, edge cautiously into Miss Hargreaves bedroom, peer down through the hole in the floor, and then take the dressing gown off the hook on the back of the door.

Two minutes later an ashen faced Gilly returned clutching Miss Hargreaves' dressing gown. She brushed the worst of the snow off it and then crept under the bed and helped Miss Hargreaves drape the garment around her shoulders. A minute or so after that Miss Hargreaves emerged from her unusual prison. The five of us let the bed and the rubble it was holding crash back down onto the sofa. Miss Hargreaves looked around her at the ruin that had been her home, opened her mouth, said nothing, and then fainted very neatly into Peter Marshall's arms.

*   *   *

Miraculously, Miss Hargreaves wasn't badly hurt. Her cottage was a ruin and would clearly need rebuilding but, trapped as she had been between her chintz covered sofa and her bed she had been well protected from the debris which had buried her. We carried her out of her cold and roofless cottage and across into the school where Frank had kept the boiler alight and the

31

kettle on the boil. I gave her a quick but thorough examination but could find nothing physically wrong. When she came round I explained what had happened to her cottage and then I gave her a full check up. Her heart seemed as sound as a ship's engine and her blood pressure was excellent. She didn't even have a bruise! To say that I was relieved would be an understatement of heroic proportions. When I had first seen the wreckage I had for a few awful moments feared that I might need to amputate a trapped limb or, at the very least, administer a series of pain killing injections.

We wrapped Miss Hargreaves in a couple of blankets and lay her down on a small camp bed that Frank had found in a store room. The wind and the snow had stopped and everywhere seemed strangely still, calm and quiet. The storm had raged for so long that the peace around us now seemed unreal and ghostly.

All around the classroom weary bodies were stretched out in repose. Peter Marshall, wearing his ever present cap, the one with the finger marked peak, was curled up in a ball and snoring in the far corner of the room. Patchy Fogg, who had been up into Miss Hargreaves' bedroom and had brought down a selection of warm, winter clothing for her to wear when she was ready, was also snoring loudly. I felt tired and my ankle hurt but it felt good to be part of a village where the inhabitants worked so willingly and so hard to help one another.

Through the steamy classroom window I saw something fluttering outside in the small garden which Miss Hargreaves kept for her pupils. She had spent years, and much of her own money, stocking it with a huge variety of shrubs, flowers and herbs and every summer the children were encouraged to grow their own vegetables too. I leant forward, cleaned a small area of the glass so that I could see through and watched a red breasted robin fly down and land on a snow covered gate post. I wondered where he had been hiding for the last few days. Although his feathers were fluffed up I couldn't help noticing how thin and hungry he looked.

Wearily, I limped into the small kitchen where Frank, who had worked as hard as any of us, was washing up a pile of dirty mugs and plates. 'Have you got any bread crusts?' I asked him.

'Still hungry?' he asked, putting down the tea towel he was

holding and reaching for the bread knife. 'Let me make you a sandwich!'

'It's not for me,' I told him. I nodded towards the window. 'I thought I'd throw a few crusts out for the birds.'

Now it was his turn to rub at the glass. 'They'll need more than a few crusts,' he said, looking out at the white of the garden for a moment and then picking up an almost untouched loaf from the small, green work surface on his right. 'Here,' he said, 'catch!' It was a kindly and unexpected gesture. I'd never thought of Frank as having any great love for the non paying customers of this world.

I put a hand on his shoulder. 'Thanks, Frank!'

Outside the back door of the school I trod down a few square feet of snow and then spread small lumps of bread around on the surface of the hardened snow. When I'd done that I walked over to what looked like a massive white snowball. Tentatively, I brushed away at the snow. As the snow fell away to the ground beneath I could see scores of moist red berries glistening in the thin winter sunshine. Working quickly because my ungloved hands were soon uncomfortably cold I shook and brushed the snow from the bush. Then I hurried back into the kitchen. Frank had poured me another cup of hot tea.

'Do you want sugar?' he asked as I leant against the wall and stamped my good foot and rubbed my hands to get the blood circulating through them.

'No thanks,' I answered with a smile.

Outside, in the garden, the cock robin had returned and was hungrily chopping crumbs from one of the small pieces of bread I had thrown down. Within a couple of minutes there were twenty or thirty birds feasting on Frank's loaf and the berries on the uncovered bush.

'Makes you feel good, doesn't it?' whispered Frank.

I looked at him, slightly surprised.

'I always feed the birds at the back of the Duck and Puddle,' he said. He frowned, as though suddenly alarmed that this unexpected sign of tenderness might adversely affect his hard drinking image. 'But don't you dare tell anyone!' he added, with a nervous smile.

*   *   *

We waited there for six hours until Samuel Houghton, who has a farm on the road to Little Mitcham and has a contract with the local authority to keep the smaller, single track roads clear of snow, fought a way through the snowdrifts, reached us on his tractor and reconnected us with the rest of the world. We heard him coming, and saw stuttering bursts of black smoke long before we could see either Samuel or his tractor. He had an enormous snow moving attachment fixed to the front of the ancient red monster and behind him left two huge, high, parallel, mounds of chunky, tumbled snow.

Samuel, who won't be celebrating many more birthdays with a seven at the front, had his pipe jammed in his mouth and wore the rusty brown tweed jacket which I've never seen him without. A length of baler twine was tied around his waist. He wore no coat, no hat and no gloves and told us that the storm had left behind it a trail of terrible destruction. All over North Devon the wind had removed the roofs from scores of hotels, houses, cottages and farm buildings. A silage bin had been spotted three miles from home. A sixty foot long corrugated iron barn roof had been seen twenty feet off the ground resting in the branches of neighbouring oak trees. Samuel insisted that a small car, whisked from a car park outside a public house on the outskirts of Shirwell, had flown over a hedge and had finished up, upside down, in the middle of a field a quarter of a mile away. Later I was to discover that this story was not only quite true but that the car, which had landed in thick snow, was virtually undamaged after its adventure and, almost unbelievably, started first time when it had been tipped the right way up by its owner and a couple of passing strangers.

By the time we were reconnected with the rest of the world Miss Hargreaves had woken up again, dressed herself ('What a terrible selection of clothes! Who brought me this old pink sweater?') and had bravely and forcefully started to make plans for the rebuilding of her shattered cottage.

'I'll have to get Mr Lathwell booked straight away,' said Miss Hargreaves, making a mental list of things to be done. Mr Lathwell, the thatcher, doesn't live in Bilbury but has over the years repaired, restored or rethatched most of the thatched roof cottages in the village. He is regularly booked three or four months ahead, especially through the summer. It was good to hear Miss Hargreaves making positive plans. There would, I suspected, be plenty of sadness to come, and probably a few tears and sleepless nights, but Miss Hargreaves' determined attitude seemed to augur well for a quick recovery from her terrible ordeal.

I was more concerned with the immediate problem of where Miss Hargreaves was going to sleep for the next few nights.

'Do you have any friends you could stay with?' I asked her.

Miss Hargreaves thought for a moment. 'I've no doubt I could stay with Miss Anderson or Miss Jilks,' she said. She pulled a face and shook her head. 'But I wouldn't want to. Miss Anderson is a terrible worrier and she'd drive me potty, always wanting everything in just the right place. And Miss Jilks is a congenital gossip. I can't abide gossip.' She thought for a moment. 'I'll rent somewhere,' she said, firmly.

It might have sounded a good idea but a few moments thought quickly made it clear that finding somewhere for Miss Hargreaves to rent wasn't going to be as easy as it sounded – particularly since she insisted that she would only rent somewhere in the village, so that she could reach the school on her cycle each day. Bilbury is rather light on available rental accommodation. In the end it was agreed that as a temporary measure Miss Hargreaves would go back to the Duck and Puddle with Frank and Gilly Parsons and would spend the next night or two with them. Samuel Houghton agreed to give all three of them a lift to the pub on the back of his tractor.

'But it's only temporary!' Miss Hargreaves insisted, firmly.

We all agreed that it was what Patchy described as an 'interim measure' and promised that we would do our best to help her find somewhere of her own to stay. And then we all set off to our respective homes. I was keen to get back to Bilbury Grange to make sure that Patsy and the animals were all unharmed by the storm. Limping slightly, and with Ben bounding along by my side, it took me little over thirty minutes to walk back along the road to the Grange.

*   *   *

CHAPTER FOUR

I was relieved and delighted to find that Bilbury Grange had survived the snow storm without suffering any damage. Now that the wind had dropped and the blizzard had stopped the house and garden looked calm, peaceful and immensely beautiful. Everywhere I looked there were trees and bushes and fields draped in huge expanses of smooth, virginal, white snow. It was as though the countryside had been put into storage by some cold handed celestial super-being. I stood for a moment in the lane and stared up our driveway. Ben barked once and wagged her tail and then looked up at me to check that it was all right for her to run up to the house. 'O.K.!' I said to her and then couldn't help laughing out loud as she struggled to fight her way through several feet of powdery snow. I limped after her, picked her up out of the snow and carried her up to the house.

I gave Patsy a hug, said 'hello' to Emily and Sophie and fed Ben. Then, while Patsy put the kettle on to boil, and went upstairs to start running a bath for me, I went out to the stable to check on the sheep. They all made an enormous amount of noise when they heard me walking through the snow. When I opened the stable door Lizzie and Cynthia both edged past me and slipped out into what they thought was the field; and what *had* been the field the last time they'd been there. When they discovered that the tasty, fresh green grass they expected to find had turned into cold, tasteless snow they both looked up. Their faces were a picture. First there was simply surprise, then there was puzzlement, next there was horror and finally there was absolute disgust.

Lizzie and Cynthia stared at me, as though it was my fault that all the grass had disappeared and had been replaced by snow, and made lots of loud and very complaining 'maaarring' noises. Then, giving me another look of disgust, they turned round, and walked back into the stable. I went into the tack room next door, picked up half a bale of straw and spread it around on the stable floor. Next, I took down the hay net which was now empty, and hung up another full one. Finally, I broke the ice on the water butt outside the stable and replenished the sheep's supply of fresh water. The four of them gathered around the hay net and furiously began to drag out clumps tasty hay. Quietly, I crept out of the stable, closed the bottom half of the door, bolted it shut and walked back through the snow to the house.

*　　*　　*

An hour later, having lain soaking, half asleep, in a hot bath until my skin had gone all white and wrinkly, I was sitting in the kitchen drinking my third cup of hot tea and wolfing down slice after slice of hot buttered toast, liberally spread with Patsy's home-made orange and rhubarb marmalade (the oranges were from the twelve old orange trees in Dr Brownlow's conservatory and the rhubarb was from our garden), when Patsy suddenly announced that she had had an idea.

She sounded so excited that I stopped my hand midway between my plate and my mouth. 'What?' I asked her.

'Why don't we let Miss Hargreaves stay in the flat over the coach-house?'

It was such an obvious idea that I couldn't understand why I hadn't thought of it myself. Patsy had restored and renovated the coach-house flat soon after we had bought Bilbury Grange. The idea had been to earn a little extra money by letting it to holiday-makers during the summer months but during the winter there weren't any tourists and so the flat stayed empty. At the end of October Patsy, who was in charge of this venture, had cleaned the flat thoroughly, turned off the water, emptied the pipes, removed any bedding which might have got damp, firmly closed all the windows and doors and shut up the flat until April the following year. The flat was, therefore, quite empty and would provide Miss Hargreaves with a perfect home for a few months.

I told Patsy that I thought this was a terrific idea.

'You don't mind the idea of her staying there?'

'No, of course not!'

'She can be a bit, well, sharp occasionally.'

I said I knew this but that I didn't mind in the least.

'She can easily ride her bicycle to school from here.'

'Absolutely. Less than ten minutes on a bike.' I agreed. I looked at Patsy and then at the toast. The conversation seemed to be over. I took a bite from the toast.

'Shall I go and ring her now?' asked Patsy.

With a mouthful of freshly inserted hot buttered toast impeding any further attempt at speech I nodded.

'She's staying at the Duck and Puddle?'

I nodded again, thought about saying something, realised that there wasn't anything useful to add to my nod and so instead took another bite from my slice of toast. Patsy disappeared into the hall to ring the pub. She came back less than a minute later.

'The telephone lines must still be down,' she said. 'I can't get through. I'll try again later.'

*   *   *

It was lunchtime the following day before the engineers could get through to repair the phone lines and Patsy was able to ring the pub to speak to Miss Hargreaves. By then the main road between Barnstaple and Bilbury had been cleared too and although there was only enough room for traffic to travel in one direction at a time it did at least mean that we were once again fully reconnected with the outside world. Inevitably, perhaps, the postman was the first to get through, delivering several days' worth of accumulated bills and with them the news that a dozen even more outlying villages were still cut off.

The snow had stopped falling but the weather was still freezing cold and the snow which had fallen before and during the blizzard had not yet started to disappear. In towns and cities fallen snow soon becomes slushy and messy and starts to look horribly dirty and unattractive. Traffic, air pollution and endless streams of pedestrians all help to turn clean, crisp, white snow into a brown, unwholesome looking sludgy mess. But out in the country we had no such problems. Our Bilbury snow still looked as white, as pure and as thrilling as it had when it had fallen. The snow on our driveway was disturbed only by a narrow, foot trodden trail.

Being cut off entirely from the world had, I have to confess, been rather fun. It certainly wasn't a trial. Our old AGA boiler served us proud, keeping the kitchen warm, providing us with a constant supply of hot water and enabling us to have hot meals. Some people might have found the absence of television difficult to live with but we had books to read, candles to read them by and plenty of logs with which to light fires to keep us warm in the rest of the house.

I didn't miss having a television at all – and neither did Patsy. I fear that television has become a repository for quiz shows, soap operas and situation comedies that may amuse the man operating the canned laughter machine but which never seem to amuse me very much. Some people I know spend three hours a day watching television. That means that in a year they will spend over a thousand hours watching other people do things. That is the equivalent of roughly twenty five full working weeks a year, slumped in front of the TV set. You could write a book, learn to play golf or grow prize winning onions in that much time. Television, the oh-so-easy way to entertain yourself, is wrecking companionship, friendship and conversation and smothering the imaginations of millions. Television is blanc-mange for the mind. How can a child who watches three or four hours of television a day grow up into a balanced, intelligent human being? A child who watches that much television every day will, by the time he or she is 18 years old, have watched twenty thousand hours of TV. That's nearly twice as much time as he or she will have spent at school. The child's imagination will have been allowed to wither and decay. I once read a survey in which a group of four to six year olds were asked so say which they preferred – daddy or television. Around half said they preferred television.

Snowbound but with no television to distract us from real life Patsy and I got on with living. We looked after our animals and made sure that the house stayed in good condition and we both managed to get a considerable amount of work done. I wrote a short story (which I never managed to sell but which I much enjoyed writing) and two practical articles (which were less fun to write but which, I was delighted to find, found a ready market). Patsy ploughed her way through several huge, rather daunting seed catalogues which had arrived with the first post-blizzard mail delivery. Peter Marshall sells seeds at the village shop but his selection is small and sometimes he accidentally conceals the 'sell by' dates on his packets of seeds with his little price stickers.

Most important of all, of course, Miss Hargreaves arrived from the Duck and Puddle and set about settling into the flat overlooking the courtyard. Frank brought her over in his rather ancient and battered Land Rover and stopped off at her cottage to pick up her clothes and as many of her other belongings as could conveniently be carried. In some parts of the world a half derelict cottage would have been looted of all its valuables within a few hours but I'm pleased to say that things like that don't happen in Bilbury.

While Patsy showed Miss Hargreaves round the flat, apologised for the fact that it didn't have a garden, and helped her put away her clothes in the wardrobe and the dressing table, Frank and I made three trips back to the cottage to rescue what we could of Miss Hargreaves' furniture. None of the curtains or carpets were worth saving.

'It'll do me until my cottage is ready for me to go back into,' said Miss Hargreaves, when we'd finished, Frank had gone back to the Duck and Puddle and the remaining three of us were sitting around in her tiny flat. There were those in the village who claimed that graciousness was not Miss Hargreaves' strong point and it wasn't always too difficult to see why she had acquired this reputation.

'Have you contacted your insurance company, yet?' I asked Miss Hargreaves. With the rooms filled with her furniture (Frank had helped me move most of our furniture down into one of the empty stables underneath) Miss Hargreaves looked very much at home. It is surprising what a few square yards of chintz, half a dozen Victorian water colours, and a packing case full of assorted knick knacks and bric-a-brac can do to a room.

Miss Hargreaves looked surprised. 'Insurance company?' she said, as though I had suggested that she might have a bookmaker. 'I'm afraid I don't really know anything about insurance. I let the School Board looks after that sort of thing.' She wrinkled up her nose as though she found the conversation rather distasteful. To be honest, I rather suspect that she did find the conversation unwholesome in a sweet, rather old fashioned sort of way. Other people, ordinary people, had insurance. Miss Hargreaves had an annual subscription to the National Geographic magazine and considered that to be rather adventurous and twentieth century of her.

'Who's the Chairman of the School Board?' I asked Miss Hargreaves. 'I'd better ring him and make sure that he's put in a claim for you. We'll need to get the insurance company to look at things as soon as they can so that they can give the go-ahead for the repair work to start.'

Miss Hargreaves, was clearly and quite genuinely surprised at this apparently unexpected complication. I have a feeling that she rather expected that the repair work would have started automatically the moment her belongings had been removed from the battered building. She ignored my question. 'How long do you think it will take?' she wanted to know. 'I'd like to be back in the cottage in two weeks time.'

I looked across at Patsy. Patsy looked back at me. Neither of us really wanted to say what clearly had to be said. But, it *had* to be said. So I took a deep breath and said it.

'I'm afraid I don't think the cottage will be ready in two weeks,' I told Miss Hargreaves, rather warily. She raised an eyebrow. 'Well, not completely,' I added, instinctively backing away. If Miss Hargreaves' eyebrow had been at Neville Chamberlain's disposal Adolf Hitler would have never dared try anything on in 1939. I have never known another human being able to express so much emotion, disapproval and contempt with a simple flicker of an eyebrow. 'I don't think you should actually, positively *bank* on being back in the cottage in a fortnight,' I said rather weakly. Secretly, I rather thought that we would be lucky if we'd got the go ahead from the insurance company by then. And I rather thought that the rebuilding work could take four or five months or maybe, perish the thought, even longer. And even that was assuming that we could find builders who were prepared to start work straight away. With all the damage the blizzard had done both in Bilbury and in neighbouring villages I had a feeling that builders would suddenly find themselves in the enviable position of being greatly in demand. Every dog has his day, so the saying goes, and builders have their days when lots of people want their roofs putting back on straight- away - and - a - little - bit - quicker - if - you - can - manage - it - please - don't - worry - too - much - about - the - price - the - insurance - company - is - paying.

Miss Hargreaves didn't say anything but she had a way of not saying anything. Some people can say a great deal when they don't say anything. Miss Hargreaves was one of those people. She could perform extensive, impressive feats of oratory without saying anything.

'I'm sorry,' I said, hardly recognising the feeble little voice which seemed to have come out of my body. I wasn't sure why I was apologising but it seemed the sensible thing to do.

I remembered my unanswered question and asked it again. 'Who is the Chairman of the School Board.'

'A pompous half-wit called Palfrey,' replied Miss Hargreaves, with disdain. 'He's an estate agent,' she added, giving me this information in the same sort of tone that she might have used if she had told me that he had a penchant for gambling or some other morally indefensible activity.

'Do you know where he works?'

She gave me the name of an estate agents' office in Barnstaple.

'I'll go and ring him,' I said, standing up.

'Just tell him that I want to be back in my cottage in two weeks time,' said Miss Hargreaves firmly.

I smiled weakly at her and left.

*   *   *

It took me about ninety seconds to decide that I didn't much like Mr Palfrey. I had never before spoken to anyone who managed to give the impression of being both obsequious and condescending at the same time.

'Bilborough, did you say?' he asked me, when I explained where I was calling from.

'Bilbury,' I repeated. 'Bilbury School. Am I right in thinking that you are the Chairman of the School Board?'

There was a pause. 'Oh, yes, I know it,' said the estate agent at last. He sighed a little when he realised that I hadn't rung to make an offer for a house. 'Tiny little place isn't it? Sweet village. Nice amenities. Conveniently situated. Hunting country. Yes, I'm Chairman of the School Board.' There was another pause. 'I have a lot of other political and social commitments and appointments, you know.'

'The storm took the chimney off Miss Hargreaves' cottage,' I told him. I had had to bite my tongue when he had told me that Bilbury was hunting country. It was true that the hunt did gallop over much of the land around Bilbury but they did this without the support of the villagers; most of whom disapproved of hunting. 'The chimney came straight through into her bedroom and has demolished most of the house. She's staying with my wife and I at Bilbury Grange. Well, not exactly with us, you understand. We have a small, self contained flat that she's borrowing.'

'What has all this got to do with the school?' asked Mr Palfrey.

'Miss Hargreaves is the schoolteacher,' I explained. 'She lives in School Cottage. It's an insurance claim.'

'Oh, yes, I know it,' said the estate agent. I could almost hear him nodding. 'Nothing to do with us, though. Miss Hargreaves has a lease on the cottage. She's responsible for her own insurance.'

I went cold.

'Are you sure?' I asked him.

'Absolutely,' insisted Mr Palfrey. 'I remember the subject of insurance coming up at a meeting a few months ago. We had a very lengthy discussion about the school's insurance policy. One of the Board members thought we were paying too much and we managed to obtain a considerably cheaper quotation from his company. I distinctly remember that the cottage was excluded from the policy.'

I didn't say anything. I felt a little dizzy. 'Are you absolutely sure that Miss Hargreaves isn't covered under the school's insurance?' I pulled a chair towards me and sat down.

'Absolutely sure,' said Mr Palfrey, rather wearily. 'She was expected to make her own insurance arrangements since the property is her responsibility.' There was another pause. 'You aren't telling me that Miss Hargreaves has no insurance, are you?'

'Good heavens, no!' I lied quickly, not wanting to get Miss

Hargreaves into trouble. 'I'm sure she's arranged something,' I added.

'Good,' said Mr Palfrey. 'Thank you for calling.'

'By the way,' I said, before he could go, 'I know you'll be pleased to hear that Miss Hargreaves wasn't injured.'

'Oh, yes,' said Mr Palfrey. 'Jolly good.' And he put the phone down.

I sat there for several minutes listening to the buzzing of the disconnected telephone and wondering how on earth I was going to tell Miss Hargreaves that she wasn't insured.

*   *   *

CHAPTER FIVE

The local witches coven was having a meeting upstairs at the Duck and Puddle and the car park was full of Ford Populars, Austin Minis and other, comfortable, 'compact' English motor cars. The witches, there were eleven of them, met once a month and exchanged recipes, spells and incantations. Since one of the members of the coven was also a part-time slimming adviser they also borrowed Gilly's bathroom scales. The floorboards above our heads were groaning and we could hear them giggling as they took it in turns to strip down to the bare essentials and weigh themselves.

I rested my chin on my hands and looked out of the window. A thin layer of salt, left by spray brought inland by the wind, had clouded the glass. Outside the snow had now almost gone completely. It had virtually disappeared overnight, leaving every low lying piece of land in the area flooded. The thaw had, inevitably, turned into something of a plumber's bonanza as householders all across North Devon suddenly discovered the twin laws of plumbing: that burst pipes leak and that water obeys the laws of gravity. All that remained of the blizzard now were those few small pockets of snow which the wind had pushed into corners and which the sun had not yet managed to melt. The village green, which had been temporarily converted into a village white, had been restored to its original green glory.

'Why on earth didn't she get herself some insurance cover?' asked Dr Brownlow for at least the fifteenth time. No one bothered to answer because although we had all asked the same question roughly the same number of times no one had yet managed to come up with an answer.

There were six of us: myself, Dr Brownlow, Thumper Robinson, Peter Marshall, Gilly Parsons and Kay McBride, the bathukolpian local district nurse. Kay had been the first person I had met when I had arrived in Bilbury although then she had been called Mrs Wilson and had been married to the local policeman. Now she was married to a tractor engineer from Ilfracombe. Mr McBride was twenty two years younger than the former Mrs Wilson.

We had formed a sort of unofficial 'Help Miss Hargreaves' group to try to work out a way to make sure first that Miss Hargreaves didn't spend the rest of her life tramping the streets or slumped in a debtors' prison and second that the school didn't close down through lack of a teacher.

When I had broken the news to Miss Hargreaves that she was not insured, and therefore could not realistically expect any of Britain's insurance companies to pay for the repairs on her cottage, she had seemed remarkably phlegmatic about it all. I had rather expected her to throw what is usually regarded as 'a bit of a wobbly', firing deadly eyebrows off in all directions, but nothing of the sort had happened. Instead she had simply sighed, said something that sounded rather like, 'Oh, dearie, me!' and smiled rather thinly in my direction.

'Have you got any savings?' I asked her, rather brashly.

Miss Hargreaves had visibly brightened at this and had instructed me to pass her handbag. This was not as simple a task as it sounds for the piece of luggage in question was far too large to be accepted as cabin baggage on any airline I've ever travelled on. It was the sort of item usually known as a 'carpet bag' although this one looked as though it had been made from a whole carpet roll rather than an offcut. From this capacious piece of luggage she had extracted a thin and rather dogged National Savings Book which she had handed to me with considerable caution. From the way in which she handled it the passbook was clearly not an item which she handed over to any Tom, Dick or Harry and I felt rather honoured.

'£129 17s 6d!' I read, from the bottom line. Miss Hargreaves hadn't had her passbook updated since decimalisation. For a brief moment I harboured the joyful thought that the interest on the capital might have built up into a sizeable sum. I once read a news story about a man who put a dollar in a bank account during the American Civil War. When a descendant found the pass book compound interest had turned the dollar into a fortune so large that the pass book holder owned the bank. But a look at the date on Miss Hargreaves' National Savings Book dashed this slender hope. I am no mathematical genius but even I could work out that at four and a half per cent interest £129 isn't likely to grow into a fortune in three and three quarter years.

'I'm afraid I don't think that will be anywhere near enough,' I said, glumly.

'Oh dear,' said Miss Hargreaves. 'I always intended to save but somehow I never got round to it.' This was, I knew, not because she was self indulgent but because she was generous. She was always buying clothes and books for children and she supplemented the Bilbury School's meagre book and equipment allowance with much of her own money. Her earnings had been frittered away not on secret bottles of sweet sherry, French cigarettes or horses with a penchant for travelling slowly and a preference for grazing rather than running but on second hand copies of Robinson Crusoe, Treasure Island, Black Beauty, Swiss Family Robinson and similar classics for the school library. It was Miss Hargreaves, said Patsy, who had taught her to love books and to find friendship, companionship and comfort among the novels of many different writers.

When the School Board somehow found out that Miss Hargreaves had not bought any insurance, and furthermore, had no savings with which to pay for the repairs to her cottage, they held an Emergency Special Meeting in Bilbury Village Hall. This meeting was held in secret and so it was not until later that evening that we discovered that the members of the board had decided to close down our village school completely and transfer all seventeen pupils to a school in nearby Combe Martin. It was only about a year since National Health Service Administrators had decided to close down my surgery in Bilbury and transfer patients to a medical list in Barnstaple, so this additional bad news was greeted with considerable dismay by those villagers who felt that this was just too much to bear and that the village was rapidly losing its personal identity.

'The school has no funds to pay for the repair to the School Cottage,' Mr Palfrey had explained when I had telephoned him about it. 'We've decided that the only viable financial route is to sell the school to be used as a personal residence and to real-locate the proceeds among the other schools in the area.'

'Less a fat commission for selling the property,' I had thought but hadn't said. I really didn't like Mr Palfrey. Only an estate agent could refer to a 'home' as a 'personal residence'.

Mr Palfrey had, however, rather unwillingly agreed that if we in the village managed to raise enough money to get School Cottage repaired then the School Board would allow the village school to stay in business.

'So,' said Thumper. 'There's only one thing for it!'

We all looked at him expectantly.

'We'll have to raise the money ourselves,' he explained, as though it was the most obvious thing in the world which in a way I suppose it was. 'The School Board isn't planning to close the school down until the beginning of the autumn term so that gives us,' he looked at a calendar on the wall and did a quick calculation (the calendar was for the year 1963 but since the government hadn't got round to changing the names of the months the principle was the same), 'eight and a half months.'

'How much is it going to cost?' asked Peter Marshall, the village shopkeeper, taxi driver, undertaker, postman, florist and pessimist. Peter can always be relied upon to think about these mundane matters although I do think that his reputation as the meanest man on Exmoor is, in my view, rather un-justified. Although I have been living in Bilbury for a long time I still haven't had a bill from him. Every time I ask him how much I owe he just smiles at me and tells me not to concern myself with such trifles. I do sometimes worry that one of these days I am going to have to take out a second mortgage to settle up with him.

'There won't be much change from £8,000,' said Thumper.

I've noticed before that builders seem rather to like the phrase 'there won't be much change from … '. This quite inaccurately implies that there is likely to be some change. Strictly speaking Thumper Robinson isn't a builder, for he earns his living doing what he describes as 'a bit of this and a bit of that', (After living in Bilbury for a while I understand that this is the rural equivalent of being in the 'import-export busi-ness'), but he has done enough brick and mortar work in his time to know his way around a building estimate.

'That means it'll be £10,000,' said Dr Brownlow, with a weary sigh. Dr Brownlow, who lives in a house which is so large that not even he knows how many bedrooms there are, has much experience of dealing with builders.

Thumper waved a hand backwards and forwards to indicate that he didn't entirely disagree with this interpretation. 'There's a new thatch, a new chimney, new ceiling, new bedroom floor and then there's the decorating.'

'It's all a bit academic, isn't it?' said Mrs McBride. 'How on earth are we going to raise that much money?'

This realistic but gloomy thought successfully silenced the discussion for a while.

'Why don't we organise a Revel?' asked Dr Brownlow, suddenly and quite unexpectedly.

'A what?' I asked. I'd never heard of a Revel before. I had no idea what one was.

'What a brilliant idea!' cried Peter Marshall, looking genuinely excited. I hadn't seen Peter Marshall look excited since a coach-load of Japanese tourists had stopped outside his shop. Within ten minutes he had not only got rid of a whole box of out of date photographic film but had also sold his entire stock of sticky fly paper. The Japanese had been fascinated by it.

'Of course!' agreed Thumper. 'A Revel!'

'What's a Revel?' asked Mrs McBride.

'We haven't had one of those for years!' said Peter Marshall.

Gilly Parsons looked at me. 'What's a Revel?' she whispered. I shrugged.

'When was the last one?' asked Thumper.

'It must have been 1961,' said Peter Marshall.

'It was before that,' said Dr Brownlow, shaking his head. 'Maybe 1957 or 1958.'

'What on earth is a Revel?' demanded Gilly Parsons, laughing.

Dr Brownlow looked at Thumper, Thumper looked at Peter Marshall and Peter looked at Dr Brownlow.

'It's a bit difficult to explain,' said Dr Brownlow. 'It's a sort of fair.'

'Spelt f-a-y-r-e,' said Thumper.

'We always used to have them,' explained Peter Marshall.

'I remember that we always used to raise a lot of money,' said Dr Brownlow.

'That was one of the main reasons why we stopped them,' said Thumper. 'No one could agree on what to do with the money.'

'But what is a Revel?' demanded a very impatient Mrs McBride.

'It's whatever we want it to be,' said Dr Brownlow, after a lengthy silence. 'Side shows, cricket tournament, bowling for the pig, dancing, vegetable show, all that sort of thing.'

'A real Revel lasts for a whole week,' explained Thumper. 'Traditionally it starts on a Sunday after morning service and ends at midnight on Saturday. Sometimes they go on for longer.'

'How will a fayre pull in that sort of money?' I asked.

'Grockles!' said Peter Marshall, with a broad grin. 'Grockle' is the local term for a tourist.

'We'll have maypole dancing, morris dancing and all that stuff,' said Peter Marshall. 'The grockles love it!'

'I hate to throw cold water on this but can anyone in the village actually do morris dancing?' I asked quietly. I'd once seen men morris dancing and it had looked very complicated. There looked to be much more to it than having little bells sewn onto your socks and then dancing around banging sticks.

'No problem!' said Peter. 'My grandfather used to be a great morris dancer. I've got a book on it somewhere. Philip Dinsdale knows all about morris dancing. He used to run the Bilbury Morris Dancers. We'll get him to start them up again.' He rubbed his hands together. 'What a great idea!' he said. 'A Revel!' He looked around the table and grinned at us all. 'You've got a real treat in store,' he said to me. 'My old granddad always used to say that if you ain't seen a Bilbury Revel you ain't lived properly!'

'So, shall we do that then?' said Dr Brownlow. 'Organise a Revel to pay for the repairs to Miss Hargreaves' cottage?'

We all formally agreed with this.

'Now that we've sorted out where the money is going to come from I can get a few of the lads together to start work pretty well straight away,' said Thumper. 'The quicker we start the sooner we'll be finished. I can get all the stuff we need on tick.'

He, like everyone else, seemed to take it for granted that by organising a Revel we would automatically raise enough money to pay for all the repairs that Miss Hargreaves' cottage needed.

Peter Marshall then decided that this would be a good time for someone to go for another round of drinks while he popped upstairs to see if one of the witches would run a Fortune Tellers' tent for us.

*   *   *

CHAPTER SIX

I was helping Patsy clear away the breakfast things when there was a sudden, sharp knock on the back door. Patsy looked at me and I looked at her. Neither of us could think of anyone who would knock on the back door at that time in the morning. Anyone from the village would have just walked into the kitchen.

There was one easy way to find out who was there. I put the plates I was carrying into the sink and opened the door.

'Good morning!' said a rather scruffy individual whom I had never seen before. He wore a suit that looked as if it had once been rather smart and a floppy tweed hat which looked at least two sizes too small for him. He had a grey, curly beard and handfuls of curly grey hair escaped from underneath his hat. He looked a bit like a pixie.

'Good morning!' I replied.

'Lovely house,' said the pixie.

'Thank you.'

'Beautiful garden.'

'Thank you.'

'Do you need any help with it?'

'I beg your pardon?'

'Your garden,' explained the pixie. 'Do you need any help with it?'

'I don't really know,' I mumbled. 'We hadn't really thought about it.' I half turned to look back at Patsy who couldn't see who was at the door but had obviously heard the conversation. She raised an eyebrow and shrugged her shoulders.

'Give me a trial week,' suggested the pixie.

The truth was that we undeniably did need someone to help us with the garden. It was far too big for us to be able to cope

with without any outside help and although we had successfully restored the vegetable garden we had still done nothing at
all to the area around the small ornamental lake.

'I don't think we can afford anyone,' I confessed, deciding
the truth was better than a made up excuse.

The pixie looked up and around the courtyard, clearly finding this difficult to believe. 'I'm not expensive,' he said, with
another big grin.

'I know it's a big house,' I said, 'but we aren't rich.' I thought
I caught a touch of disbelief in his eyes. 'Honestly!' I added.

'I tell you what I'll do,' said the pixie. 'I'll work for you for £5
and somewhere to sleep – then you see what you think and if
you're satisfied with my work you pay me what you can afford.
Give me a trial for a week.'

I half turned again and looked at Patsy. She made it clear
that she was happy to leave the negotiations up to me.

'Come in,' I said, stepping back from the door and making a
snap decision. He looked trustworthy enough. 'We'll find you a
room. We'll pay you £5 a week and we'll share the income from
selling fruit and vegetables to the local shops and hotels.'

'That's very fair!' said the pixie. He didn't enter the house.
'But I didn't mean a room in the *house*!' He seemed genuinely
embarrassed and looked around the courtyard. 'You must
have a bit of a stable somewhere, a loft, something like that ...,'
he waved a hand around airily to make it clear that he wasn't
fussy.

We found him a dry loft above one of the unused stables and
he seemed well pleased with this. When he had deposited his
bag, a small canvas holdall which would have made a scarcely
adequate weekend bag for most travellers, Patsy and I led him
on a brief guided tour of the garden. He seemed quietly impressed with the state of the walled vegetable plot but tutted
and oohed and aahed when he saw the overgrown and out of
control gardens around the ornamental lake.

'There's a lot to do,' said Patsy.

'There is that,' said the pixie. 'But you've got the makings,'
he added quietly and appreciatively. 'Oh, yes, you've certainly
got the makings.'

I thought I knew what he meant.

We walked slowly back towards the house together.

'I've suddenly realised that we don't know your name!' said Patsy.

'No,' said the pixie. He had engaging, twinkly eyes but there was a sadness in them. He looked the sort of man who liked smiling but hadn't had much to smile about recently. But he still didn't tell us his name.

'What is it?' I asked him after we'd walked on together for another half a dozen paces.

'Parfitt,' said the pixie, almost reluctantly.

'Welcome to Bilbury Grange, Mr Parfitt,' said Patsy.

'Thank you,' replied the pixie. We showed him where there was a water tap and an outside lavatory, told him that he could help himself to any winter vegetables still growing in the garden and warned him about the existence of Miss Hargreaves whom we hardly ever saw and who had settled into the coach-house flat very well.

And so we acquired a gardener; albeit only on trial for a week.

When we got back to the house we discovered that a delivery van had been out from Barnstaple with a parcel for me. Because there had been no one in the house the driver had left a card to say that he had taken the parcel all the way back into town. I went and fetched the car keys and set off straight away. I rather thought I knew what the parcel might be and I was anxious to collect it without too much delay.

*   *   *

The road from Bilbury to Barnstaple twists and turns a hundred times. People who believe that crows fly in straight lines would probably estimate that a flying crow would measure the distance between our village and the nearest town as no more than five miles. But for earthbound travellers, who have to obey the whims of centuries old track makers, the distance is twice as far. The A39, the main coast road down through North Devon and North Cornwall skirts around the edge of the straggling village of Kentisbury, passes Arlington Court on the left and climbs up a steep hill around the edge of Woolley Wood before dropping down to skirt past the edge of the village of Shirwell and enter Barnstaple from the north east. I know the road well and because it was winter and there were

54

no visitors around I drove quickly, taking particular care on those corners which were sheltered from the sun and which might therefore still be icy. The weather had become a little milder since the big blizzard but there were still patches of drifted snow to be seen on the northern side of many hedgerows.

I had just negotiated the severe hairpin bend half way up the hill past Woolley Wood when I saw a couple of red flags sticking out of the side of the hedge. The flags were faded, dirty and drooping and I very nearly missed them completely.

I stamped my foot on the brake and skidded to a halt just in time to avoid smashing into the back of a very grubby pick up truck. The truck was so dirty that it was quite impossible to see what colour it had been when it had been first driven out of the showroom. In fact it was so grubby that it was difficult to believe that it had ever even been in a showroom. Not that this was anything unusual. As a general rule in North Devon it is fairly safe to assume that any vehicle which isn't battered or dirty belongs to a visitor.

The truck had been parked less than fifty yards after a blind bend. A small grey saloon was parked a few yards in front of the truck. Three scruffy figures and a man in a suit were standing in the road talking. The man in the suit was holding a clip board. He looked very cold. A fallen tree trunk lay across half the road and two of the scruffy men were holding chain saws. The road was littered with sawdust and small branches.

A tall, long haired figure wearing a green jacket, a beige woolly hat, dark brown corduroy trousers and a pair of heavy boots waved to me and wandered over towards me. I didn't know his name but I recognised him. During the summer months he operated a hut renting out surfboards and selling ice cream on one of the nearby beaches and during the winter he earned a living doing anything that wasn't overtly illegal.

'Hello, doc!' he cried, grinning cheerfully when he recognised me. It seemed clear that whatever was going on was going to take some time so I got out of the car and wandered over to him. I sometimes think that living in Devon is a bit like living in Spain. There isn't a lot of point in trying to hurry because by and large things will get done when the people doing them are ready to do them and no amount of cajoling or threatening will make any difference. Since I've lived in Bilbury I've known of

55

three couples who have left London to live in the area. They all returned to their more familiar haunts within a year, claiming that they found the slow, laid back pace of life far too stressful for them.

'You'd get on quicker if you didn't cut everything up so small!' insisted the man in the suit. He shivered uncontrollably. He pointed to the pile of logs at the side of the road. They looked as if they'd been cut to fit perfectly into the average sort of fireplace.

'We have to cut them into small pieces or else we can't get them into the back of the truck,' said one of the woodmen. I recognised him too. I'd seen him at the Duck and Puddle.

The man in the suit frowned, clearly unconvinced.

'I've got a bad back,' said one of the men.

'Hernia,' said another.

'It's me chest,' said the third.

The man in the suit scribbled something on his clip board, glowered at no one in particular, shivered and walked back to his car. He got in, performed an eighteen point turn and drove away. When he'd gone the three men dragged the tree trunk out of the way so that I could drive past.

'Don't strain yourselves!' I shouted.

They grinned back at me and the man in the woolly hat who rented out surfboards in the summer winked.

*　　*　　*

The parcel was, as I had expected and hoped, from my publishers in London. It contained my six author's copies of my very first book. I signed the forms that the brown coated man behind the counter handed to me and took the parcel carefully into my arms.

'You don't need to worry,' said the man in the brown coat, pointing to the form I'd signed. 'It's only books.'

Only books! He might as well have said: 'It's only holy relics' or 'It's only the crown jewels'.

I could have not felt more tenderly towards that parcel if it had contained my first born baby. In many ways that was exactly what it *did* contain. I had spent nearly a year writing the book, a serious exposé of the international drug industry, and when I had finished the researching, and the writing, and the editing and the proof reading and the answering of queries from the libel lawyers (that alone had taken three months and by the time I'd finished the book was less than two thirds of its original length) I was as exhausted and as careworn as a mother at the end of a full nine month pregnancy.

I glowered at the insensitive bibliophobe in the brown coat, tucked the parcel safely under my arm and walked out to my car. There I sat and stared at the parcel for what seemed like an hour or two (but was probably no more than a couple of minutes). I desperately wanted to open the parcel and see what one of my babies looked like. But I also wanted to share that magical moment with Patsy.

Something the publisher had said to me kept coming back. 'However many other books you write this will always be your first book,' he had said when I was flagging during the lengthy editing process. 'You must make it as good a book as you can.' I had done just that.

I made the decision to delay the opening of the parcel until I got home, put the unopened package down on the passenger seat, fastened the seat belt around it and set off on the winding journey back to Bilbury Grange.

The three wood cutters were still working near Woolley Wood, though the tree trunk they had been chopping up had more or less disappeared. I slowed down as I approached their truck and the ice cream salesman in the woolly hat waved to me. I wound down the car window and stuck my head out into the cold.

'Is the hernia O.K.?' I asked.

'Fine, thanks, doc!' he grinned. He rubbed his hands together. He wore no gloves and it really was bitterly cold. 'Do you want some logs?' he asked me, pointing to the large pile of neatly cut small logs in the back of the pick up truck. The three of them had been busy.

'How much do you want for them?' I asked him.

He suggested a price that seemed half way between outrageous and absurd. I offered a price that was mid way between mean and theft. We then quickly agreed on a sensible compromise; the price both of us had probably thought of in the first place. Patsy and I had burnt up quite a large proportion of our stock of logs during the blizzard and it seemed an excellent opportunity to replenish our supplies. Patsy's father had explained to me that logs burn best if stored for a year or more and so I didn't want to have to buy logs at the last minute. Green wood is slow to ignite, burns poorly and tends to give off more steam than anything else.

'We've just got a bit more tidying up to do,' said the man in the woolly hat. 'Shouldn't take us more than half an hour or so.'

'I'll be back home by then,' I told him. As I drove away I couldn't help smiling to myself. The men had been paid by the council to remove the tree trunk and they had now managed to get paid by me for the logs. I rather suspected that they would all be doing a little celebrating later that evening. Being a townie who relied on central heating the man in a suit from the council probably hadn't even realised that a chopped up tree can have a cash value in the countryside.

*   *   *

Patsy and I sat in the kitchen staring at the parcel for a while.

'Aren't you going to open it?' asked Patsy at last.

'You open it.'

'No, you. It's your book.'

I picked up the parcel, found the knot and picked eagerly at the string. Whoever had packed the parcel had certainly taken no chances with it coming undone.

'Cut it,' suggested Patsy, handing me a sharp kitchen knife.

'I can't do that!' I said, rather shocked. When I was a boy my mother would never let anyone cut string. I don't know whether this was because she thought it was bad luck to cut string (she had a lot of superstitions and quite a few of them seemed to involve black cats, the number thirteen and pieces of string) or because she just thought it was a waste (I suspect that the latter may have had some influence on her thinking for I don't think she ever threw away anything – her kitchen always contained mountains of neatly folded paper bags). We always had to undo string, roll it up neatly and put it into the string box before we could even think of unwrapping the rest of the parcel.

Patsy smiled and put the knife away. She had enough superstitions of her own not to dismiss mine as entirely silly. When I had eventually managed to unravel the knot, had unfastened the string, folded it, tied it neatly and put it away in a drawer (we didn't at the time have a string box though we did eventually acquire one) I carefully unfolded the thick brown wrapping paper. Inside that there was another thick layer of wrapping paper, made up of large proof sheets from another author's book. And inside that layer of wrapping paper lay my six author's copies. I stared at the small neat pile of books for a moment and could feel my heart beating wildly. A *With Compliments* slip lay on top of the books. I picked that up first and carefully laid it down on the table. Then I picked up one of the books and handed it to Patsy and picked up another book to look at myself. On the front cover there was the title and my name. On the back cover there was a small piece of blurb about the book and a photograph that made me look quite respectable. I examined the jacket spine and then I slowly undressed the book and examined the binding. Then I put the dust wrapper back around the book and flicked through the pages. I could hardly believe it. But the proof lay in my hands. I had written a book.

'It's just like a real book!' said Patsy, holding her copy book very gently, as though frightened that it might suddenly fall apart.

'Yes!' I said.

'Here's that chapter that you had all those worries about!'

'It's nice paper isn't it?'

'It's a good photograph of you.'

'Do you think anyone will want to buy it?' I asked, suddenly overwhelmed by an awful feeling that after all this trouble the book would not be of any interest to anyone.

Patsy looked up at me and reached out to hold my hand. 'It doesn't matter whether they do or they don't,' she said quietly.

She was right.

For that moment I didn't care what the critics said or whether anyone bought the book or not. The important thing was that I had written my first book. No one could ever take that away from me.

And then for the second time that day there was a loud knocking at the back door and I had to go and show the wood cutters where to unload the logs I'd bought.

'I almost forgot,' said Patsy, when I came in from helping to move the logs from the back of the yellow truck into the back of our log shed, 'there were two telephone calls for you while you were in Barnstaple.' Inevitably, the wood cutters had wanted to dump the newly cut logs at the front of the shed. I had had to give them an extra pound each to persuade them to help me to put the logs right at the back where there was plenty of room and where they would be able to dry out in peace for a year or so. The first call had been from a girl called Tanya who worked for a publicity agency in London which had, apparently, been hired by my publishers to promote my book. They wanted to know if I would go up to London to meet with them and discuss the various ways of publicising the book. The second telephone call had been from Peter Marshall who hadn't left any message apart from the fact that he wanted me to ring him back.

I rang the publicity people in London first and got hold of Tanya straight away.

'First,' she cooed, 'I have to tell you how *thrilled* we all are to be handling your book. It's going to be a real joy and a privilege to work with you.'

Not realising that this was publicity-agent-speak for 'hello' I felt a little embarrassed at the effusiveness of this greeting. 'That's very kind of you,' I stuttered back, rather hesitantly.

'Oh no,' said Tanya. 'We really are most terribly, terribly excited by this project. I can't tell you how honoured we are to have been chosen to help promote your book. Mr Leytonstone himself has told us that the book must be given every priority. He is convinced that it's going to be a major, major bestseller.'

'Oh,' I said, rather taken aback by all this. 'Thank you.' Then after a moment's hesitation I asked who Mr Leytonstone was. This question clearly threw poor Tanya who obviously lived in a world where everyone not only knew who Mr Leytonstone was but also regarded him as being only slightly less important than the gods of fire, water and earth.

'My Leytonstone is our Senior Account Director,' she answered, in a whisper. I realised that she was probably whispering because she was embarrassed at having to explain who Mr Leytonstone was.

'Ah,' I said, as knowledgeably as I could.

'We would all love to meet you so that we can take on board your views about how the book should be promoted,' said Tanya. 'And, of course, we would like the opportunity to tell you about our plans for you and your book.'

'Er, yes,' I said. 'Thank you.' I was naturally keen to go and talk to the publicity people who were going to turn my book into a bestseller but I really didn't fancy the idea of a trip to London.

'We'll be fixing up lots of radio and television interviews for you,' said Tanya. 'Deborah has already started talking to people about you.'

'Radio?' I said. 'And television?' I could feel my palms becoming sweaty. I wondered who Deborah was.

'Oh, yes, absolutely. Have you done any broadcasting before?'

'Broadcasting? Er, no, I don't think so,' I muttered. I was beginning to get very cold feet about this whole business.

'You'll be absolutely marvellous,' said Tanya. 'I just know you will. Now, when can you come up and have lunch with us all? Would next Wednesday be convenient?'

I looked at the calendar hanging on the wall near to the telephone. There was nothing at all written on it. 'Yes, I think so,' I said, hesitantly. 'Next Wednesday would be fine.'

'Wonderful. Everyone here will be so thrilled that you're coming! It's going to be a real treat for us all to meet you.'

'Er, thank you,' I mumbled.

'Goodbye then,' said Tanya.

'Goodbye,' I said and found myself listening to the brrrr of a disconnected telephone.

*   *   *

After all this it was a real relief to telephone Peter Marshall and get back to the real world. After the telephone had rung for what seemed like a lifetime Peter eventually picked up the receiver and then immediately asked me if I could wait for a moment, explaining that a potato sack had split, spewing its contents all over his store room. I sat there listening to him huffing and puffing and cursing in the background as he picked up the potatoes.

61

'Who is it?' he demanded eventually. He sounded very bad tempered.

I told him.

'Oh, hello!' he said. 'What can I do for you?'

'You rang and left a message for me to telephone you,' I reminded him.

'Did I?'

'Yes.'

'Oh.' said Peter. 'Well I must have wanted to speak to you about something, I suppose. I wonder what it was. Wait a minute.' Again the phone went dead and this time I heard him rummaging around on his desk. There was a loud crash as something breakable fell on the floor and broke.

'I know what it was,' he said eventually. 'I'm sorry about all that but I've had an absolutely terrible day. Can I put you down for the cricket team?'

'The cricket team?' I exclaimed, horrified. 'Do you mean you want me to *play* cricket?'

'Well I'm not selling tickets and I don't want you to make the teas.'

'I haven't played cricket since I was six years old!' I protested.

'Doesn't matter,' said Peter without hesitation. 'I was appointed secretary of the cricket club at the last meeting and we've only got ten members.'

'What do I have to do?' I asked.

'Turn up,' said Peter baldly. 'You'll only have to field a bit and maybe bat. You can bowl if you like. We're going to play a few matches as part of the Revels.'

'What's the team called?'

'We're the Old Bilburians,' replied Peter.

'The *what*?'

'I know,' sighed Peter. 'I don't know how we got that name. I think someone said it would make us sound more important than Bilbury Village Cricket Club. Can I put you down?'

'Who else is in the team?'

'Thumper, Dr Brownlow, Frank, Patchy,' began Peter.

'O.K.' I agreed. 'Put me down then.'

'Jolly good,' said Peter. 'There's a meeting at 8 tonight at the Duck and Puddle.'

'I'll be there,' I sighed.

* * *

The Old Bilburians Cricket Team had what a generous sports writer might describe as a 'patchy' history. A less generous, more realistic, critic might have preferred words such as 'useless' or even found the plain 'not very good' suitable. An unkind commentator might have found the word 'pathetic' irresistible. It was the sort of team which is usually described as being reliable (roughly translated this means that at least eight men usually turned up for most of its matches) and 'the backbone of the local cricket league' (translated as meaning that no one alive could remember it ever having won a match).

The team, I learned from Peter in the Duck and Puddle that evening, had not actually played any cricket matches for four years. It had, however, had four annual dinners, four summer barbecues, eight committee meetings and five car boot sales and had played six darts matches, four skittles matches and a snooker match.

'I thought we could organise a few matches as part of the Revels Week,' said Peter, when he finally decided that it was time to start the meeting.

'Cricket matches?' asked Dr Brownlow, seemingly startled at the prospect of the Old Bilburians Cricket Team actually playing any cricket. From the looks on the faces of the others I gathered that I was the only one who had been made aware of Peter's plans.

Peter nodded.

There was a lengthy silence as this information sank in.

'Does anyone here actually know how to play cricket?' asked Thumper at last.

There was then another fairly lengthy silence while we all considered this question.

'I used to be a pretty mean leg break bowler,' said Patchy, picking up a beermat and wrapping his fingers around it as though it were a cricket ball.

Dr Brownlow studied Patchy's grip critically. 'Isn't that the grip for an off spin bowler?' he asked cautiously.

Patchy stared at his fingers, at Dr Brownlow and then back at his hand. He frowned. 'Is it?'

'I'm not sure,' confessed Dr Brownlow, with a shrug.

'It's a long time since I was at school,' admitted Patchy quite unnecessarily. He carefully put down the beer mat and flexed his fingers. 'Maybe I was an off spinner,' he said thoughtfully. He picked up the beer mat and tried out the grip again.

'Have we got any equipment?' asked Frank.

We all looked at him. This was an unusually specific, and unexpectedly relevant remark for Frank who, when faced with social events of any nature, is usually more concerned with problems such as 'Will there be enough beer' and 'Who will carry me home afterwards'.

'Equipment?' frowned Dr Brownlow.

'Bats, balls, stuff like that,' explained Frank.

'I can get bats and wickets and balls,' said Peter quickly.

We all looked at him. Peter's shop sells toy beach cricket kits which contain little bats made of balsa wood, stumps that are barely more than eighteen inches high and balls that are so light that they travel no more than ten feet however hard you hit them.

'I'm not sure that the stuff you sell will be quite the sort of equipment our opponents will be used to,' said Dr Brownlow, tactfully.

Peter looked at him blankly.

'The stuff in the shop,' explained Dr Brownlow. 'Good, though it is,' he added quickly. Peter can be a little touchy if his wares are criticised. He once hit a French visitor who had dared to criticise his sprouts. He didn't hit him with his fists, of course, but with a rather large piece of broccoli. Afterward a representative from the French Embassy travelled down from London to issue Peter with an official protest. He subsequently needed to have a length of cucumber removed from his person. On another occasion a weekend inhabitant of the village was foolish enough to compare Peter's unwashed, organic carrots unfavourably with those on sale in the Harrod's Food Hall in London. The man, who had also made the mistake of threatening to report Peter to the authorities for not making sure that his outside window blind was the regulation height above the ground, had been promptly banned for life from Peter's shop. A full two years after the incident Peter proved that he isn't a man to bear a grudge lightly by refusing to sell the weekender a newspaper. Peter tutted impatiently and shook his head. 'No,' he said, 'I mean real cricket bats. Real balls too.' He paused, realising perhaps that he got carried away a little. 'Well, nearly real.'

'Ah,' said Dr Brownlow, impressed. 'Nearly real will do us very nicely.'

'I'll get them at cost,' said Peter. He took the small red notebook in which he writes down all his orders and cash transactions out of his inside jacket pocket, licked the business end of a small stub of a pencil which he took from behind his left ear and carefully wrote down the order.

'Will anyone want to play us?' I asked, feeling rather foolish but thinking nevertheless that the question ought to be asked.

'Finding opponents won't be a problem,' Dr Brownlow reassured me. 'Every summer there are hundreds of teams from the Midlands down in the West Country looking for games. Any village that has a picturesque ground can get as many matches as it wants. Over at Yoxley they play four or five times a week all through the summer.'

'When the village last had a cricket club we went for years without ever playing an away fixture,' said Thumper. 'Visitors love playing here because we've got a pretty ground.'

'Where is our cricket ground?' I asked.

Everyone looked at me as if I was mad.

'The village green!' said Thumper, pointing through the window.

It was, when I stopped to think about it, a pretty obvious setting though the village green didn't look very much like a cricket pitch. The grass was nearly a foot long and most groundsmen would have regarded it as something of a challenge to get it ready for a football match – let alone a cricket match.

'It'll need a bit of a rolling,' said Dr Brownlow, who has a nice ear for the understated phrase.

'No problem, doctor,' said Thumper. 'I can borrow Herbert Thurlow's roller.'

'Splendid!' said Dr Brownlow.

'Forgive me for asking what is probably another daft question,' I said, 'but if we're going to start playing cricket seriously doesn't it mean that we have to start practising?'

Peter looked at Frank, Frank looked at Thumper and Thumper laughed.

'I don't think we have to be *that* serious about it!' said Thumper.

'Besides,' said Frank, 'practising isn't exactly the gentlemanly thing to do, is it? Not for amateurs.'

'Look at this way,' said Peter, 'our role is to make the other team feel good – they are the visitors after all.'

'And if they feel happy because they've won,' said Frank, 'they'll buy all the drinks!'

'Since I seem to be asking all the stupid questions,' I said, 'can I just ask one more?'

'Certainly!' said Frank. He paused. 'One more.'

'The idea of organising the Revels is to make money to pay for repairing Miss Hargreaves' cottage, right?'

'Right,' agreed Thumper with a nod. Everyone else murmured assent.

'How will a few cricket matches help us make money?'

'Ah!' said Dr Brownlow. 'That's easy. First, the visiting teams will spend money when they're in the village. They'll drink a lot of beer, smoke a lot of tobacco and eat a lot of chips. Frank will sell them the beer and the chips and Peter will sell them the tobacco.'

'And we'll sell them raffle tickets,' said Thumper.

'And we give a cut of the extra profits to the Revels Committee,' said Frank.

'Second, if we advertise the fact that we're holding cricket matches on the village green we'll get a lot more visitors to the village. And they'll ... '

'... drink a lot of beer, smoke a lot of tobacco, buy a lot of raffle tickets and eat a lot of chips!' I interrupted.

'And buy a lot of postcards, maps, tinned sweets and magazines!' added Peter with a broad smile. I felt silly for not having thought of all this. I should have known that Peter is not a man to organise anything if there isn't a shilling or two to be made out of it.

'Does the Revels Committee get a cut on all those things?' Dr Brownlow asked Peter, apparently innocently.

Peter looked as though he would have gone red if he'd been

the sort ever to get embarrassed or cross with himself. 'Hrrmph, er, well, not exactly the postcards,' he mumbled.

'What about books?'

'Books are a rather difficult commodity, you know. Margins are poor you know,' said Peter, continuing to mumble.

'Magazines?' asked Dr Brownlow.

'I don't think my contract with the wholesalers allows me to have any arrangements with a third party,' said Peter, quite earnestly and without the hint of a blush.

'Sweets?'

'Oh, the profit on sweets wouldn't be worth having,' said Peter with a shake of his head.

'What do we get a cut on, then?' asked Dr Brownlow.

Peter hesitated. 'Tobacco!' he said at last, giving us all a rather hollow smile.

'We perhaps ought to have a little meeting,' murmured Dr Brownlow, giving Peter a wink. 'See if we can't sort out a few more items where the Revels Committee might conceivably expect a little payment.'

'What about your bottled water, then?' asked Peter.

'I'll certainly be giving ten percent of all my sales during Revels Week,' said Dr Brownlow.

'And we'll give ten percent of the take from the Duck and Puddle during Revels Week,' promised Frank.

Everyone looked at Peter expectantly.

Peter looked glum and for a moment or two didn't say anything. I thought he was probably going to brazen it out. But it turned out that even Peter had a breaking point. 'All right,' he agreed at last. He sighed. 'Ten per cent of all my sales during Revels Week.' He had to drag the words out as though they were sewn in.

'Splendid!' said Dr Brownlow. 'I'd drink to that but my glass is empty.' He leant a little closer to Peter. 'I think it's your round!' he said with a rather wicked smile.

* * *

67

CHAPTER SEVEN

The human body is equipped with an enormous range of subtle and sophisticated mechanisms; many of which are as yet quite unexplained by doctors and some of which you are probably unaware that you have. Should a speck of dust find its way into one of your eyes tears will flood out in an attempt to wash the irritant away. The tears contain a special bactericidal substance designed to kill off any infection. When you have a fever, the rise in your temperature is probably a result of your body trying to help you cope more effectively with any infection that may be present. There is even a quite remarkable mechanism which will enable you to go to bed at night, tell yourself what time you want to wake up and then wake up at that time!

In order to get to London in time to have lunch with the people who had been hired to promote my first book I had to get up at half past five in the morning. When I was working as a doctor I often had to get up out of bed during those parts of the night when I would have preferred to have been fast asleep but I never grew to like it. Many of the other inhabitants of Bilbury, being farmers, probably thought nothing of getting up at half past five in the morning but to me it was still a chore which required discipline and effort.

However, since I was a child I've been able to wake myself up at whatever time I wanted simply by telling myself the specified time. Just how this internal mechanism works is a mystery. But work it does.

On the morning I was due to go to London to meet Tanya and the publicity people who had been hired to promote my book I woke suddenly and carefully reached out, cautiously grasping for the alarm clock. The illuminated hands showed that it was 5.25 am. I turned off the alarm, due to go off in five minutes time (even after all these years I am, I am rather ashamed to admit, still sceptical about my powers to wake up on cue and so whenever I need to get up particularly early I always put the alarm clock on as a mechanical 'back up') picked up the small torch that since the blizzard I had kept on my crowded bedside table alongside the alarm clock, the lamp and the telephone and stealthily crept out of bed. Ben, who had been curled up next to my feet, woke instantly and leapt down off the bed. I reached down and touched her mouth to tell her not to make a sound and took my flannels, my old and faithful sports jacket, a clean woollen shirt and my underwear into the bathroom so that I could get dressed without waking Patsy. I heard Sophie and Emily, our two young cats, follow Ben down off the bed.

Cats are supposed to be silent creatures but those two, particularly Sophie, made so much noise when they moved about that I could never understand just how they managed to catch as much wildlife as they did. Sophie was pretty clumsy as well as noisy and whenever a pot plant was found mysteriously smashed on the floor we knew who to blame. (Not that we ever did blame her, of course. We knew that in reality it was our fault for leaving the plants scattered around in such silly places. Anyone who puts a pot plant on the mantlepiece when there is a cat living in the house must expect to come in one day and find a smashed pot in the hearth.)

It was still dark outside and I couldn't see a thing, though I could hear the wind and the rain lashing against the windows. As usual it was freezing cold in the bathroom. I shaved and then dressed and started to tiptoe down the stairs when to my surprise I heard Patsy calling from the kitchen.

'Your porridge is ready!'

I hurried downstairs. I could smell fresh toast too. The morning was looking better already.

'I didn't even know you were up!'

'You don't think I was going to let you creep out of the house without any breakfast, do you?' Patsy poured boiling water from the kettle into the teapot.

'But it's horribly early!' I said, sitting down at the breakfast table. Ben, Emily and Sophie all sat around looking underprivileged.

'I was brought up on a farm. This isn't early. Come on, start your porridge and I'll boil you a couple of eggs. Do you want syrup on your porridge?'

I said 'yes, please', accepted the proffered tin and put two large dollops of sweet, sticky, golden syrup into the middle of my bowl of porridge. Twenty five minutes later, with a bowlful of porridge, two boiled eggs and two slices of toast inside me, and feeling infinitely better than I had when I'd woken, I stuffed my feet into my shoes, pulled on my coat and gloves, crammed a hat onto my head, scraped the ice off the car windscreen and set off to drive to the railway station in Barnstaple.

It's difficult to feel in a hurry on the journey between Barnstaple and Exeter. The train stops at Lapford, Eggesford and what seems like every other village in the county. When you look at the map it seems as though the railway takes a pretty direct line between Barnstaple and Exeter. In real life I suspect that the train prefers to take a more adventurous, circuitous route.

In Exeter I had a twenty five minute wait before I caught the main line express from Cornwall to Paddington. I bought a newspaper and joined the hardy bunch of early morning travellers waiting to journey East. I can never quite believe it but I have it on the firmest authority that the early morning passenger list from Exeter to London includes a number of daily commuters – most of whom catch an earlier train than the one I was catching! I suppose it's all right if you enjoy travelling and find working and reading on the train easy to do but I would find it an enormously tedious and quite exhausting business.

I was in London by eleven o'clock and since I didn't have to be in the south of the city for my meeting with Tanya, Mr Leytonstone and the others until one o'clock I decided that instead of catching the tube or taking a taxi I would walk from the station. A quick look at the elderly and rather dog eared copy of the map of London that I had brought with me suggested that it couldn't be more than a few miles. It was much warmer in London than it had been in Devon and even though there was a thin, misty rain falling a walk through Hyde Park seemed a much more pleasant proposition than being cooped up in an underground train.

By the time I had stopped at a cafe in Knightsbridge for a cup of tea and a bun (I could have bought a three course meal at the Duck and Puddle for the same price), lingered in a bookshop where I bought a fistful of paperbacks which filled the pockets of my coat and bought a brooch in the shape of a butterfly from a street trader for Patsy it had started to rain more steadily.

There was something distinctly odd about the rain which for a moment or two I couldn't quite put my finger on. Eventually, I realised what it was. The rain was coming straight down and as a result pedestrians who were carrying umbrellas were staying quite dry. In North Devon the rain tends to pay more attention to the wind than to gravity and usually travels horizontally. No locals in Bilbury, Combe Martin, Ilfracombe, Lynton or Barnstaple ever bother carrying umbrellas because they know that if rains then it will probably also be windy. In London businessmen in suits were successfully keeping keep themselves dry by holding newspapers over their heads!

By the time I got to the offices of Taggart, Leytonstone, Mortehoe and Evans (the publicity firm which my publisher had hired to promote my book) my coat and hat and shoes were soaking wet.

'Good morning, can I help you?' asked a stunning young lady with long blonde hair, bright blue eyes and improbable looking eyelashes. The eyelashes were heavy with mascara and pulled her upper eyelids down so low that she had to hold her head back in order to look at me. She wore a high neck, skin tight, Chinese silk mini dress and had a tiny pair of headphones and a miniature microphone hanging around her neck. The dress looked about three sizes too small for her. Her bosom was straining as though anxious to escape and the dress was so short that the welt at the top of her tights was clearly visible. She wore a white enamelled name badge with gold edging and gold writing on it. The badge told me that she was called Felicity.

'I've got an appointment to see Tanya,' I said.

The receptionist leant forward and gingerly tapped at a small telephone switchboard with the end of a pencil, presumably to avoid damaging her finger nails. She held the headphones to one ear and twisted her neck so that she could speak into the microphone. She clearly didn't want to upset her hair by wearing the headphones. 'Hello, Tan,' she said, 'there's a person here to see you.' She looked up at me as she spoke and was clearly not impressed with what she saw. The person at the other end, presumably Tanya, said something which I didn't hear.

'What's your name?' asked the receptionist.

I told her.

The receptionist passed this information on to the person at the other end of the telephone.

Tanya said something which, again, I didn't hear.

'Are you an author?' asked the receptionist, lowering her voice a little, as though anxious lest anyone overhear my embarrassing secret.

I confessed that I was, indeed, an author.

'Yes, he is,' said Felicity. She put a hand half over her microphone as though anxious to stop me overhearing what she was going to say next but the ploy was pointless and I could hear perfectly well. 'He's very wet,' she murmured. There was a lengthy pause while Tanya said something else. 'No,' continued Felicity, with her hand still wrapped around the microphone, 'dripping wet!' She giggled at something that Tanya had said and unplugged the connection. 'Please take a seat,' she said, waving a hand airily towards a sofa. 'Tanya will be with you shortly.'

I hung my coat and hat on a chromium plated hat rack, sat on a black and white striped sofa and waited. There were a dozen, glossy magazines scattered around on a glass topped table but none of them looked particularly attractive. I reached up to my dripping coat and took one of the paperbacks I had bought, 'Walden' by Henry David Thoreau, out of my pocket and settled back to read it.

'Hello! Sorry to have kept you waiting!' said a chirpy young girl about fifteen minutes later. She looked about nineteen, maybe twenty, years old. She had tousled blonde hair that made her look as though she'd just got out of bed and wore a baggy, rugby shirt and a pair of very tight jeans. She rolled her eyes heavenwards. 'I've just had the most ghastly row with a TV producer in Manchester,' she told me. 'He promised me faithfully that he'd get one of our authors on his show but now he says he can't squeeze him in and we've already fixed up newspaper and radio interviews around his wretched show so it's all very beastly and damned inconvenient. Would you like a drink?'

I started to reply but was too slow.

'Felicity, would you be an absolute darling, and bring us three coffees?' She turned to me. 'Follow me, darling, I'll take you along to meet Deborah who'll be working with you.' As she turned she caught sight of my coat and hat, and the puddle that had formed around the base of the hat stand. 'Good heavens, are those yours?'

I said they were. 'I don't actually drink ... ,' I started to add but Tanya wasn't listening.

'Couldn't you get a cab? Oh, you poor darling!' She put a hand on my arm in apparently genuinely concern.

'I walked,' I explained.

'You walked?' It was a question, quite clearly born of disbelief.

'It wasn't far.'

Tanya stopped and stared at me. 'Where did you walk from?'

'Paddington station.'

'Paddington? Oh my god! You must be exhausted. That's the other end of town. Oh my god! That's miles. Oh how awful. Your publisher would have paid for a cab you know. Where have you come from?'

'Devon.'

'Devon? Good heavens! That's where people go for their holidays isn't it? Do you mean to say you actually live there? Oh how absolutely divine! But I could never live there. All that clotted cream! I'd be the size of a house in a week. You simply must meet Tiffany before you go. Her parents come from Devon. Well, they have a holiday home down there. I think it's Torquay or Newquay or somewhere with a quay in it. They're called Parkinson. Tiffy's father is THE Parkinson, the one whose firm makes all those witty advertisements that you see all the time on the television, but you wouldn't know it to talk to her. She's an absolute gem. Do you know them? I'm sure you must. I gather they know just about everybody in Devon. Did you really walk all the way from Paddington?'

I muttered something that sounded suitably inconsequential in reply to this barrage of questions and comments and strode along behind Tanya who had shot off down a corridor at a surprising speed.

'Hugo, this is the wonderful man who has written that absolutely sensational book on drugs!' said Tanya, stopping at an open door. She giggled nervously. A balding man who wore a large pink bow tie, had his trousers held up with a pair of bright yellow braces and was holding a Sherlock Holmes pipe in one hand a telephone in the other put his hand over the telephone and waved to us both. 'He lives in Devon and walked here in an absolute storm!' explained Tanya, pointing to me.

'Pleasure to meet you! I'm sure your book is going to be a tremendous success,' said the man with the bow tie, waving his pipe around airily. His office was lined with bookshelves. All the shelves were crammed with books. His desk was covered with books, manuscripts, magazines and loose papers. 'Jolly good timing. There's a tremendous amount of interest in the drug abuse problem. Heroin, cocaine, cannabis and all that. Tremendous interest. Big problem. I'm sure your book will make a vital contribution to the debate.' He nodded wisely, held his pipe aloft in some sort of salutation, took his hand away from his telephone and continued with his conversation. He had an airy, superior, rather condescending manner which I found slightly disturbing. Some men command respect, some demand it, a few deserve it; Hugo simply seemed to expect it.

'It isn't actually about drug abuse,' I tried to tell him, but he wasn't listening. 'It's about drug companies and, er, doctors...,' I continued lamely, abandoning my reply when I realised that Hugo was ignoring me.

'That was Mr Leytonstone himself,' whispered Tanya, hurrying along the corridor again. 'Isn't he an absolute angel? Absolutely brilliant, of course. He personally masterminded the Stuart Wallis story and when he was in advertising he thought up that completely sensational campaign for Tracey's Ales. He's a writer too so he has a special affinity with our authors. He wrote a book about advertising which is an absolute classic I'm told. I haven't actually read it, of course, because you can't get a copy – they're like absolute gold dust – but everyone says it's really the most important thing ever written.'

I didn't have the faintest idea who Stuart Wallis was and I

hadn't heard of Tracey's Ales but I made what I hoped were suitable noises to let Tanya know how impressed I was.

'And this,' said Tanya, pausing in the doorway of an office the size of a broom cupboard, 'is Deborah who'll be looking after you. She's going to take over your life completely, aren't you Debsie? Call her Debsie everyone does.'

I peered over Tanya's shoulder at a girl of about eighteen. She looked up at me and smiled. She had a thin, nervous looking face and shoulder length jet black hair. She wore a tee shirt with a message I couldn't quite decipher.

'He lives in Devon and he walked all the way here in the pouring rain! Isn't he divine? You're going to be fighting off producers when they see him.'

I hesitated, but thought I probably ought to correct Tanya before I developed too much of a reputation as a long distance walker. 'I didn't actually walk from Devon – only Paddington. And it wasn't raining all that much.'

Tanya waved a hand dismissively, as though none of this was important. 'Debsie is going to have you flying all over the country! Manchester, Glasgow, Birmingham, Cardiff. Everywhere! You'll be a household name by the time she's finished with you!'

'Golly,' I murmured. I wasn't sure that I was ready for any of this.

'And that's Fawn and that's Vanessa,' continued Tanya, pointing first at a plump, buxom blonde in a white silk blouse and then a freckled, redhead in a mauve jumper. 'They are the rest of my team!' Fawn and Vanessa, who were both busy on the telephone, beamed at me and waved their pens. I smiled back and waved rather diffidently.

'Do you want to come with us to my office, Debsie?' asked Tanya. 'There's a bit more room there and you can explain to us all the exciting things that you've got planned!'

'Shall I order some coffee?' asked Deborah, picking up all her telephone. As she reached across her desk I could read the message on her tee shirt but I still couldn't understand it.

'It's all done, darling!' cried Tanya, rushing off again. I hurried after her and heard Deborah clip clopping along behind me. Intrigued by the sound I turned, looked and saw that she was wearing white, high heeled, backless, toeless sandals. I couldn't help wondering if she'd travelled through wintry London wearing such impractical footwear.

'Sit yourself down!' said Tanya, as she led me into her office. It looked like another broom cupboard. Like every room I'd seen in Taggart, Leytonstone, Mortehoe and Evans the walls were covered with bookshelves, the bookshelves were bending under the weight of the books they were carrying and the desk was littered with books, manuscripts, press releases, letters and scribbled notes. Three mugs full of steaming hot black coffee stood in the middle of the desk. I hadn't seen Felicity bring the coffee although she must have walked down the corridor behind me. I sat down on an uncomfortable metal chair. Deborah, sat down beside me on a similar chair and lay down a huge diary across her knees. The open pages of the diary were covered with tiny, scribbly hand writing and there were at least fifty bits of paper sticking out of other pages in the book. I could see my name printed in large letters under the day's date. It was spelt wrongly.

'Debsie is really thrilled to be working on your book. Aren't you Debsie?' Deborah confirmed that she was, indeed, quite thrilled to be working on my book and added that she was envied by both Fawn and Vanessa. I don't know why but I got the feeling that this was an ego boosting routine served up to all authors. 'Do you take milk?' Tanya asked me, rummaging in the drawer of her desk. 'Sugar?'

'I don't...,' I started to say.

She pulled out two tiny cartons of milk and a handful of sugar sachets. 'I have to filch them from cafes and pubs,' she admitted with a nervous laugh. 'We never have any milk or sugar here because we all drink it black – we need the caffeine! So, how's it going so far, Debsie?'

Deborah glanced at me and smiled and then looked down at her diary. 'It's going terrifically well and there's an absolutely enormous amount of interest. I'm pretty certain that the producer of 'All Together!' is desperate, absolutely desperate to have us on the programme and I've got really firm maybes from Radio Manchester and Radio Birmingham.'

'Er ... what's 'All Together!'?' I asked, diffidently.

'Haven't you seen it?' asked Tanya, seemingly astonished.

I admitted that I hadn't.

'Oh, it's an absolutely wonderful programme, darling! It goes out in the early afternoon and it's really terrific. You'll be marvellous on it. They'll love you to bits.'

'Oh.' I said. I swallowed and felt uncomfortable. I wasn't sure that I was ready to be loved to bits by people I didn't know and would never know. In the end I need not have worried. I never heard any more about 'All Together'.

'It's looking good, Debsie!' said Tanya. 'What else is there in your little book?'

'The producer of 'Youth Culture' on Radio Leeds is pretty sure that they'll want to do something – they've having a week long series of programmes on drug abuse next month so our book fits in really well!'

'It isn't actually about drug abuse,' I said quickly.

'What isn't, darling?' asked Tanya.

'My book.'

Tanya looked at me and frowned. 'I thought it was about drugs?'

'It is.'

'Well, there you are then!'

'No, but . . . ,' I stumbled. 'It's not really about drug addiction. It's more about prescription drugs.'

Tanya looked rather startled. 'Oh!' she said. 'Oh. That's a terrible pity. It's a wonderful programme.' She turned to Deborah. 'Is Eden Taylor still presenting it?'

Deborah checked her diary and nodded.

Tanya turned to me. 'He's wonderful, isn't he? Absolutely brilliant.' She must have seen the look of incomprehension on my face. I knew it was there but had tried to conceal it. 'Have you not heard his show?'

'Er . . . no, I can't say I have,' I admitted.

'The next time you go to Leeds you make a point of tuning in,' said Tanya. 'He does a lot of our authors. What time does his programme go out, Debsie?'

'Eleven until midnight on Sundays,' said Deborah quickly.

'I don't get to Leeds much,' I admitted. It was a dramatic understatement. I couldn't remember ever having been there before.

'Well you'll be there if you're on Eden Taylor's show!' Deborah pointed out.

I said that this was undoubtedly true and that I looked forward to hearing Mr Taylor.

'Not that you'll be able to listen to the show if you're there with us!' said Tanya, with a giggle.

Deborah and I both looked at her.

'You'll be ON the programme, won't you!'

'Er, yes...,' I agreed. 'I suppose I will.'

'Do you not know anything about drug addiction?' Tanya asked me. She picked up her mug and took a noisy slurp of coffee. Deborah picked up her mug and followed her example. I left my mug of coffee where it was. It looked more like black soup than coffee and I wondered how many hundred milligrams of caffeine each mug contained. There was, I thought, probably enough caffeine in those three mugs to keep an entire platoon awake throughout a long night of manoeuvres.

'Well, yes, I suppose so...,' I agreed. 'A bit.'

'So you could talk about it?'

I thought about it for a moment. 'I suppose so,' I said. 'As long as it wasn't anything too complicated.'

'Oh, don't worry,' laughed Tanya. 'It won't be anything complicated! Not with Eden!'

'So I can still pencil in Eden and Leeds?'

'Oh, yes, absolutely, absolutely, Debsie!' said Tanya enthusiastically. 'What else have you got? Any nibbles from the nationals yet?'

'Well a nice lady at the Express said she thought they might be prepared to do something and your friend at the Telegraph – who sends his love by the way and told me to tell you that Freddie is pining for a big kiss – says he'll try and get something in if the conference on sewage treatment is cancelled.' Tanya, who was blushing heavily, tried to hide behind her coffee mug but seemed secretly quite thrilled.

'I think – and this negotiation is at a very early stage so we mustn't get too excited – but I think there's a chance that The Guardian will buy serial rights.' Deborah looked at Tanya and then at me and smiled as though waiting for praise.

'Oh, you clever thing! That's absolutely marvellous, darling! You are a wonder! Isn't she a wonder?'

I agreed with Tanya that Deborah was, indeed, a wonder and

that the news was absolutely marvellous. 'But what, er, what are 'serial rights'?' I asked.

'If The Guardian buy serial rights they'll publish an extract from your book!' said Tanya. 'It's very, very exciting news!'

I agreed that this was, indeed, exciting news.

'The 'West Country Post' is pretty sure that they think they probably want to do a interview,' went on Deborah, blushing now with pride at having almost persuaded The Guardian to publish an extract from my book. 'Your friend Kathy on 'Good Homes and Beautiful Gardens' says she's almost absolutely certain they'll do a short review and that man you told me to ring said we're pretty sure to get a piece on the diary page of 'Music Week'.'

'Marvellous!' said Tanya. 'Isn't that marvellous!'

'Well, yes,' I agreed.

'Of course, the 'Music Week' piece depends on the book being about drug addiction,' said Deborah, 'so I suppose we might have to do a bit of arm twisting there.'

'Oh, I'm sure you'll manage something,' said Tanya, confidently. 'Is Bernard Crossweather still the news editor?'

Deborah looked at her diary and nodded.

'Just take him for a long, boozy lunch and wear something with lots of cleavage,' said Tanya. She looked at her watch. 'Talking of lunch,' she said, 'it's time we left. I've got a table booked at Le Déjeuner Sur L'Herbe. I hope that's O.K.'

'I'm sure it will...,' I began.

'They do the most divine veal and lamb pie,' said Tanya.

'Er, actually, I'm, well, sort of vegetarian,' I confessed.

Tanya, who had been busy filling a huge leather satchel with diaries, appointment books, a Filofax and half a dozen books, stopped as though suddenly frozen. 'Oh my God!' she said. 'Did you tell us?'

'I don't think...,'

'I should have guessed,' said Tanya. 'Walking all that way. You must be a bit of a health freak. I suppose it's with you being a doctor and so on.'

'Well, no, in fact it hasn't got anything...,' I began.

'Never mind,' said Tanya, 'I'll have a word with Felicity on the way out and get her to ring Maurice and make sure he can do you an omelette or something.'

'Please don't go to any . . . ,'

Tanya carried on throwing books and papers into her satchel. I began to wonder if she was taking advantage of her lunch break to move offices. 'Debsie, darling, have a word with Felicity on the way out will you, my love and get her to ring Maurice and make sure, absolutely double certain sure, that he can do an omelette. Tell her to make sure he understands that it is for a very important author, won't you?'

Deborah hurried off to have a word with Felicity.

'Debsie is an absolutely angel. She's a fiend in the office and can be quite utterly ruthless with some of these self important media types but she's such a sweetie really. She's been with us for nearly a week now and I can't imagine how we ever managed without her.'

'Where was she before she came here?' I asked. I was surprised to hear myself finish a sentence.

'Rodean, darling,' said Tanya.

'Rodean?'

'School! You know, hockey sticks, blue knickers and all that . . . !' Tanya giggled. 'Come on, we'll be late for lunch and Maurice will never, ever forgive me!'

I went to lunch slightly chastened by the thought that the publicity expert who was looking after my book had slightly less than a week's experience behind her. As we walked along the corridor back to where my still damp coat and hat were waiting we passed another open door and another small office wherein three more teenage girls were busy being charming on the telephone.

'That's Jacantha, Arabella and Fiona,' said Tanya, stopping in the doorway and whispering to me. 'They all work with Imogen. She's one of our other executive directors.' 'This is one of our authors,' whispered Tanya to the three teenagers. 'He's just walked from Devon in a thunderstorm! Isn't he an absolute wonder?' The three girls all smiled at me and waved their pens.

*　　*　　*

'Now I absolutely don't want you to take this the wrong way,' said Tanya as she signed the credit slip for lunch. 'But do you have another jacket?'

I was still coming to the terms with the fact that I'd been

bought a meal by a woman. I looked down at my jacket and brushed at a blue ink stain on the lapel. 'Is there something wrong with it?'

'Not in the slightest,' said Tanya, a little too quickly. 'It's an absolutely splendid jacket. Isn't it, Debsie?'

Deborah agreed that it was, indeed, an absolutely splendid jacket.

I put my hand over the leather patch on my left elbow. It had been loose for rather a long time but I hadn't got round to getting it put back on properly.

'But I'm not sure that it's going to give you the image we're searching for!' Tanya continued. 'It's an absolutely lovely jacket for the country – on the moors in Devon and so on – but we want you to have a certain, what's the word I'm looking for...,' she paused. 'Gravitas!' she added explosively.

'I don't actually...,' I began.

'Charcoal with a pale blue shirt and a dark tie,' suggested Tanya. 'Some people still have black and white sets and blue looks a really bright white on a black and white set.'

'Oh.'

'And maybe it would be possible to get a little something done with the hair?'

'The hair?'

'It's lovely hair. Really lovely, isn't it, Debsie?'

'It is,' agreed Deborah rather too vehemently. I looked at her, surprised. She blushed at her own over enthusiasm and looked down as a waiter whisked away the remains of her traditional veal and lamb pie and my Italian herb omelette, Iberian sun dried tomatoes and French field mushrooms.

'But...,' sighed Tanya, shaking her head, '... and I know that Hugo would be the first to agree with me on this ... if you could have it cut a little shorter.'

'Hugo?' I couldn't think of anyone called Hugo.

'Yes, Hugo. He gets his hair cut twice a week!'

'Hugo?' I still didn't know who she was talking about.

'You know ... you met him in his office ... Hugo Leyton-stone.'

'Ah, yes.' I remembered. I tried to picture Hugo Leyton-stone. He had, I felt quite sure, been more or less completely bald.

'Isn't he, er, bald?' I asked, rather undiplomatically.

'Only on the top of his head,' said Tanya, rather sternly. Hugo's lack of hair was clearly not a suitable topic for conversation. 'He has quite a luxurious growth around the back and the sides and he says that the less you've got the more care you need to take of it.'

I automatically brushed my fingers through my hair. There did seem quite a lot of it. I tried to remember when I had last had it cut but couldn't.

'I'm afraid I haven't got a suit,' I said.

'Oh,' said Tanya, clearly rather stunned by this confession. 'Well, just wear something sober. Try not to wear anything too flashy – it'll make you look like a game show host on television and no one will take you seriously.'

'I'm afraid this is the only jacket I've got,' I said. 'I don't own a suit. And I don't think I can afford one. I've just bought a rather old house. Besides, there doesn't seem an awful lot of point in buying another jacket when I've got this one.'

Tanya looked at Deborah and Deborah stared back at Tanya.

'Don't tease me,' said Tanya.

'I'm not,' I said. I examined the jacket again. 'It was new when I bought it,' I said rather defensively.

'Well, I'm sure it will be fine,' smiled Tanya.

'It's Harris Tweed,' I continued. I opened the jacket and showed her the label. 'I remember the salesman saying that it was the sort of jacket that would last a lifetime. The buttons are genuine . . . ,' I examined the one on my left cuff carefully but couldn't work out what it was made of and couldn't remember what the salesman had said it was made of, 'well, I'm not entirely sure what they are but they're genuine, anyway.'

'I'm sure they are,' said Tanya.

I wondered if there was going to be anything else. There was.

'And you need to push yourself forward a little more,' said Tanya. 'You don't mind me telling you these things, do you?'

I shook my head.

'That's good,' Tanya smiled. 'I'm just keen to help you promote your book successfully. Some of the interviewers you meet will be quite tough with you but you mustn't take it personally.'

'Er, no,' I said, thinking that writing books seemed a lot easier than promoting them. I had, rather naively imagined that I could leave the selling of the book to the professionals.

'Will it be all right if I'm assertive?' I asked, rather diffidently. 'I don't want to appear pushy or arrogant.'

Tanya nodded furiously, and handed the signed slip and her credit card to a waiter. 'Absolutely, darling!'

'O.K.,' I said, with a slight shrug. 'I'll try and be more assertive.' I paused and looked at first Deborah and then Tanya. 'If you're sure that will be all right,' I added. I paused, smiled and looked at them both in turn. 'Anyway,' I said with a brave attempt at confidence, 'It's surely what I say that really matters – not how I say it or what I look like!'

Tanya smiled at me and I knew from the way that she smiled that I had said something stupid. That smile said volumes. 'Television is all about image,' she told me kindly. 'Hugo always says that perception is far more important than reality and that reality and substance have very little to do with anything on television and are of very little consequence.'

I suppose I should have thought of something sharp and witty to say but I couldn't and I didn't. Some people complain that they always think of their bon mots and acerbic responses seconds too late. I envy them. At least they can replay their conversations in their mind and imagine themselves handing out a suitably reproving put down. Only rarely can I think of the right thing to say; even months later I tend to feel deflated and noticeably inconsequential when I have been thoroughly patronised.

*   *   *

'Deborah will ring you as soon as we've got things firmed up a bit more,' promised Tanya, as the three of us stood on the pavement outside Le Dejeuner Sur L'Herbe. She wore a thin summer raincoat and shivered in the cold. 'We've got to rush back to the office to do some more frantic telephoning on your behalf but it's been absolutely, wonderfully marvellous to meet you!' She stood on tiptoe, put her arm around the back of my head, pulled my face down to her and kissed me several times on both cheeks.

'It's been a real thrill,' said Deborah. She too stood on tiptoe and kissed my cheeks. She wore no coat at all and was shivering even more violently than Tanya.

'Oh, one more thing – send us a photograph of yourself!' instructed Tanya, as she edged away. 'If you haven't got one then get one taken.'

'Right,' I said.

'Bye!' they both cried, hurrying off back to their offices to tell the editors of Motoring Weekly, Gardening Today and the Leamington Spa Review just why they had to include a review of my book. The rain had more or less stopped and Deborah's impractical, summery sandals clip clopped furiously on the hard, wet London pavement as she struggled to keep up with Tanya's furious pace.

I looked around to see if anyone was staring at me. I'd never been kissed so many times by women I hardly knew. It was, I supposed, one of the small perks or penalties of being a modest, new entrant to the world of show business. No one seemed to be staring so, pulling my coat collar up against the light London breeze, I walked briskly back across London to Paddington. After four hours I'd had quite enough of life in the big city and was keen to get back to the sharper winds and narrow lanes of Bilbury just as quickly as I could.

On the way back to the railway station I narrowly avoided being run over on two occasions. Each time it was my fault for I was quite mesmerised by the traffic. In London the roads are wide enough for the traffic to travel in at least two directions. In Bilbury the lanes are all so narrow that if two vehicles approach one another from opposite directions then one of them will have to reverse.

When I finally got back to Bilbury that evening Patsy reported that we had frogspawn both in the lake and in our ponds and that Sophie had caught a vole. Through the window I noticed that a single, glorious, impertinent primrose had appeared to add a dash of yellow to the carpet of snowdrops in the shrubbery. It was good to get back to the real world.

*   *   *

CHAPTER EIGHT

Patsy and I were having quite a struggle to make ends meet without my income from the practice. Repairing the structure of Bilbury Grange had taken all the money we had borrowed from the bank and keeping up the repayments on the mortgage wasn't easy without a regular income. I earned £40 a week for writing my newspaper column and although I still hadn't received the cheque I had another £250 due on the publication of my book. In addition I was managing to earn something (but not much) by writing articles and stories for magazines and newspapers. Patsy was bringing in small and irregular sums of money by buying books at auctions and selling them to a dealer in London but with Miss Hargreaves living in the stable flat we wouldn't be able to earn an income by letting it out to holiday-makers.

We were toying with the idea of having paying guests in the house during the summer months and I had started to make discreet enquiries about finding some locum work in the area. Most of the medical practices in Devon have more work to do in the summer months when the local population is dramatically increased by an influx of holiday-makers and so I was hoping to find a niche where I might earn a regular income by doing a few surgeries every week. In the end, however, we didn't take guests in and I didn't get a job doctoring.

Surprisingly, perhaps, being broke never really worried either of us. We both loved Bilbury Grange but we both had faith in fate and we believed that something would turn up. Besides, worrying wasn't going to change anything – other than to make us miserable as well as poor!

Meanwhile, being poor did have one big advantage: it meant that since we had to ration the number of times we used our car (both because we didn't have the money to spend on petrol and because the more we used it the more likely it would be to wear out and break down) we had taken to using our bicycles; old but extremely sturdy machines which we had bought from the lost property office at the local police station. As a result we had discovered footpaths and bridlepaths that even Patsy, who had spent all her life living in the area, didn't know about.

After my London meeting with Tanya and the other publicity people I had not arrived back in Bilbury until late. Although I had spent at least six hours of the day sitting down on the train I had felt exhausted by the time I finally slipped off my shoes and climbed the stairs to wash the grime and smell of London away. I comforted myself after my adventure in the city with the promise that I would go for a bicycle ride around Holdstone Down the following morning. Patsy who had fallen down the cellar steps and banged her knee said that if I didn't mind she would stay at home.

* * *

As Patsy had reported the lake and all our ponds were full of frogspawn, always a sign to me that spring can't be far away. The wind, which seemed to have been howling for ever, had miraculously died down and although the sun wasn't shining the grey of the winter sky had acquired a hint of blue. Most important of all it wasn't raining! I put on my old jeans and the thick, oily sweater which Patsy's mother had knitted and felt far more comfortable than I had while wearing my flannels and sports jacket.

While I checked my bicycle, making sure that the chain was tight and the tyres fully inflated, Patsy made a packet of sandwiches, wrapped in greaseproof paper, and then packed the sandwiches, a banana, an apple and two rock cakes into a brown paper bag (Peter at the local village shop still uses old fashioned brown grocery bags and refuses to have anything at all to do with bags made of plastic, though I suspect this is more because he has a large cache of old fashioned paper bags rather than because of any matter of principle or environmental concern).

Patsy also filled a thermos flask with hot, home-made vegetable soup. Patsy's soup is the mainstay of our diet: its contents vary with the seasons and the stores in our cellar and outhouses but everything in the soup is grown in the Bilbury Grange garden.

With the picnic safely packed away in my saddlebag I set off for the sea with Ben bounding along beside me as excited as a puppy! Sophie and Emily would have come too if I hadn't set off quite so quickly; they both ran after me for a few yards as I cycled down the drive. When I looked back they were sitting in the middle of the driveway staring after us like two children who've been told that they can't go to the party.

From Bilbury I rode across Kentisbury Down until I met the main road from Blackmoor Gate to Combe Martin. I turned left at the main road, rode down Silkenworthy Knap and turned right at Waytown, pedalling down the lane past Truckham Farm.

When I got to Stony Corner I took a right hand turning to Trentishoe and Heddon's Mouth. The route is undulating but beautiful, rich with hidden promises, and bordered by thick hedgerows. My bicycle, built and geared for flat suburban roads and city thoroughfares, creaked and complained as I forced the pedals round. Ben, unhindered by sprocket or crankcase, pounded along ahead of me apparently tirelessly; stopping every hundred yards or so as though to say 'What's keeping you? Hurry up!' and then bounding back towards me in a flurry of flying paws; her tongue dangling from the corner of her mouth and her tail high with excitement.

Holdstone Down is a beautiful, windblown, rockstrewn piece of moorland covered in tight, scrubby heather and gorse. It is aptly named for the wind blows so fiercely along the cliffs that not even rocks are safe here. In summer its undulating contours are covered in purple and yellow and it looks like a giant five day old bruise. Half a dozen stunted, bent over, scrubby trees struggle to survive and it is easy to see which way the wind usually blows from their bizarre shapes. Higher up there is nothing over a foot tall and the ground is scorched by searing, salt laden winds which blow almost endlessly from the south west. Small, hardy sheep, their coats ragged from the wind and the gorse, struggle to find enough to eat and the few patches of grass are eaten almost down to the bare earth. Across the Bristol Channel lies the coast of Wales. During the winter the coast is usually only dimly visible through the mist which so often lies across the channel. The coastline is at its most beautiful late on a summer evening when the Welsh lights shine and flicker like a valuable necklace laid out on the horizon.

In summer the sea between Devon and Wales is dotted with fishing boats, yachts and pleasure craft. Holiday-makers try sea fishing for the first and only time in their lives. Brave yatchsmen dart along the coast, hopping from one small port to the next and, if they are sensible, listening regularly to the weather forecast for even in summer the conditions can change quickly and a friendly, warm blue mill pond sea can become a fierce and unmistakeably unfriendly monster.

In the winter it is difficult to believe that this is the same stretch of water. Whipped into a constant frenzy by the wind there is more white than grey and mountainous waves crash down onto the jagged rocks, creating towers of spray and filling every tiny inlet with thick, creamy foam.

If you tried to sell this land for farming you would get only pennies for it. But if you measure land by its beauty then this is territory that, inch for inch, matches the value of the Mona Lisa.

The path which stretches, sometimes precariously, often spectacularly and always unpredictably, along the coast of North Devon runs around the foot of Holdstone Down. In summer the wide grassy footpath is alive with walkers for people come from all over the country to tread this path. They come in many different sizes and shapes; women in their fifties in shorts and stout boots with maps strung around their necks, men in breeks or plus twos wearing thick socks and brogues and carrying tiny rucksacks; young hikers led by earnest, bearded school masters or scout troop leaders and lone adventurers carrying their tiny tents and neatly packed supplies on their backs. But in winter the footpath is deserted. No one wants to walk this desolate route in the cold and savage months between October and April.

I turned left onto the coast path just before the lane veered down and to the right. From here, high up above the sea, the view along the cliffs is breathtaking. The lane heads down towards the village of Trentishoe, where the church of that name nestles comfortably in a cleft in the hills, and then twists sharply down a steep hill to Hunter's Inn and to Heddon's Mouth Cleave, a spectacular river valley which leads down to the tiny bay of Heddon's Mouth. Huge puddles lay across the path heading west towards Blackstone Point and Combe Martin and my bicycle left tyre tracks in the occasional patches of soft, sodden earth; not that I was despoiling virginal countryside for someone, probably a farmer fetching a dead or injured sheep, had driven a Land Rover along the path and had left deep ruts behind. Most of the path had, however, long since been worn down to rock and the puddles lay on the top. Ben, a little slower now, jogged happily along beside me; politely and professionally ignoring the attractions of the grazing sheep and rabbits scattered around on either side of the path.

Pleasantly wearied by my ride along the lane I free wheeled down the path, bumping and jolting my way around Holdstone Down, frequently having to take avoiding action in order to steer around particularly large rocks or potholes and constantly having to brake in order to stop my machines running away with me. I thought once or twice of the over-enthusiastic Tanya and Deborah and the others beavering away in their tiny, claustrophobic offices in London and felt myself fervently hoping that I would never have to leave Bilbury to work in a town or city. I felt at home in North Devon; comfortable, safe and at peace.

I rode my bicycle around Holdstone Down until I reached the path leading down into the tiny valley of Sherrycombe; a hidden, deep gorge where a clear, fast flowing stream bubbles and gurgles over a rocky bed. The path there is far too steep to ride down and so after I had taken the bag containing the food supplies from my saddlebag I pushed my bicycle underneath a bush to protect it in case it rained (I had no fear of my bicycle being stolen – in winter you could safely leave a well-stuffed wallet on Holdstone Down and go back and collect it a week later) and, much to Ben's obvious delight, continued down the hill on foot.

I ate my picnic sitting on a rock by the stream; sharing my sandwiches with Ben and a friendly robin. It was surprisingly warm in the valley. I was tucked away between rocks and trees and although I could hear the wind howling above me I could neither feel it nor see any evidence of its presence. All the really enjoyable meals I have ever eaten have been consumed out of doors. I have never been much of an enthusiast for starched linen tablecloths, obsequious waiters or restaurants where men in bow ties, oozing false bonhomie, charge fancy prices for undersized portions of overcooked food. I would be happy never to eat again in a restaurant where diners snap fingers, ties are essential items of apparel and everything on the menu is handwritten in French. Few meals could ever provide me with as much pleasure as a bagful of sandwiches and a piece of fruit eaten out of doors. I have eaten – and enjoyed – picnics in howling gales and the pouring rain and though I enjoy outdoor dining best when the weather is clement I must have an ounce or so of adventurer's blood flowing through my veins for I would turn down an invitation to dinner in the smartest restaurant in London for a chance to sit on wet grass and eat squashed cucumber sandwiches.

*　　*　　*

Since the age of four, when I first learned how to read, I have rarely moved anywhere without a book (or sometimes two) in my pocket. When I had finished my lunch I took out my by now rather battered paperback copy of Henry David Thoreau's 'Walden'.

Thoreau is without doubt my favourite philosopher; simple, honest and unpretentious and yet infinitely wiser than many more austere and apparently more intellectual philosophers. The kindness and compassion pours from his pen and I have always found his wonderfully anarchic distaste for bureaucracy and government, tempered as it is by genuine, heartfelt concern for the rights and responsibilities of both men and animals, truly inspirational.

Thoreau abandoned society for a while and lived in a rough cottage by the side of Walden Pond. He believed that 'the mass of men lead lives of quiet desperation' and argued that man's desperation is often born of the consequences of his desire to accumulate material possessions which he doesn't really need. I sat there, half dozing, and thought of some of the friends I'd had at medical school. As students they had worked long, hard hours but they had enjoyed life too and although their hours were full they had enjoyed a real sense of freedom. Their lives had been structured but despite the structure there had been freedom. Without exception they had all changed, almost beyond recognition. A few months earlier I had attended a reunion dinner and had hardly recognised any of my former friends. The men all wore suits and looked very earnest and respectable. The women all wore sensible shoes and carried sensible handbags. The system had pulled them in and sucked them dry.

The truth, I realised, is that most people are dead at twenty five: their ambitions, hopes and aspirations confined to acquiring a car with 'genuine' vinyl seats and a fully paid up pension plan. They won't be buried for another half a century but they are doing little more than killing time until life runs out. They watch life drift by; never grasping their destiny or taking control.

I realised then, with genuine sadness, that most of my former friends were doing jobs that they hated – but excusing themselves by arguing that they needed the money to pay for the things with which they had littered their lives. I wondered how many of those possessions – paid for with blood, sweat and tears – were worth the price they had paid.

I thought of people I knew who had sold their souls so that they could receive a pension in their old age. One friend had taken a job with a drug company, although he had always professed to despise the industry. When I gently chided him about his dreams he replied: 'I'll have plenty of time and money to enjoy myself when I retire.'

The truth is that we only get one chance at living. We should not sell our bodies, souls or minds so that we can buy an ice cream maker, a timeshare apartment in Marbella or a three piece suite in mushroom velour. I swore there and then that I would not make the mistake of wasting my life on low expectations. I would not let my possessions own me or direct my life. I would take some chances and accept the consequences.

Three days earlier I had received a telephone call from one of the consultants I had worked for in hospital. He had been sent an advance copy of my book to read and, through kindness and genuine concern for my welfare, had rung me to ask me not to publish it.

'It will wreck your career,' he had warned me. 'You'll never be able to get a decent job in medicine.'

He had explained that the medical establishment didn't like people who rocked the boat or who spoke out in public about injustices or irregularities. 'These things are best dealt with within the profession,' he had told me. 'There is no need to worry patients with all this sort of nonsense.'

I had thanked him for his call, told him that I appreciated his concern and promised to think about it. I think he meant well. I think he really believed that the men in pinstripe suits and old school ties really did know best.

I had thought about what he had said. But not for long. I felt that my book, which denounced the close links between the medical profession and the pharmaceutical industry, and which named a number of prescription drugs which confidential papers I had unearthed had shown to be far more dangerous than the manufacturers had admitted, deserved to have its chance. I had conceived, nurtured and given birth to it and I did not feel that I now had the right to destroy it.

And what, in truth, had I got to lose? Maybe, in a strange way, I was lucky in that I no longer seemed to have a career to worry about. I had abandoned the chance to work in hospital to work as a general practitioner. But then, through a mixture of my own bloodymindedness and sheer misfortune over which I had no control, I had lost my practice.

Many of my former student colleagues now seemed afraid. But I didn't really understand what they were afraid of. I knew that they had dreams when they were students. We had shared our dreams in those late night conversations; sitting at one of the Formica-topped tables in the hospital canteen. But their dreams had been buried, pushed deep down out of sight. And I felt far sorrier for them, with no dreams, no independence and no pride, than I did for myself, with no career and no future in medicine. I was merely giving up a place on the ladder. In order to retain their places on the ladder they had given up their dreams. I still had my dreams. I still wanted to change the world. It seemed to me that I had come off best.

Lying on the soft, sheep shorn grass by the side of the stream I read another chapter of Henry David Thoreau's masterpiece and then, as the weak rays of early spring sunshine faded away,

I gathered up my sandwich wrappings and started back up the hill towards the spot where I had left my bicycle. And then, with Ben bouncing along beside me, I pedalled back home.

* * *

While I had been refreshing my spirit, battered and dented by a day in London, the telephone at Bilbury Grange had apparently been ringing incessantly. Tanya had rung three times and a man called Reynolds from a television programme called 'Alive and How!' had telephoned twice. Peter Marshall, never a man to waste money on making two telephone calls when one would do, had left one message.

'Did any of them say what they wanted?' I asked Patsy, who was surrounded by mounds of fresh vegetables.

'Tanya said it was vital that you rang her the moment you came in and wanted to know why you didn't have a bleeper.'

'I used to have a bleeper when I worked in hospital,' I said. 'Why would I want to take a bleeper with me to Holdstone Down?'

'Well Tanya seemed to think you ought to have one so that she could get in touch with you.'

This didn't seem to make any sense to me. I'd gone to Holdstone Down to recover from going to London to see Tanya. 'I'll ring her later,' I said. 'I'll ring Peter Marshall first.'

'He said it wasn't urgent,' said Patsy. She finished scraping the carrot and tossed it into a bowl.

'What are you making?'

'A vegetable pie.'

'Great!' Patsy makes a terrific vegetable pie. 'Are we expecting someone to dinner?' I asked. She seemed to be making a larger than usual pie. One of Patsy's ordinary pies would feed six. This pie looked as though it would feed at least a dozen. She was making it in a gigantic dish which I had never seen before.

'I invited Miss Hargreaves round for a meal,' said Patsy. 'She popped in this morning to see if I wanted anything bringing from the shop and we got talking and I felt that she was probably a bit lonely so I invited her round.'

'That's nice. I like Miss Hargreaves. She's got a terrific library, you know. Where did you get that pie dish from?'

93

'I found it in the cellar. Is that what was in all those card-board boxes we brought round from her cottage?'

'What?'

'Books.'

'Yes. She's sweet. She keeps all the male authors in the bookcase in the living room and the female authors in the bookcase in the bedroom.'

'She doesn't!'

'She does.'

'How do you know that?'

'Because I helped her unpack and I asked her if the books had to go anywhere in particular and she told me.'

'That she keeps her books segregated by the authors' sex?'

'Yes.'

Patsy giggled.

'I think she's worried that if she lets Daphne du Maurier and Charles Dickens get together there could be trouble,' I explained.

The telephone rang.

'That'll be Tanya!' said Patsy. 'And I invited Mr Parfitt too,' she added.

Brrr Brrr.

'To dinner?'

'Yes.'

Brrr Brrr.

Mr Parfitt was the pixie. Our gardener.

'Do you think they'll get on?'

Brrr Brrr.

'Miss Hargreaves and Mr Parfitt?'

Brrr Brrr.

'Yes.'

'I don't know. Why shouldn't they?'

Brrr Brrr.

'I don't know.' I shrugged. 'I'll answer the telephone.'

I went into the hall and picked up the telephone.

'Tanya here,' said a voice I recognised instantly. 'Thank heavens I've found you!' said Tanya. 'Are you all right?'

'Yes, of course,' I said. 'Why shouldn't I be?'

'Your wife said you were riding your bicycle on the cliffs!'

'Yes, that's right.'

'We were terribly worried that you might have an accident. When no one answered the telephone I was terrified that you'd fallen off.'

'What – the bicycle or the cliffs?'

'Oh, don't joke about it!' said Tanya. 'You mustn't take any risks! We've got a tremendous amount of exposure planned for you.' She sounded genuinely concerned.

'I'll take care.' I thought I was probably much safer riding my bicycle around Holdstone Down than I would have been walking through London.

'Good,' she said. She still sounded worried. 'You'll be getting a telephone call from Simon Reynolds.'

'He's already rung.'

'Oh no! And you were out!'

'Yes. I was riding my bicycle on the cliffs.'

'Oh dear. Never mind. I'll get a message to him to let him know that you're in now. You're not going anywhere, are you?'

'Not that I know of. Who is he?'

'Who?'

'This Reynolds fellow.'

'Simon Reynolds?'

'Yes.'

'Haven't you heard of him?'

'No.'

'He's one of the producers of 'Alive and How!' – he's married to Celeste Peters.'

'Who?'

'Simon, of course.'

'No, who did you say he was married to?'

'Celeste Peters.'

'Is she a singer?' I asked. I thought I might have heard of her.

'She reads the weather on television.'

'Oh.' I hadn't heard of her. 'I think I must have got her confused with someone else. Isn't there a singer called Celeste something?'

'Celeste Bartholomew?'

'That's it!'

'She's an American jazz singer. I think she's around seventy years old.'

'I used to have one of her records. She sang with Duke Ellington.'

'Probably.' said Tanya, rather impatiently. 'But Celeste Peters is a big star. She opened three supermarkets last month.'

'Ah,' I said. 'And she's married to Simon ... ',

'... Reynolds. That's right. She's married to Simon Reynolds. And Simon Reynolds rang you because he absolutely adored your book and he wants you to appear on 'Alive and How!'!'

'Oh, good.'

'If I put the telephone down do you promise not to go anywhere?'

'Yes.'

'Really promise?'

'Yes.'

'O.K. So I'll put the telephone down and ring Simon and tell him that you're at home waiting for his call.'

'Fine,' I said. I thought that while I was waiting for Simon to call I would find out what Peter Marshall wanted. I put the telephone down, picked it up again and dialled Peter's number. Or, rather, I was about to dial Peter Marshall's number when the telephone startled me by ringing again. I picked up the receiver.

'Hello,' said a girl's voice. 'Mr Simon Peters is calling you. Please hold the line.'

I started to say 'thank you' but she had gone. I stood there in the hallway for what seemed an eternity but no one came onto the line so I put down the receiver and headed back for the kitchen. I was still several paces short of my destination when the telephone started to ring. I turned round, walked back and picked it up again.

'Hello,' said the girl again. 'Mr Simon Peters is calling you. Please hold the line.' She sounded rather cross and put great emphasis on the last sentence.

'Hello,' said a male voice a moment or two later. 'I've just been talking to Tanya about you. It's a great honour to speak to you, sir.' He didn't sound as though he was taking the mickey so I muttered something polite about the honour being mutual.

'I believe that Tanya told you about our little show,' he said. I confirmed that she had.

'And we're all absolutely thrilled that you're prepared to come on and talk to Vivienne about your book.'

'Vivienne?'

There was a silence at the other end of the telephone line. 'Vivienne Nugent,' said Simon, as though he felt sure that he was simply jogging my slightly addled memory. 'Our presenter!'

'Of course,' I said. I had never heard of Vivienne Nugent.

'It's a wonderful, wonderful book,' said Simon enthusiastically. 'I'm sure it's going to be an enormous bestseller and earn you millions.'

Enthusiastic as I was about my book I thought that this was probably a little over the top. Even I suspected that the market for an earnest polemic about prescription drugs might be severely limited. But it was my first book and I wasn't blasé enough about the experience of publication lightly to dismiss such enthusiastic praise.

'That's very kind of you,' I said.

'I know that Vivienne is just as excited as I am,' said Simon. 'She can't stop talking about your book! She's a real fan!' I had never heard anyone sound quite so full of enthusiasm.

I didn't really know what to say to this so I said nothing.

'We'd like to have you on the show on Friday,' said Simon, positively bubbling. 'We'll send a car for you, of course!'

'Friday?' I said, surprised. 'This Friday?' Friday was only two days away.

'We'll have a car pick you up at six. You should be with us by ten. That'll give you time to meet Vivienne, go into make up, have some breakfast and relax a little before the show.'

'Er ... what time is the programme?' I asked, more because I couldn't think of anything else to say than because I particularly wanted to know. I was beginning to get cold feet and wondered if there was any way that I could get out of appearing on the programme.

'We go on air at two and we'll probably put you in the first segment of the show,' said Simon. 'Which name do we use when we talk to you on air?' he asked. 'The one on the book jacket, I guess!'

'Yes,' I replied, puzzled. I started to say that I didn't have any other names but Simon wasn't listening. 'I'll go and tell someone to order the car to collect you,' he said. 'What's your address?'

'Bilbury Grange, Bilbury, North Devon,' I told him. 'But I'm not...,' I began.

'Wonderful!' said Simon. 'Absolutely marvellous. One of our cars will pick you at six am on Friday!'

And before I could say anything else he put the telephone down.

It rang again immediately.

'Have you spoken to Simon?' demanded Tanya.

I said that I had and that Simon had invited me to appear on his programme in two days time.

'Oh that's fantastic!' said Tanya. 'Absolutely terrific. Isn't he a wonderful man?'

'I don't...,' I began.

'Are they sending a car for you?'

'Yes, b-b-b-but...,' I stuttered.

'I'll get Debs to meet you at the studios,' promised Tanya, 'just to make sure that you're O.K. Marvellous, marvellous news, darling! I'm so thrilled. I'll speak to you later.'

I thought I ought to return Peter Marshall's call quickly before anything else happened. I dialled his number and waited. Unlike most of us Peter never allows the telephone to interrupt him but insists that it should take its place in the queue for his attention. If he is serving a customer and the telephone rings he won't answer the call until he has dealt with all the customers who were in the shop before the telephone started ringing – and since he never hurries any of his customers this can take quite a while. His attitude is that whereas the customer standing in the shop is almost certainly going to spend money the caller on the other end of the telephone may not even be a customer at all.

'Are you all right?' asked Patsy coming out of the kitchen a few minutes later.

I put my hand over the telephone mouthpiece, though there was no need for this since the telephone was still ringing, and explained that I was calling Peter Marshall at the village shop.

'Ah,' said Patsy, with a knowing nod. 'Would you like a cup of tea and a rock cake?'

I said I would. I had drunk the tea and eaten the rock cake when Peter finally picked up the receiver.

'I think all the houses round the village green should be painted,' said Peter when he recognised my voice. 'We must make sure that the village looks smart for the Revels.'

'That's a good idea!' I agreed. 'But do you think we'll be able to get people to agree? Some of the villagers living round the green might not be able to afford to get their cottages repainted.'

'I'd thought of that,' said Peter. 'So I think the committee should pay for the paint.'

'But the committee hasn't got any money!' I pointed out. 'And it won't have any money until the Revels are over!'

'That's all right,' said Peter, cheerfully. 'I'll let the committee have the paint on account. It can pay me when it has some money.'

I told Peter that I thought that would be fine. Foolishly I forgot to ask him the colour of the paint of which he had such large quantities in stock.

*   *   *

CHAPTER NINE

I'd had to pop into Barnstaple to take a copy of a lengthy article I'd written to the main post office and by the time I got back to Bilbury Grange both our dinner guests had arrived. I found Miss Hargreaves, Mr Parfitt and Patsy all sitting in the living room, each clutching a glass of the parsnip wine that Patsy's uncle had made three years earlier. Emily and Sophie were both curled up on Patsy's lap and Ben, who I had left behind, was curled up on the rug in front of the log fire.

Not having been lived in for a long time Bilbury Grange had been in terrible condition when we had bought it and Patsy and I had decided that we had to concentrate first of all on mending the roof and replacing the rotten windowframes. Repairing the fabric of Bilbury Grange had taken all our money, most of our time and much of our energy and there had been little of any of these left to spend on decorating or furnishing the inside of the house.

We had, however, managed to buy a huge quantity of cheap white paint from Peter Marshall and with Thumper's help we had decorated all the downstairs rooms, the staircase and several rooms on the first floor. We had furnished the house by attending auctions and buying the cheap reproduction furniture that is always left over when the dealers and collectors have taken their pick and bid against one another for the real antiques.

As I entered the living room and looked around I couldn't help thinking how homely and inviting the room looked. Our plain white walls and simple, cheap and slightly battered furniture wouldn't have won any plaudits from smart interior designers with expensive tastes, and we weren't likely to find ourselves besieged by photographers working for smart monthly magazines, but the room looked lived in. Most important of all, perhaps, it looked a happy room.

The chintz covered sofa on which Patsy and Miss Hargreaves were sitting was designed to accommodate four large adults and we'd bought it for two pounds at a house auction in South Molton. It was far too large for a cottage or a modern house but looked very much at home in front of the fireplace. The springs weren't quite as firm as they once had been but most people who sat on it agreed that it was one of the most comfortable pieces of furniture they had ever come into contact with. The only snag with it was that it was so soft and squashy that levering yourself up out of it was sometimes a bit of a problem – particularly if you'd been sitting in front of a nice, cosy fire for a few hours and had drunk a glass or two of anything brewed locally.

Grouped on both sides of the sofa, also facing the fireplace, there were three huge armchairs. None of these matched the sofa and all had come from different auctions. The leather one had come from a house in Lynton, the green one from a hotel in Barnstaple and the dark brown one from a flat in Bideford. We couldn't afford to have any of the chairs recovered and so Patsy had strewn a dozen or more brightly coloured cushions around and had draped multi coloured shawls (found in a suitcase we'd bought at an auction in Hatherleigh) over the backs of the sofa and the chairs. The white painted walls were almost covered with old paintings, all bought for next to nothing, and above the fireplace hung a huge but slightly flawed mirror in a chipped, gilt frame. Apart from the flickering orange red light from the flaming beech logs in the fireplace the room was lit by two old fashioned, wooden-based standard lamps. The dark, gloomy night was shut out by a wall of red velvet drawn across the windows. The curtains, which had come from a hotel in Ilfracombe, had cost us £1 to buy and Patsy's mother had altered them by hand for us. Altogether we hadn't spent more than £30 on furnishing the entire room but because all the furniture was old the room looked as though it had been the way it was for half a century or more.

I kissed Patsy on the cheek, said 'good evening' to our two guests, apologised for being late, rubbed Ben's head, poured myself a glass of wine and filled up Mr Parfitt's glass. Miss

Hargreaves put her hand over her still nearly full glass to make it clear that she didn't want any more and Patsy just smiled at me and gently shook her head to give me the same message.

'Have you two met before?' I asked our two guests. It wasn't just an attempt to break the ice but was a genuine question, inspired by curiosity.

'Sadly no,' said Mr Parfitt. He looked across at Miss Hargreaves and tentatively smiled.

Miss Hargreaves didn't reply but pursed her lips and shook her head.

'Miss Hargreaves is the village schoolteacher,' I explained to Mr Parfitt.

'So I understand,' said Mr Parfitt.

Miss Hargreaves glared at him. 'Who's been talking about me?' she demanded, frostily.

'Just someone in the pub,' replied Mr Parfitt, going slightly red.

'Hmm!' said Miss Hargreaves tartly. She clearly disapproved of something though whether this was Mr Parfitt, people talking about her, the Duck and Puddle or all three it wasn't quite clear.

There was a slightly uncomfortable silence for a moment. Mr Parfitt looked as though he was about to say something but then changed his mind. I thought I ought to try and defrost the atmosphere but I was too frightened of saying something that might lower the temperature still further to dare say anything at all.

'I read your book,' said Miss Hargreaves. I didn't even know that she knew I'd written a book.

'Ah,' I said cautiously, not quite sure how to respond to that.

'Is it selling well?' she asked.

I hesitated. 'Well not terribly well,' I said. 'It's not a very commercial book.'

'There have been some super reviews,' said Patsy quickly.

'So I gather,' said Miss Hargreaves.

'And The Guardian serialised it,' added Patsy.

'I'd like to read a copy,' said Mr Parfitt.

'I'll lend you one,' I said.

'He can borrow mine,' said Miss Hargreaves. 'It's a very

courageous book,' she said. She glared at Mr Parfitt. 'But I want it back, mind you!'

'Er, of course!' said Mr Parfitt.

There was then another long silence which Patsy broke by carefully moving Sophie and Emily off her lap, putting them down on the sofa beside her and then standing up. 'Dinner is ready so if you don't mind I think we ought to eat before it spoils!'

We all politely murmured our readiness to eat and after I'd put up the huge brass fireguard (bought, together with a brass coal scuttle, a set of dog irons and a full set of brass hearth tools for £1 from an auction in Porlock) to protect the carpet (given to us free by an auctioneer in Combe Martin who was under strict instructions to make sure that he got rid of everything at a house clearance sale) we all followed Patsy into the kitchen.

We did have a dining room at Bilbury Grange (it was connected to the kitchen by a hatch in the wall) but we still didn't have a dining table (we had got nearly bought a massive old refectory table and eight matching chairs for £20 but then two dealers spotted the table and within minutes the price had gone up to £350) so we ate all our meals in the kitchen.

As soon as we were all sitting around the kitchen table Patsy served out large portions of tomato soup (made with fresh tomatoes and four different herbs) and put a basket full of home-made bread into the middle of the table.

*   *   *

'Have you always been a gardener?' Patsy asked Mr Parfitt.

Mr Parfitt, his mouth full of bread, shook his head. 'No,' he said, when he'd emptied his mouth. 'Not exactly.'

'Well, you're very good at it!' said Patsy.

'Thank you,' said Mr Parfitt. 'I've always been interested in plants. Gardening has always been a love of mine.'

'What did you do before you became a gardener?' I asked him, innocently.

'I worked in a bank,' said Mr Parfitt.

Patsy and I both stared at him. He smiled back at us.

'What did you do in the bank?' asked Patsy.

'Up until fairly recently I was in charge of the securities trading room,' replied Mr Parfitt, rather unexpectedly. I would have been no more surprised if he had told me that he had been an astronaut, a bull fighter or a Minister of State.

I tried to lift my spoon out of my soup bowl and put it into my mouth but my muscles seemed to have frozen. Miss Hargreaves seemed neither impressed nor surprised by this revelation. She simply carried on sipping at her soup.

'In London, I presume?' I said, more to make sure that I could still speak than because I thought the comment was worth making.

'Oh, yes,' confirmed Mr Parfitt. He told us the name of the bank he used to work for. It was such a large and well known bank that even I recognised it immediately.

'What, er, what took you into gardening?' asked Patsy, hesitantly. 'I mean, it seems quite a career change ... '

Mr Parfitt grinned and shrugged. 'I ran away,' he said.

'Oh,' said Patsy, weakly. Miss Hargreaves reached out and plucked another piece of bread from the basket.

I went cold inside and wondered how much he had stolen, whether Patsy and I would be sent to prison for sheltering him and who would look after our animals.

'Don't look so worried,' said Mr Parfitt, with a mischievous grin. 'I didn't empty the vault before I ran away!' he told me, as though reading my mind.

'Oh good heavens,' I laughed weakly, but with considerable relief. 'I never thought you did!' I murmured, rather dishonestly.

'I just woke up one morning and decided I'd had enough,' said Mr Parfitt.

I wondered why I had automatically believed him when he'd told me that he hadn't stolen anything. Would he have told me if he had? If he was a thief wasn't there also a good chance that he would be a liar?

'It must have been quite a big step to take,' said Patsy.

Mr Parfitt shrugged as though the decision had been inevitable and out of his control.

'Did you have a family?' she asked him.

Mr Parfitt nodded.

Miss Hargreaves, apparently oblivious to all this and clearly not on a diet, took yet another piece of bread. I like to see people enjoy their food but I had never before seen anyone work up a sweat while eating.

'A wife?'

Another nod.

'Two children. Rodney, who is 21 and Polly who is 20,' said Mr Parfitt.

'Won't they be worried?'

'No,' replied Mr Parfitt, simply. 'We only had three cars so I expect they're quite pleased I've gone,' he explained.

'Oh, surely not!' said Patsy, horrified.

'You don't know my family,' said Mr Parfitt. 'When I first realised that I was wasting my life I talked to my wife and asked her if she'd stay with me if I gave up my job and started doing something I enjoyed. It would have meant selling the house and having a less expensive lifestyle but we would have had more time together.' He paused. 'Do you know what she said?'

No one said anything.

'She said: 'happiness isn't everything'.' said Mr Parfitt. He broke a small piece of bread into two and popped the smaller half into his mouth. He chewed slowly and then swallowed. 'Anyway I sent them a couple of postcards so they know I'm still alive,' he added.

'That was thoughtful of you,' said Patsy.

'I didn't want them having me declared officially dead,' said Mr Parfitt, with disarming honesty.

'Would you like some more soup, Miss Hargreaves?' asked Patsy, suddenly noticing that our other guest had emptied her bowl.

'I don't mind if I do,' said Miss Hargreaves.

Patsy stood up, brought the saucepan full of tomato soup from the stove where it had been kept warm, and replenished Miss Hargreaves' bowl.

'Would you like more bread?' Patsy asked her.

'If it's not too much trouble,' said Miss Hargreaves.

Patsy refilled the basket with hunks of bread.

'Did you decide to leave suddenly or was it something you'd been planning for some time?' I asked. I hesitated. 'I'm sorry is that rude? I don't mean to pry ... '

Mr Parfitt waved a hand. 'Don't worry,' he said. 'I don't mind talking about it.' But he lifted his spoon and sipped at his soup before answering. 'I suppose I had been thinking about it for a long time,' he told me. 'I don't know when I first realised how dissatisfied I was with my life. The funny thing is that although we all think we have choices, and we think we control our own lives, we don't, do we? Most of the time we allow ourselves to be led by destiny, by chance and by the ill thought out ambitions and prejudices of those around us.'

I felt myself warming to Mr Parfitt. His must, I knew, have been a difficult decision. I remembered what I'd been thinking about during my picnic on Holdstone Down.

'But when it came to it everything happened quite suddenly. The government had just put a new range of gilts on the market and the dealing room was frantic. I was talking to half a dozen people at the same time and suddenly, for no reason, it occurred to me how pointless the whole thing was. I had my usual bad indigestion and the noise in the dealing room was giving me a headache. I was looking around thinking how much I hated my job – and always had – when my wife rang in an absolute panic to tell me that we had twelve people coming to dinner that night and that she had discovered that we only had ten matching ramekins. She said I had to go to Harrods immediately and either buy two to match the ones we already had or else buy a dozen new ones.'

Mr Parfitt looked around and shrugged, rather apologetically. 'It probably sounds silly to you,' he said. 'But I just got up and walked out of the dealing room, left the bank and started walking away from the City. Then it started raining so I got on the first bus that came by and when the bus stopped at Paddington Station I got off the bus and got on a train. I got off at Exeter because I was hungry and there was no buffet car on the train and after I'd eaten a couple of sandwiches and drunk a cup of tea I caught the next train out which happened to be the train up to Barnstaple.'

'How long ago was that?'

'A month or so.'

'Any regrets?'

Mr Parfitt shook his head.

'When I first arrived down here I was a nervous wreck. I walked past a cottage on the edge of the village green and heard a telephone ringing. I instinctively found myself waiting for someone to open the window and tell me that the call was for me.'

'Do you think you'll go back?'

'I don't know. I haven't even thought about it,' said Mr Parfitt. He thought for a moment. 'And I don't want to think about it,' he added, quite firmly.' He looked around at each of us in turn, and smiled. 'I'm happier and more content now than I can ever remember being before. I just want to take things day by day.'

'That's fine with us,' said Patsy.

'You stay as long as you like!' I told him. 'The garden has never looked as good!'

'Thank you!' said Mr Parfitt. 'You know, it's a real joy to have a job where you can see an end result, where every day brings a new challenge and where there is always something to look forward to tomorrow. And the wonderful thing is that when I finish for the day I stop thinking about work.' Mr Parfitt looked around at us with a wonderful smile on his face. 'I don't worry about it!' he said. 'That's the real luxury. I don't worry because there isn't any point in worrying. I can't change the weather. I can't control nature. When I worked at the bank I used to go home at night and carry on working in my study until one or two in the morning. And then I'd lie awake worrying about the decisions I'd made – wondering whether I'd thought of all the angles and worrying about whether someone else might have stitched me up. And telephoning people in Japan or America to see what was happening there.'

'Now I live in a tiny room and I have virtually no possessions to speak of but I'm happier than when I lived in a massive house and had an expensive car. The snag with wealth and power is that if you have either or both then you're always frightened of losing what you have – and losing what you think of as being the security that goes with them. If you have nothing then you have nothing to lose and so only then are you truly free. I knew some very rich people when I worked in London but they were among the least secure people I've ever met.'

We finished our soup and while Patsy served up her vegetable pie I opened a bottle of her father's potent bilberry wine.

*   *   *

'That was a lovely meal,' I said, when our two visitors had gone and Patsy and I had washed up the dirty dishes.

'Did you like the apple and blackberry pie?'

'It was lovely!'

'Not too tart?'

'Not at all.'

'I really admire Mr Parfitt, don't you?'

'Yes.'

'You don't ever feel trapped do you?'

'No, of course not. I don't do anything I don't want to do. I'm very lucky. How about you?'

'What?'

'Do you feel trapped?'

'No! Of course not.' Patsy paused. 'If you ever thought that Bilbury Grange was too much of a burden and you wanted to sell it and live in a tiny cottage I'd be just as happy.'

'I know,' I said. 'That's one of the reasons why I love living here.'

*   *   *

CHAPTER TEN

The car sent by the television company arrived bang on time. By eight thirty a.m. we were the other side of Bristol, having breakfast at a motorway service station. I had egg on beans on toast while the driver, a short, overweight, taciturn man with terrible dandruff and a voracious appetite for boiled sweets (which he crunched all the way between Bilbury and Birmingham) ate a huge plate piled high with heart attack fodder: four slices of very fatty bacon, two huge fatty sausages, two eggs, and two slices of fried bread all floating on a small lake of grease. He washed all this down with two huge mugs of tea and finished off with two slices of thickly buttered toast upon which he spread a generous layer of marmalade. We then climbed back into the car and continued our journey north; finally arriving at the television studios at about the same time as the locally resident staff.

The driver handed a slip of paper to a uniformed man behind a desk who examined it carefully before picking up the telephone. After speaking to the person he'd called for a moment he told me that someone would be with me in a minute or two. The someone turned out to be a very businesslike young woman in a red trouser suit. 'Would you like some breakfast?' she asked me. She had very short blonde hair, carried a huge clipboard, had a pen and a stopwatch hanging around her neck and had introduced herself as Louise. She was, she said, a programme researcher, though she had advised me that this was just a temporary stepping stone and that she would soon be working as a fully fledged producer on her own show. Impressed by her confidence I shared her lack of doubt in her ability to succeed.

I politely declined her offer of food, pointing out that I had eaten at a motorway service station and did not yet feel able to subject my stomach to any more excitement.

'Then I'll take you straight along to make up,' said Louise. 'Follow me!'

She scurried off along the corridor as though she was in training for a fast walking competition and I hurried along behind her, struggling hard to listen to the running commentary she was giving me. The media world seemed to be full of fast talking, fast walking young women. Eventually we stopped outside a door upon which there was a small sign bearing the words MAKE UP. Louise reached for the door handle but before she could grasp it the door flew open and a dozen waiters and waitresses streamed out past us. I was at first puzzled by this for I had not realised that even the catering staff had their make up applied professionally when working at television studios. I was about to make some comment about this when Louise whispered something to me about feeling sure that I would recognised them as being from the 'Royal Hotel'.

'Where is the 'Royal Hotel'?' I asked, timidly, too confused by everything around me to think it odd that the staff of a hotel should be got ready for work by a television make up department.

Louise sighed and looked at me as though I'd asked her if she knew the name of the occupant of Buckingham Palace. ''Royal Hotel' is one of our top rated comedy dramas!'

I apologised, and tried to explain my ignorance by pointing out that I didn't get much time to watch television. Louise just tutted and walked through the now open door. I followed her into the make up room and found myself standing between a huge pirate, complete with beard, eye patch and wooden leg and a young woman dressed as a fairy. They were having a row.

'I did warn you that I'd be late,' said the pirate, apologetically.

'You said you'd be a bit late,' corrected the fairy. 'I don't call three hours a bit late!'

'I had to go and get the car serviced.'

'Since when have they sold beer at the garage?' demanded the fairy, hands on hips. 'You stank of the stuff!'

'I took John to the 'Bear and Flagstaff' for a pint to thank him for getting me that job as a bar of soap,' said the pirate sheepishly.

'Ha!' snorted the fairy with a toss of her head. 'You just wanted to drool over that trollop behind the bar!'

Underneath his make up the pirate blushed. 'Don't be silly, Brenda!' he whined. 'You know I love you!'

The fairy glared at him and then smashed her wand over his head. The wand, made of silver painted balsa wood, broke into two pieces. 'Now look what you've made me do!' she said, angrily. The pirate bent down and picked up the two pieces of shattered wand.

'Give those to me!' snapped the fairy, close to tears.

'Who's next?' demanded a cheery and attractive young woman in a pink overall. She had a powder puff in one hand and a pot of powder in the other. The name, Karena, was embroidered on the breast pocket of her overall.

Neither the pirate nor the fairy moved. They were both trying to fit the two pieces of the broken wand back together again.

'I think that'll be us, then!' said Louise, pushing me forwards. She looked at her watch and wrote something down on her clip board.

The make up girl smiled at me and pointed to a chair. I sat down and she draped a white cloth around me, tucking the ends in at the back of my neck. 'What are you here for?' she asked me.

'I'm appearing on ... ' I began and suddenly realised that I had forgotten the name of the programme. 'I've forgotten the name of the programme.' I said, feeling rather foolish.

'Alive and How!' whispered Louise from behind me. She put a hand on my shoulder. 'Don't be nervous!' she said. 'You'll be marvellous!'

'I'm not nervous,' I said. 'I just couldn't remember the name of the programme.'

'What are you talking about?' asked Karena, dabbing powder over my face.

'I was just telling Louise that I couldn't remember the name of the programme,' I explained.

'No. I mean what are you talking about on the programme?' She did something around my eyes.

111

'Ah, sorry. My book,' I said.

'Would you like to comb your hair?'

I felt in my pocket for a comb but couldn't find one. 'I don't seem to have a comb,' I said.

'Would you like me to brush it for you?'

I said I would be grateful.

'What's your book about?'

'Drugs and drug companies and doctors and ... things,' I said.

'How interesting!' said Karena. 'My brother once smoked cannabis at a party in Fulham. He said it made him feel sick for three days afterwards but I think it was just as likely to be the lager, don't you?'

'I don't, er ...,'

'Do you have a parting?'

'Yes. On the left.'

'He drinks too much but won't listen to anyone.'

'Er, sorry. The other side.' I realised I'd been looking at myself in the mirror.

Karena ignored me and carried on talking about her brother while she brushed my hair. When she had finished she sprayed half a can of lacquer over it. I reached up and gingerly touched the top of my head. It felt as though it as covered with chicken wire. If someone had tried to mug me by hitting me over the head with a blunt object I would probably not have noticed.

'I'll take you along to the canteen in a moment and you can get a cup of tea,' said Louise.

The make up girl whisked the white cloth away from me and disappeared in search of her next customer. I stood up, edged carefully between a human sized carrot and a police constable with his arm in a blood stained sling, and followed Louise back out into the corridor where twenty or thirty children, all dressed as elves were waiting in an unruly line. A morose, red faced fellow in a Father Christmas costume stood at the end of the queue surreptitiously smoking the last half inch of a home-made cigarette. He had his beard pulled down underneath his chin so that it looked rather like a bib.

'Isn't it a bit late for Christmas programmes?' I whispered to Louise.

Louise half turned her head. 'They're filming a special show for *next* Christmas in Studio B!' she explained.

* * *

The canteen was full. Roughly half the customers seemed to be large, scruffy men, identically dressed in grubby tee shirts, jeans and worn sneakers. These customers were all busy wolfing down platesful of bacon sandwiches and noisily drinking tea from huge mugs. The other half of the customers were in fancy dress. There were pirates, policemen, chambermaids, nurses, doctors, elves, vegetables, dancing girls in spangly leotards and fishnet tights and a dozen men in white ties and tail coats. I spotted one clergyman, an Elizabeth I, complete with ruff and bustle, two gypsy girls and half a platoon of soldiers – all equipped with balsa wood rifles. These customers were daintily nibbling biscuits and sipping tea and taking great care not to spill any food.

I bought myself a can of lemonade, a packet of crisps and an apple and carried my tray around the room looking for a spare seat. I had just found one, and had sat down between a potato and a chambermaid, when I noticed Louise, still carrying her clip board, walk briskly through the door. She was accompanied by a tall red-haired, harassed looking man in a lilac coloured shirt and a pair of very tight lemon coloured trousers. Behind them there stood a third figure. The red-haired man had a pair of headphones and a microphone around his neck and he too carried a clipboard. The microphone he wore was connected by a wire to a large metal box which was clipped to his belt. The two of them stood in the doorway for a few moments, clearly looking for someone. Eventually Louise tapped the red-haired man on the arm and pointed in my direction. He looked at me, looked back at her and frowned. She nodded and said something. He seemed surprised but, shrugging off the confusion he obviously felt, minced briskly across the room towards me. As he moved I could see that the third person was Deborah, Tanya's assistant. Louise and Deborah followed the red headed man across the canteen.

'Darling!' cried the red headed man, holding out both hands as though we were long lost brothers. 'How wonderful of you to come!'

I looked to either side, just in case I was mistaken. But the potato carried on sipping his or her limeade through a straw and the chambermaid carried on nibbling at her digestive biscuit. I stood up and received a hug and a kiss on each cheek from the red-haired man. No one, apart from me, seemed surprised or embarrassed by this. The potato simply carried on sipping and the chambermaid carried on nibbling.

'We're all so absolutely thrilled that you could come!' said the red-haired man.

'You must be Simon Reynolds!' I said, feeling quite pleased with myself for remembering his name.

The red-haired man burst into a fit of giggles, as though I'd just delivered the smartest one liner he'd ever heard, and clapped himself on his chest with his left hand in a very camp gesture. 'Me?' He turned to Louise. 'He mistook me for Simon!' he said, and burst into another fit of giggles.

'This is Tony,' said Louise. 'He's the floor manager.'

I said hello to Tony and smiled at him.

'Hi!' said Deborah. She seemed rather shy and overawed by it all.

I said 'hello' to her.

'Have you been to make up, yet?' the floor manager asked me.

I said I had.

He bent closer and peered at me. 'Silly me! Of course you have, darling! Then as soon as you've finished your drink we'll get you along to wardrobe. Where are your clothes? Have they given you a dressing room?'

I looked down at my sports jacket and grey flannels and then I looked back up at him. 'These are the only clothes I've brought,' I said.

Tony the floor manager started to giggle but stopped when he realised that I was serious. He put his hands over his face as though not sure what to say. He turned. 'He does know it's television and not radio, doesn't he?' he whispered loudly to Deborah. I thought that this was pretty catty and I decided that I didn't like Tony very much. I didn't see why I should present a false front to the viewers. I knew that lots of people made a special effort to look smart when appearing on television but this seemed as dishonest as saying something you didn't agree with so as to gain popularity. I like to feel that people who read what I write will trust me. How can I expect anyone to trust me if the very way I look is fraudulent? If I give the impression of being scruffy it isn't because I want to be offensive or because I'm deliberately making some anti-fashion statement but, rather, it is because I'm unwilling to waste time making myself look pretty. I'd rather spend the time researching the things I'm going to write or talk about rather than selecting a smart looking shirt or an impressive tie. Some people say that they like their clothes to make a statement for them. I prefer my clothes to keep quiet while I make the statements.

Deborah, blushing bright red, nodded, stuttered and finally said something to the effect that she was pretty sure that I did indeed know that the programme was being broadcast in vision as well as sound.

'It's the best jacket I've got,' I said defensively. I paused. 'In fact, to be perfectly honest it's the only jacket I've got.'

'Well, we'd better get you along to wardrobe and see what they've got that will fit you,' said Tony, rather peevishly. He turned and minced back across the canteen floor, followed by Louise and Deborah. I finished my lemonade, stuffed my apple and the remainder of my crisps into my jacket pocket, said 'goodbye' to the potato and the chambermaid and followed them. Standing in the doorway to the canteen the pirate and the fairy were still arguing. They had not managed to mend her broken wand.

*   *   *

The wardrobe department was full of people trying on clothes. Half a dozen tall, beefy looking men in socks and underpants were pulling on pirate costumes. Four or five equally tall, but willowy, girls were standing around shivering in bras and panties. There were racks and racks of colourful clothes and a plump woman in a grey knitted cardigan was ironing a white blouse for a girl wearing jodhpurs, black leather boots and absolutely nothing else.

'I need a jacket!' said Tony, clapping his hands excitedly and pointing to me. 'To fit this one over here.'

No one took any notice of him and this seemed to make him angry. I watched, mesmerised, as he stamped a foot. I'd never seen anyone actually do that before. 'I need a jacket!' he shouted. This time everyone looked. 'For him!' he cried, pointing at me. Everyone looked at me. I tried to shrivel up and disappear but when you're well over six foot tall and weigh fourteen stones it isn't easy to disappear in a crowded room. A middle aged woman in a blue jumper, dark blue skirt and grey carpet slippers shuffled over, looked at me and shook her head as though she didn't hold out much hope. 'What sort of jacket?' she asked.

'Something lively!' said Tony. 'And some trousers, too!' he said, catching sight of my grey flannels.

The woman in blue disappeared and returned a couple of minutes later with two jackets thrown over one arm. One jacket was made of shiny, plastic in a leopardskin print. The other was a very bright yellow and had sequins sewn all over it.

'Try them on!' said Tony to me. He ran his fingers over the bright yellow jacket. 'Oh, isn't it absolutely divine! Who's worn this?'

'David Dunster!' replied the woman in blue.

'David's worn this? David Dunster?'

The woman in blue nodded.

Tony closed his eyes and swooned.

'Who's David Dunster?' I asked Deborah.

'He hosts a quiz show,' she replied, in a whisper.

"Tickle My Fancy!" said Louise.

Startled, I looked at her.

'That's the name of the show,' she explained, blushing.

I took the hideous fake leopardskin jacket and tried to get into it but it was at least four sizes too small. The ripping sound the jacket made as I tried to squeeze my arms into it made me wince. I hurriedly shrugged it off and handed it back to the woman in blue. Without even looking at the jacket she just tossed it across a rail which was already laden with clothes – presumably all waiting to be repaired – and handed me the yellow jacket. That too was far too small.

'Can you alter the yellow one for him?' asked Tony.

The woman in blue thought for a moment and then shook her head.

'Damn!' said Tony.

'I don't think either of those are exactly right for me,' I said, relieved.

Tony, a sulky look on his face, minced out of the wardrobe department and stopped and looked at his watch; a huge and outrageously flashy piece of gold-coloured jewellery. He then rather brusquely ordered us all to follow him to the studio. It was, so Louise whispered, time for the rehearsal.

*   *   *

The studio was much bigger than I had expected it to be; more like an aircraft hangar than anything else. A small fake living room, complete with rug, sofa, easy chairs, bookcase, potted plants and a long, low, glass topped coffee table had been built in the middle of the available space and a dozen or so men in grubby jeans and dirty tee shirts were standing around looking bored.

'I've got him here,' I heard Tony mutter. I looked across at him and he turned his head away from me. He was clearly not going to forgive me for not wearing a more fashionable jacket. I wandered across the studio and peered at the bookcase to see what titles they had chosen but the shelves were filled with strips of cardboard painted to look like rows of books. I looked at the plant; that, too, was artificial.

'Darling!' I heard someone behind me say. 'How wonderful of you to come! We've all been looking forward to meeting you!'

Idly, I turned and found myself the target of a portly, bespectacled, middle aged man who was trotting towards me with an eager look on his face. He had his arms outstretched as though we were relatives who had been parted by several continents and oceans for a couple of decades. He wore a brightly coloured Hawaiian shirt and a pair of mauve corduroy trousers and had a green and yellow patterned neckerchief knotted around his neck.

'I'm Simon, darling!' he said, grasping me by the shoulders and kissing me on both cheeks.

I said that I was pleased to meet him and thanked him for inviting me.

'Did you have a good journey?' he asked.

'Yes...,' I started to reply. But he'd turned away and was

telling one of the men in jeans to get rid of a wrinkle which had appeared on the rug.

'I have to worry about absolutely everything, darling!' he said, turning back to me. 'Someone find Vivienne!' he shouted. Half a dozen people, including Louise, hurried away in search of Vivienne.

'I gather Tony wasn't too pleased with your jacket,' whispered Simon.

'No, I'm afraid not,' I said.

'Don't you worry about it, darling!' whispered Simon, giving me a reassuring pat on the arm. 'I think it's absolutely divine! The leather patches on the elbows are quite, quite perfect and I'll get someone from the props department to cover up the worst of the stains!'

I thanked him.

'And we all absolutely loved your book, darling!' said Simon. 'Marvellous, absolutely marvellous!'

'That's very kind of you.'

'I loved the bit where the hero is in a lift with the bad guy and neither of them know who the other one is! Absolutely gripping. Quite sensational, darling! Divine! Terrific plot. Can't wait for the movie. Have they decided who's playing the lead yet? I read that both Redford and Newman are desperate for the part and to be honest I'm not surprised!' Simon put his arm around my shoulder. 'Perhaps we could have a word later on,' he said. 'Maybe you could put in a word for Celeste?' He winked. 'She'd be terrific as Angie.'

I frowned, puzzled and started to say something. There was no lift scene in my book. There was no hero. There was no plot. There was no character called Angie. There were no characters at all. And unless Redford and Newman were keen to play the part of a slightly discredited sleeping tablet there wouldn't be a movie either.

I tried to mention all this. It seemed important. But Simon had rushed off to the other end of the studio to greet and assist a tiny, woman who was tottering along underneath a massive, shoulder length blonde wig and on top of a pair of monstrously elevated high heeled shoes. A moment or two later Simon introduced me to Vivienne Nugent, the presenter of 'Alive and How!' She showed me a row of expensively capped teeth. Once again I tried to explain to Simon that he had confused my book with someone else's but, as before, he was too busy to listen to anything I had to say. I tried to say something to Vivienne but she just smiled at me and ignored me.

'That script you wrote for your introduction is marvellous, absolutely marvellous!' Simon said to Vivienne. He kissed her and hugged her. 'Dialogue as crisp as a freshly baked poppadom!'

Vivienne looked pleased with herself.

'Just look at this!' said Simon, holding out the script in his hand so that I could read it. 'Read it out loud!'

'Hello,' I read, 'and welcome to another edition of your favourite magazine programme: 'Alive and How!' As always it's a real pleasure to have your company and I'm delighted to be able to tell you that we've got our usual marvellous mix of entertainment and education for you!'

I looked at Simon, waiting for him to offer me another page of script. He didn't. Instead he smiled and withdrew the script. 'Super isn't it?'

I said I thought it was wonderful.

Vivienne and I were then escorted onto the set and allowed to settle down onto the sofa; a plushly upholstered piece of furniture into which I sank at least a foot and a half. Vivienne, clearly on a high from Simon's glowing praise, smiled a lot at everyone.

'I don't want to talk to you about your book until we go on air,' said Vivienne, speaking to me at last. She spoke slowly, carefully and quietly as though sharing a secret and anxious to make sure that no one else overheard. 'I always think it spoils the freshness of what we have to say if we rehearse our little chat!'

I made one last attempt to avoid what I suspected might prove to be an embarrassing moment for her. 'I think Simon might have got me mixed up with . . . ,' I began.

But Vivienne wasn't listening. She had called a make up girl across and was having running repairs made to her lipstick.

I secretly hoped that she, at least, did not think that my book contained a plot, a hero or a part for any of her friends or relatives.

When she was satisfied with her appearance she turned to me again. 'Is this your first time?'

I said that it was.

'How exciting you must find it,' she said. 'But try not to be too nervous,' she added. I waited for her to pat my knee but she didn't.

I said that I would try.

She then talked about her forthcoming memoirs, her new television programme about cookery, the shops she had opened, the carpet warehouse she was due to open, the magazine interview she'd done that morning, the fee she had been offered to pose topless for a mens' magazine (she had, of course, refused it), the modelling work she had done in Paris and the wonderful plastic surgeon she'd found in Beverley Hills (not that she needed plastic surgery herself, of course, but it's always nice to know of someone just in case you ever get asked).

Suddenly Tony rushed onto the set, clapped his hands and made very loud shushing noises. Vivienne shut up and we both stared at him. He seemed to enjoy this. 'Simon wants the table moving forwards two inches,' he said, as though Simon had asked for Tower Bridge to be moved a few hundred yards along the Thames.

'No problem!' I said, keen to be helpful. I leaned forward, moved the table two inches and leant back again. Tony stared at me as though I had just spray painted a rude graffiti message onto the carpet. The studio fell silent and, gradually, I became aware that everyone was staring at me.

'What's the matter?' I whispered to Vivienne.

Vivienne, who had already edged a few inches away from me, looked down at her knees and pulled pointlessly at the hem of her skirt. The skirt was far too tight to move and far too tight to reach her knees. She no longer seemed to want to talk to me. A huge, mountain of a man who wore a full black beard and a tee shirt with the slogan 'Alive and How!' on the front strode onto the rug and glared down at me.

'Did you move that?' he demanded fiercely. He had bunches of black hair sticking out of his nostrils and it was difficult to take him seriously.

I said I had. I thought that the bunches of black hair looked rather like wrestling spiders and wondered if he would find it amusing if I were to tell him this.

'Are you union?' he demanded.

I looked at him, not quite sure what he meant.

He repeated the question.

'No, I don't think so,' I said. I decided that it would be tactful for me to keep to myself the observation I had been thinking of making about the hair in his nostrils.

The man mountain took a silver coloured whistle out of his pocket and blew into it. He and the other men in tee shirts and dirty jeans then walked slowly but determinedly out of the studio.

'Well,' said Tony, close to tears.

'Was it something I did?' I asked.

'You touched the set!' said Tony.

'I was just being helpful.'

'No one is allowed to touch the set if they aren't in the union!' said Tony. 'Everyone knows that!'

'I didn't!' I protested.

'I just hope you're pleased with yourself!'

Tony turned and flounced off the set leaving Vivienne and I sitting together but quite separately on the sofa. Someone out of sight switched off the main lights.

'You fool!' hissed Vivienne in the darkness. I really wasn't warming to her.

*　　*　　*

I don't know how long we sat there, waiting. It seemed like hours but I don't suppose it could have been anything more than a few minutes. Suddenly the lights came back on and Simon strode purposefully towards us. He was scowling and sweating profusely. Behind him stood Louise and Deborah; both looking very serious. 'They say they'll go back to work if you apologise,' Simon said.

'What do I have to apologise for?' I asked. I noticed that he was no longer calling me darling and for this I was quite grateful.

'For moving the table.'

'But I was just trying to be helpful.'

'It doesn't matter. They don't like people being helpful.'

'But I'm a doctor. I was trained to help people.'

Simon thought for a moment, dabbed his forehead with a red, silk handkerchief and then shook his head. 'They won't buy that,' he said. 'You'll have to apologise.'

'What will happen if I don't apologise?'

'They'll black you, me the studio and probably the entire station.'

'You mean that the programme won't go ahead?'

'We'll be lucky if we get back on air within a month.'

'Do you mind if we have a word in private?' asked Deborah, moving forwards and beckoning me to join her.

'Not if you can persuade him to apologise!' sighed Simon. 'And preferably fairly quickly!' He dabbed his forehead again, blew his nose and looked at his watch. 'I've got a programme due to go on air in less than an hour.'

'I'll do my best,' promised Deborah.

I stood up and followed Deborah over to a dark, far corner of the studio.

'I just rang Tanya,' whispered Deborah. 'She said you don't have to apologise if you don't want to.'

'But I thought you'd want me to apologise?' I whispered back.

'Officially, we do!' whispered Deborah. 'And for heaven's sake make it clear to Simon that I tried to persuade you to apologise. But unofficially Tanya thinks we could be heading for a great stunt. If the programme is blacked the papers will have to say why. Your book will get a fantastic amount of publicity!'

We walked back over to where Simon and Louise were waiting for us. Vivienne had disappeared.

'Deborah wants me to apologise but I don't think I've done anything I need to apologise for,' I said. 'But as a gesture of goodwill I'm happy to move the table back to where it was.'

Simon stared at me.

'If I put it back where it was then one of the men can move it to where you wanted it putting, which was where I'd moved it to,' I explained.

Simon, dabbed his face and neck with his now very damp handkerchief and glared at me. 'I don't know whether they'll buy that,' he said.

I shrugged. 'I don't care whether they do or not,' I said.

Simon, now looking a broken man, turned and scurried away. Louise, still carrying her clipboard, hurried after him. Deborah and I stood and waited.

'You were brilliant!' whispered Deborah.

'I haven't got the foggiest idea what is going on,' I said. 'This place is like a lunatic asylum.' I just wanted to get back home as quickly as I could and I no longer cared whether or not I made my television debut.

A few minutes later Simon reappeared. This time, in addition to Louise, he was followed by Tony, the floor manager, the large man with the fighting spiders up his nose, and the rest of the offended crew.

'Bill says that in view of your lack of experience they'll accept your offer,' said Simon. The sweat was dripping off his nose. Bill folded his arms and looked very stern.

I walked across to the table and moved it back to where I thought it had been before I'd moved it the first time. Simon turned to Bill. 'Is that O.K.?'

Bill walked over to the table and stared at it. He moved around it and looked at it from the other side. He bent down and examined it from a different angle. Then he went back to where Simon was standing. 'It needs to be another inch nearer to the bookcase,' he said.

'It needs to be an inch nearer to the bookcase,' Simon said to me.

I moved the table so that it was an inch closer to the bookcase.

Once again Bill walked across and examined it carefully from all possible angles. This time, when he walked back to Simon, he nodded. Simon closed his eyes in relief and blotted his face once more. Bill then called to two burly looking men who were standing about ten yards away. They walked over and, under his directions, moved the table back to where it had been after I had moved it the first time.

'O.K.?' Bill asked Simon.

'Marvellous,' said Simon, weakly. He turned to Louise. 'Would you like to take him to the canteen?' He gave me what was intended to be a smile. But there wasn't much fun in it. 'We'll come and get you when we need you,' he said.

'You were wonderful!' whispered Deborah as we followed Louise back to the canteen.

'Is television always like this?' I asked her.

'I don't know,' admitted Deborah. 'I've never been in a studio before.'

*　*　*

Eventually, I found myself sitting on the sofa watching the second hand on a huge clock tick slowly round and round. A man in a grey pullover knelt by my side fitting a tiny microphone to my tie.

'Is this a club tie?' asked the man in the pullover.

'No, I don't think so.'

'Oh.'

'Why?'

'I didn't think anyone would wear a tie this awful unless it was a club tie.'

I looked down. I'd never really looked at it before. I didn't usually wear a tie but had put it on simply in honour of my television debut.

'Shall I take it off?' I asked him.

'No!' he said, rather insistently. He glowered at me. 'Where am I going to fix my microphone if you take it off?'

'Three minutes to air!' cried Tony, his voice breaking with excitement.

I remembered having read that performers work better when they are nervous and so, conscious of the fact that I felt merely bored rather than excited, I tried to feel more apprehensive. It didn't work. I looked across at Vivienne. She was carefully studying a thick sheaf of notes. On the coffee table in front of her lay a thick, fat book. On the cover of the book a buxom young woman who was bursting out of her dress was running away from a horde of bad tempered looking men brandishing guns. The author's name, a name I had never heard before, was printed in very large type. I realised for the first time how Simon had made his mistake. The book had exactly the same title as my own book.

'Any good?' I asked.

Vivienne looked up at me.

I nodded towards the coffee table. 'Is the book any good?' I asked.

Vivienne showed me her dentist's handiwork again. It really was more of a dental display than a smile. 'I loved it,' she said. 'Perhaps you'd like to sign it for me afterwards?' she suggested.

'Me?'

'Authors often do sign books, don't they?'

I envy people who can produce a bon mot at the drop of an insult or who can produce incisive, relevant comments at exactly the right moment. As I've already pointed out I don't often think of sharp or witty things to say, but just once in a while the right words trickle out at exactly the right moment. They weren't particularly witty or incisive words. But they were the right words.

'Yes,' I said quietly. 'But usually only the books they've written.'

Vivienne's response to this apparently harmless comment was instant and quite predictable. She panicked. She looked at the book and then at me and decided that I must be joking. 'You did write this didn't you?'

I shook my head.

'That isn't funny.'

'It isn't meant to be.'

I shall for ever treasure the memory of the look which crossed Vivienne's face at that moment. It contained a rare mixture of emotions though fear was, I felt, by far the most dominant.

She picked the book up and held it up so that I could see the cover more clearly. 'You didn't write this?'

'I've written a book with the same title but I didn't write that book.'

Vivienne looked around.

'Two minutes to air!' called Tony.

'Simon!' screamed Vivienne. 'Simon! Come here!'

I don't know where Simon had been but by the time he arrived on the set he was quite breathless. He had abandoned his handkerchief and was now mopping his brow with a small, white hand towel.

'He didn't write this book!' squealed Vivienne, waving the book in the air.

Simon looked at me. He now had the same look in his eyes as Vivienne had had for a few moments. His skin was the same colour as the towel he was holding.

'Ninety seconds to air!' croaked Tony, who had realised that something wasn't right.

'I've written a book with that title,' I explained. 'I did try to tell you that I thought you'd got confused but you wouldn't listen!'

'How can you do this to me?' demanded Simon. He started tearing at the towel and I thought he was going to have a fit of some kind. 'Do you hate me?'

'It'll be O.K.!' I said. 'My book is quite interesting!'

'What's it about?' demanded Simon.

'It's about doctors and drug companies,' I replied. 'If Vivienne asks me what it's about I'll explain it all. But it's better not to talk about it beforehand, isn't it?'

Vivienne had now also gone white.

'Sixty seconds to air!' whispered Tony, who had moved closer to find out what was going on. He too looked terrified.

'I didn't mind when I didn't know what questions you were going to ask me,' I said, trying to cheer up Vivienne. 'Now neither of us know the questions or the answers! It'll be more exciting this way!'

I heard someone or something hissing on my right. I turned my head but could see nothing except a camera. Then I heard the hissing noise again. I looked over the arm of the sofa and saw the man in the grey pullover lying on the floor.

'Hello!' I said. 'What are you doing there?'

He said something but didn't actually speak and I've never been able to lip read.

'Pardon?'

'You're crackling!' he hissed. 'Every time you move you crackle.'

'Thirty seconds!' muttered Tony, who looked as though he was about to faint.

Still tearing at his towel Simon stumbled off the set and fell to his knees just out of camera shot. Louise rushed over to him and put her arm around his shoulders. I couldn't see his face but his shoulders were shaking and I got a strong feeling that he was crying.

I looked down at my microphone but could see nothing wrong.

'What have you got in your pocket?' shouted the man in a pullover who, although he had shouted had managed to do it in a whisper.

I put my hand in my left hand jacket pocket. Nothing. I put my hand in my other jacket pocket and found the packet of crisps I had bought in the canteen but hadn't finished eating. I pulled the packet out.

Tony, who was now using his fingers to tell Vivienne the number of seconds that were left before we went on air, looked really ill. I handed the packet of crisps to the man in the grey pullover. 'Don't eat them!' I told him, sternly. He took the packet from my outstretched hand and wriggled away.

'Are you O.K.?' I asked Tony. 'You look terrible!'

Tony weakly pointed a finger at Vivienne and nodded. He then backed away a couple of yards and sank gracefully to the floor.

'Hello, and welcome to another edition of 'Alive and How!'' said Vivienne to a camera which had a little red light lit up on its snout. 'Today my first guest is the author of an exciting new book.' She turned to me. 'Tell us what your book is about!' she said.

*   *   *

'You were marvellous!' said Deborah afterwards.

'Wonderful television! Absolutely wonderful, darling!' said Simon. Judging by the reappearance of the word 'darling' he was no longer quite so cross with me. 'But don't you ever put us through that again, darling!' he added, with a nervous laugh. I couldn't help wondering how Thumper, Peter Marshall or Frank Parsons would respond if I started calling them 'darling'.

'Terrific, darling!' said Vivienne, giving me a kiss on the cheek and immediately disappearing to talk to someone else more interesting.

'Can I go home now?' I asked. I had seen enough of the world of television not to believe any of them. It was, it seemed to me, a very superficial, artificial, unpleasant world.

'Your car is waiting at the front door,' said Louise.

On the way home the short, overweight, taciturn driver and I stopped at a motorway service station for food and fuel. While the driver was chewing his way through a plateful of sausages and chips and a dishful of spotted dick and lumpy looking custard I telephoned Patsy to tell her that I was on my way home.

Since we didn't have a television set at Bilbury Grange she hadn't seen the programme.'How did it go?' she asked.

'It was O.K.,' I said.

'I've heard that making television programmes is very boring,' she said.

'It is,' I agreed.

'The first swallow arrived this afternoon!' said Patsy.

And that was truly the most exciting news I'd had all day. Spring had come.

* * *

CHAPTER ELEVEN

I'd only been away from Bilbury for a day but the arrival of the first swallow of spring hadn't been the only notable thing to have happened in my absence. Even though the Revels Fund didn't have a penny in it, and they all knew very well that it would be several months before they could receive any money for their labours, Thumper Robinson, Alf Lillywhite, Geoff Taylor and Ian Entwhistle had cheerfully started work repairing Miss Hargreaves' cottage. And on the other side of the village Frank and Gilly Parsons had erected a plaque on the outside wall of the Duck and Puddle to tell the world that the North Devon writer and naturalist Henry Williamson had once been a much loved customer. Finally, Patsy also told me that Peter Marshall had called round to let me know that the cricket team would be holding its first practice session on Saturday evening.

Still, despite all this excitement it was, without doubt, the arrival of the first swallow of spring which had really delighted me. I stood in the courtyard and watched as he (or maybe she: like everyone else I know I am quite unable to differentiate between the male and the female of the species) explored our outbuildings. It was, we were both quite certain, one of the same swallows which had lived with us the previous summer.

Mr Parfitt, who had been working on some flower tubs he had installed in the courtyard, had been the first to see our first resident of the season arrive.

'He knew exactly where he was going,' said the gardener, standing beside Patsy and I as the three of us watched the swallow swoop straight down out of the sky, fly rather languidly around the courtyard and dive immediately and without hesitation into the stable where he and his colleagues had nested last summer.

Suddenly, there was another flash as a second swallow arrived. This one perched on the electricity cable which runs across the courtyard to provide the flat and stable block with power. It sat there for a moment, looking lonely, miserable, bedraggled and rather weary after what must have been a flight of several thousand miles across Europe.

Moments later the three of us witnessed one of the most joyful reunions any of us had ever seen. The swallow which had arrived first came out of the stable and immediately spotted the second bird perched on the electricity cable. The quiet and peace of the morning was shattered when the two birds saw one another. The two birds soared and dived and gave us a most extraordinary display of aerobatics. They flew together, never more than an inch or two apart, in absolutely perfect harmony. They flew around us and around our legs. They circled our heads and dived into and out of every opening on the stable block. They flew, no more than two feet above the courtyard floor, at such speed that it seemed inevitable that they would smash into the wall of the house and destroy themselves. But at the very last moment they swerved upwards, soaring high up into the sky, disappearing from sight and then racing back down earthwards again. From the way that they checked out all their old haunts it was clear that these were indeed two of last summer's residents. And from the way that they stayed with one another, never moving more than a few inches away from one another's side, it was clear that they were mighty pleased to see each other.

Most birds fly to get from one spot to another or to catch food but swallows alone seem to fly for fun. They always seem to enjoy their wonderful ability to dance and soar and play with one another. It is always the same; they always seem to fly as though they have just discovered their wings. And although they have their off days (particularly when the weather is grey and gloomy – for they love the sunshine) they never seem to lose their ability to enjoy life. I always get pleasure from watching swallows; they always bring bright sunshine into my heart. And even on a cool, rather dank spring morning the very sight of them reminds me that it will soon be summer and that we will soon be enjoying still, sun bathed mornings, warm days and balmy evenings.

I know it's always too easy to anthropomorphise when watching animals or birds but I couldn't help wondering where they had been separated from one another. I wondered if the sadness they had experienced when they had been parted had matched the joy they now expressed at the sight of each other.

After twenty minutes or so Patsy said she had to go into the house to check on something she'd put in the oven. Mr Parfitt asked me to walk down to the walled garden with him.

'I love watching you two together,' said Mr Parfitt.

I looked at him, slightly puzzled. I didn't really know what he meant. I said so.

'You remind me of those two swallows,' he said. 'You love each other totally, don't you?'

I nodded.

We walked another few paces.

'Did you love your wife?' I asked him.

'To begin with,' replied Mr Parfitt. 'But I don't think she ever really loved me,' he said, sadly. 'I think that was part of our problem.'

'Why did she marry you if she didn't love you?'

Mr Parfitt shrugged. 'I've thought about that,' he said. 'But I'm still not sure of the answer. Maybe she was running away from something. Maybe she was so desperate to leave home that she didn't need to love me to marry me. Maybe she can't love anyone. I don't know. Her father had died when she was seven and her mother had married again. She didn't get on with her stepfather and she fought with her mother all the time.'

'But you must have had some good times.'

'I suppose so,' agreed Mr Parfitt. 'But they were never really carefree times. When we married I was trying to make it as a racing driver. I'd inherited some money from an aunt and I'd spent a big chunk of it on buying a car. I wanted three years to see if I could really make it into the big time. Although I think it was the wildness and excitement of racing which had first attracted her to me, Clarice – that's my wife – didn't really approve of my lifestyle. Once we got married she worried that I was wasting the money I'd inherited. She wanted me to get a job

131

and race cars at the weekends. You can't do that if you want to do it properly.'

'Gradually, the things about me which had attracted her to me in the first place began to worry her, to eat away at her. I won a few races and people started to say that I could become a champion. But there was never any security in it and that worried her. When I got some sponsors and started to make money out of my racing she became even more uncertain. I think she was worried about the fact that we could so easily lose what we'd got. The more we had the more she was frightened of losing it. I never made enough money to invest any for the future.'

'I'd always taken risks as a driver – you have to if you want to get anywhere professionally – but she started to worry about me crashing and not being able to drive any more. And, strangely, I think she resented my success too. She enjoyed the success but she wanted it to be her success and it was so obviously mine.

'Slowly, and in little ways, she tried to change me. No, that's not fair. She didn't try to change me. I tried to change myself. But I tried to change myself because I knew it was what she wanted – and I wanted to please her. I gave up racing and got a job in banking through one of the sponsors I'd met.'

'Gradually, what had seemed at first like a passionate, caring and genuine interest in my well being and progress became tedious and suffocating. As a young, newly married husband I was flattered that someone cared about me so much that they didn't want me to take risks. It was sweet and charming. But as I grew into middle age I felt thwarted by the knowledge that I had to tread carefully and avoid all risks. I became someone I am not. I became someone I did not like or feel comfortable with. I had to be nice to everyone above me in the bank because Clarice was terrified that if I annoyed anyone important they would wreck my career. I had to be careful about what I said – and who I said it to. I felt constantly threatened by Clarice's insecurities.'

'Because I didn't say anything Clarice assumed that I was happy with my life and that was my fault. I should have told her how I felt. I stayed quiet because I didn't want to hurt her by telling her the truth and gradually whatever love there had been

between us just seeped away until there was nothing left holding our marriage together but habit and children and social
niceties and in the end that wasn't enough.'

'Do you think you'll ever go back?' I asked for the second
time.

This time Mr Parfitt didn't even hesitate or stop to think
about it. 'No! Never!' he said firmly. He smiled at me. 'I've
never been as happy or as content as I am now,' he said.
'Besides,' he said. 'I had a letter a few days ago. My wife has
started divorce proceedings.'

'Oh,' I said. I reached out and touched his arm. 'I'm sorry...'

'Don't be,' said Mr Parfitt. He smiled. 'I'm not.' I could tell
that he meant it.

We pottered around the garden for a little while longer and
Mr Parfitt showed me some bushes he thought needed moving
and then we walked in comfortable silence back to the house.
When we got there we discovered that the courtyard was as
busy with revellers as Trafalgar Square on New Year's Eve.
There were, I suppose, no more than six or seven pairs of birds
but they were playing a complicated series of flying games and
when they saw us approaching we were incorporated into the
games. They flew around our heads and around our bodies,
never moving at anything less than top speed. Emily and
Sophie were sitting on the courtyard cobbles watching the
birds' fearless antics with confused looks on their faces. The
birds seemed completely unperturbed by the presence of our
two cats; indeed, several of them seemed to delight in deliberately flying within inches of the cats' heads. Some of the birds
were undoubtedly the offspring of last year's pairs ('Can we
come and stay with you, Mum? Just till we find a place of our
own?') but others must have been new.

'It looks as though you've got an entry in the Good Nest
Guide,' said Mr Parfitt.

I laughed. But inside I felt quietly proud that the swallows
had chosen to come back to us. I have heard people complain
that swallows and house martins make a mess and are noisy,
disruptive birds. I don't care about the mess and I love the
noise. I know of one man who deliberately shot the swallows
who came to roost around his house. He claimed that one year
they had nested in the outhouse where he stored his garden
equipment and that several times during the season he had had

to scrape thick layers of droppings from his lawn mower. What a small, insignificant price to pay for such intense and pure pleasure from such delightful companions. How anyone can be so callously cruel is quite beyond my comprehension. The man who told me this used to be a friend. I have never spoken to him since. You can judge the character of people by the way they treat animals, birds and other creatures. I considered our swallows to be part of the Bilbury Grange family and from the first day I saw them I hoped they would never stop coming back to stay with us.

*　　*　　*

I wasn't quite sure what to wear for the cricket club's first official practice session. After our last meeting I had been surprised to hear that the Bilbury cricket club was going to hold practice sessions at all! But I was keen to make a good impression and to justify my inclusion in the team.

Neither at school nor at medical school had I ever taken part in any team sports. There had been three main reasons for this complete lack of athletic experience. Firstly, I had never found the necessary time. At university the football and cricket team members had all trained on at least three or four nights a week – and their training sessions had each lasted several hours. Students studying Greek, astronomy or civil engineering might have been able to find the time for such things but, like most medical students, I found that I was working what often seemed like, and sometimes was, a twenty hour day. Secondly, I had never been attracted to the idea of running round and round a damp field in a wet track suit. Most of the training sessions I'd witnessed had taken place in the pouring rain and hadn't looked much fun. Thirdly, I had never been regarded as being any good at sports and I was therefore quite sure that even if I had wanted to play they wouldn't have let me. I've always loved cricket but at school my skills were ignored. I've always suspected that my natural sporting skills remained undetected and undeveloped because I was never the sort of child who makes friends easily. Team captains were elected as a result of their popularity among the other boys. And, naturally enough, team captains tended to pick their chums first when selecting teams. As a result, when teams were being picked I was always one of the stragglers, unwanted by either captain. My name always appeared at the bottom of batting lists, I never got a chance to show my skill as a bowler and when fielding I was always sent to ruminate in the rutted pasture-lands of long leg, long on or third man.

I have always comforted myself with the thought that if it had not been for my natural shyness, innate sense of independence and refusal to be bullied my hidden sporting talents would have brought me certain acclaim. If, at the age of six, I'd let John Boardman have my best marble he would picked me as an opening batsman and I would, in the fullness of time, have played cricket for England. It is with such slender threads of fate that the tapestry of our lives are sewn. My refusal to compromise my integrity (and my reluctance to part with my best marble – a wondrous looking beast the size of a table tennis ball) had meant that my natural talents as a cricketer had never had a chance to flower.

In the end I had stuffed an old tee shirt, my best gardening trousers and a pair of tennis pumps that I'd found in the cellar into a plastic shopping bag and had set off for my first training session. The pumps were a trifle on the small size so I had cut holes in the front of the shoes so that my big toes could poke through.

Peter Marshall had told Patsy that the club would be meeting in the tap room at the Duck and Puddle at seven thirty. Anxious not to miss any opportunities in this final chance at a sporting career I got there at twenty past. The new blue painted plaque, commemorating Henry Williamson's custom, had been fixed to the wall alongside the front door at eye level and looked very impressive.

As I walked in I congratulated Frank on the new plaque.

'Hmm.' said Frank, rather glumly.

'What's up?' I asked him.

'When that . . . ,' Frank paused, '. . . woman at the Pig and Whistle in Kentisbury heard about our plaque she put one up too. She says he drank there as well.'

'Did he?'

'God knows. Probably.' Frank automatically took down a glass and started to pull me a pint of Old Parsonage Brew.

'You mustn't say that!' said Gilly, appearing as if by magic.

Her hands were covered with flour and she was wearing a large white, starched apron. 'I don't think he ever did drink there. They certainly can't prove that he did.' She disappeared again.

I held up a hand. 'I'm not sure I should be drinking that stuff yet,' I told him.

'He drank here at least twice!' said Gilly, returning. Before I could comment she disappeared again. I'd never seen her so upset.

'Is Gilly O.K.?' I asked Frank.

'Oh she's just a bit peeved over this blue plaque business. She found some letters showing that Henry Williamson had drunk here and she thought it might help our summer trade if we put a plaque up.' He shrugged. He hadn't stopped what he was doing but he now looked up at me anxiously. 'Are you O.K.?' he asked, putting the emphasis firmly on the second word.

'Cricket team practice!' I explained, rather proudly. 'Though I'm not sure what Peter's got planned,' I confessed.

Frank laughed. 'I shouldn't worry too much!'

I said that all the same I thought I would play safe and just have a tomato juice. Frank, staring at me as though I'd just deliberately chosen to share my bed with a rubber hot water bottle instead of Lauren Bacall, finished pulling the pint of ale (it wouldn't be wasted for he would, I knew, drink it himself) and then bent down and picked up a small bottle of tomato juice. He blew the dust off it and handed me the bottle, the opener and a glass.

'Do you mind opening it yourself?' he said. 'I never feel comfortable touching that stuff.'

I took the bottle of tomato juice off him, levered off the top and poured the contents into the glass. As I was pouring the thick red juice Thumper walked in. He saw the pint that Frank had just pulled and grinned. 'Saw me coming, did you Frank?' he said. 'Nice plaque. Have you seen the one they've put up at the Pig and Whistle?'

Frank said nothing but just pushed the foam topped glass across the bar counter into Thumper's hand. Neither of us paid for our drinks. Frank just made a note in the book he kept hanging on a string behind him. We would get our bills when our entries in the book filled a page.

'He hasn't drunk there!' said Gilly, reappearing for a

moment and then disappearing again. She looked harassed and had a smear of flour across her forehead where she had wiped her hair out of her eyes with her hand.

Thumper turned to me. 'Who didn't what?'

'Henry Williamson hasn't ever drunk at the Pig and Whistle.'

'Oh. Hasn't he? They've got a plaque up. I don't much care anyway.' Thumper nodded towards the plastic bag at my feet. 'What's in the bag?'

I told him. He laughed. Before I could ask him what he had found so funny Peter Marshall and Dr Brownlow turned up, closely followed by Patchy Fogg and what was clearly the rest of the Old Bilburians Cricket Club. Patchy, who specialised in selling very nearly genuine antiques, was looking particularly pleased with himself. I discovered later that he had just sold a truckload of genuine Chippendale antique television cabinets to an American dealer. Two skilled craftsmen in Combe Martin would, as a result, have enough work to keep them going for nine months while Patchy would make enough profit to avoid doing any work for at least a year. Frank, exercising the way he knew best, pulled pints of beer for everyone.

When used to describe a sports team the word 'Old' usually implies that the members were all once students at some scholarly institution. But in the case of the 'Old Bilburians Cricket Club' the word was used in a more direct, more definitive sense. Some members of the 'Old Bilburians Cricket Club' were, to put it as simply as possible, very well qualified to be in the team. There was certainly no danger of us getting into trouble for misrepresenting ourselves.

'Do you want to practice in the room upstairs?' Frank asked. His attention was, as ever, focused on the pint he was pulling and so he didn't look up or direct the question at anyone in particular. Frank regarded the work of transferring beer from a barrel to a glass as a craft, maybe even a minor art form. He would never allow himself to be distracted and still did not like to be reminded of the time when two tall, long legged, blonde, Swedish hikers wearing very short shorts and very skimpy tops had walked into the bar and ordered drinks and sandwiches. It was as a result of that incident that the front door of the Duck and Puddle now carried a notice, similar to the ones which appear on the outside of cathedrals all over Europe, asking female customers to dress appropriately. Frank didn't like spilling beer. We all looked at one another.

'Maybe we should,' said Peter, thoughtfully. 'Secret training camp! Just in case someone from another village comes in. Nice plaque, Frank. If you want any more I can get them done wholesale.' He paused and frowned. 'Who is Henry Williamson, by the way?'

I wasn't sure that moving upstairs was an entirely practical notion. Looking around I wasn't at all sure that all the members of our team would even be able to get upstairs under their own steam.

'Safer down here,' said Thumper, settled comfortably on his usual bar stool.

We all looked at him.

'We don't want anyone getting injured,' he explained, taking a sip at his beer. 'Cricketers are always getting injured during pre-season training.'

'I don't think we're any more likely to injure ourselves upstairs than we are down here!' I said.

'It's not the being upstairs that's dangerous,' explained Thumper. 'It's the getting there. All those stairs. Trays of beer every five minutes. Someone is bound to fall.'

'Thumper is right!' said Peter, firmly. 'Is that O.K. with you, Frank?'

'Fine with me,' replied Frank, with a shrug. 'You can practice wherever you like as far as I'm concerned.'

We settled ourselves around the bar. I recognised everyone in the team, though I didn't know everyone's names. Peter introduced us all to one another but did it in rather a hurry and didn't bother to tell us whose name went with which face. I recognised all the names but was as confused and as ignorant as I had been to start with.

'First thing we've got to do is choose a captain,' said Peter Marshall.

'Josh.' said Thumper immediately.

'Josh.' agreed everyone else.

'Is that O.K. with you?' Peter asked Josh.

'Thank you very much,' said Josh. 'I'll have a gin and tonic.' He paused. 'And a packet of salt and vinegar crisps.'

I was, to say the least, surprised at this choice. Josh Wilkins is at least eighty years old and bent double with arthritis. He lives on the other side of the village green to Peter's shop and every morning at 8 am sharp he sets off to fetch his morning paper. He arrives at Peter's shop at about ten thirty, collects his paper and gets back home at about one. He then has his lunch and walks back to the shop to do his shopping. Whatever the weather his hunched and crippled form is, therefore, an almost constant sight on the round around the village green. I once asked him why he didn't do his shopping in the morning when he picked up his newspaper. He had looked at me in some surprise. 'If I did that what would I do in the afternoons?' he had asked.

I bent closer to Patchy Fogg, who was sitting next to me. 'Why Josh?'

'Because he is bent over and so close to the ground that when the toss is taken he can see whether it's heads or tails before he commits himself,' explained Patchy. 'He was the Old Bilburians Cricket Club captain in the fifties and he always got the other captain to toss so that he could call and he always called late.'

'Did he get away with it?' I asked.

'Of course!' said Patchy. 'Can you imagine anyone accusing Josh of cheating?'

I had to agree that any such remark would look in poor spirit.

'Besides,' added Patchy, 'he's completely deaf so even if the opposing captain complains Josh won't hear him!'

'But why is winning the toss so important?' I was puzzled by this. 'I thought we weren't worried about winning?'

'We aren't. But winning the toss means that we control the game. And if we can control the game we can make sure that in the unlikely event that the other side are worse than us then they still win.'

There was clearly a great deal about village cricket that I didn't understand. 'How does winning the toss mean that we control the game?'

'It means that we can always make sure that our opponents bat first.'

'Oh.'

'If they bat second they might lose. If they bat first we always

139

know what score they've got – so we know what we mustn't beat.'

'Losing sounds quite tricky.'

'It is,' said Patchy quite seriously. 'It's sometimes much harder than winning.'

After the selection of the captain had been completed Peter suggested that we had a break. Thumper and three of the others went off to play pool while a couple of team members borrowed the darts from Frank and started peppering the panelling around the dartboard. In most pubs the dartboard is surrounded by a tyre and the tyre is surrounded by a wooden board. At the Duck and Puddle the quality of dart playing is so low that such localised forms of protection would be of absolutely no value. Even the unshaded light bulb hanging from the ceiling is at risk and sits in a small chicken wire basket.

After twenty minutes Peter coughed loudly and clapped his hands. 'Time for team selection, gentlemen!' he cried.

'Thank you!' smiled Josh. 'I'll have a gin and tonic, please.'

The pool and dart players finished their games. More drinks were poured.

'Thumper,' said Peter, 'will you bat at number eleven?'

Thumper nodded and said that he would be delighted to bat at number eleven. I was, I confess, slightly surprised by this. I had thought that Thumper would command a batting place far higher up the order.

Gradually the rest of the batting order was organised. Patchy Fogg was put at number ten and Peter Marshall volunteered to bat at number nine. Frank was given the number eight spot and Dr Brownlow the number seven position. Eventually the only two people left were Josh, the newly elected captain of the Old Bilburians Cricket Team, and myself.

'Well it looks as if you two are going to open the batting for us this year!' said Peter. 'Is that O.K. with you both?'

I said I would be honoured to take such a responsible position. Josh, who clearly had no idea what was going on, said that he would have a gin but that we could hold the tonic. As an afterthought he mentioned that he would also like a packet of pork scratchings.

We then all sang 'Ten Green Bottles' and sixteen choruses of

'Eskimo Nell' before Peter officially declared the training session over.

'Are you sure you don't mind opening the batting for us?' asked Peter, as the rest of the team celebrated the end of the session by ordering drinks and Dr Brownlow and I headed for the door. Dr Brownlow had offered to give me a lift home but I had gracefully declined.

I said that I would be delighted to try and see off the new ball bowlers.

Peter looked at me rather strangely and then, apparently deciding that I was joking, laughed nervously. 'Don't try taking any quick singles!' he laughed. 'Josh likes to take things fairly slowly.'

This seemed good advice and so I nodded sagely.

'I'll try and push you up the order a bit for some of the later matches,' said Peter. He looked down. 'What's in the bag?' he asked.

I followed his eyes down. 'Oh just some old clothes,' I said. 'Patsy asked me to drop them off at the vicarage for next week's jumble sale,' I lied, saying the first thing that came into my head.

'Oh wonderful!' said Peter, taking the bag from my hand. 'I've got a pile of stuff to go there I'll take this lot round there for you.'

'Thank you,' I said, weakly, making a mental note to pop round to the vicarage the following morning to retrieve my clothes.

'Why were Thumper and Patchy put at the bottom of the batting order?' I asked Dr Brownlow as he climbed into his elderly Rolls Royce.

'We need our best players at the bottom of the batting order,' said Dr Brownlow. 'Just in case we need to lose some wickets in a hurry.'

I looked at him and frowned. 'I don't understand,' I said.

'If the other sides' bowlers aren't very good it can be quite difficult to get out,' explained Dr Brownlow. 'If they aren't bowling very accurately you can't rely on being bowled or given out leg before wicket so you have to make sure that you give easy catches.'

'Oh.' I said, wishing I hadn't asked.

Still, for a brief moment I had enjoyed the thought that my talents had been recognised and that I had been selected to open the batting in recognition of the strength of my sporting skills instead of, as had always been the case, an entirely justifiable assumption that I had no sporting skills.

As I left the Duck and Puddle I noticed that someone had stuck a small cardboard notice on the Duck and Puddle's front door. It said simply: 'Thumper Robinson drank here'. The next time I returned to the pub the notice about Henry Williamson had disappeared.

*　　*　　*

I had turned down Dr Brownlow's offer to drive me home because there was a full moon and I rather fancied the walk back across the fields. During the last week I had spent one day in London and another in the Midlands and I hadn't had time for any of my favourite country walks. I have noticed that if I don't get out into the fields very regularly I suffer from withdrawal symptoms. I get edgy, irritable and easily upset. Besides, I had a rather strong suspicion that Ben, who had spent the evening sitting obediently and quietly under my chair in the Duck and Puddle, would enjoy a chance to get a little fresh air in her lungs and a little mud on her paws.

I had got to the bottom of the main field where our four sheep usually graze when I heard the unmistakeable sound of a sheep in trouble. The noise was coming from a small copse and so, treading carefully because it was dark underneath the trees, I gingerly edged off the path. The ground between the trees was thick with dead brambles and as I forced myself further and further into the thicket I could feel the thorns scratching at my legs through my trousers. Ben, who had tried to follow me but had, to her dismay, discovered that she simply could not find a way through the brambles remained on the path, occasionally whining very quietly.

At first I had half suspected that the sheep which was in trouble might be one of ours. It didn't sound like Lizzie, Petula, Cynthia or Sarah-Louise (people who don't know anything much about sheep assume that they all must sound the same but they do not; their voices are most distinct) but a distressed sheep can sometimes sound quite different. But when I finally managed to break through the brambles to stand within a foot or so of the trapped sheep I could clearly see that it wasn't one of our tiny flock.

The poor thing must have been stuck for hours. It had strayed into the overgrown thicket, presumably in search of some tasty morsel, and had got itself naturally tethered by two long, strong brambles. It was so nervous and agitated that before I could even begin to free it I had to spend ten minutes stroking its head to calm it down. It looked no more than a year old and had enormous, trusting brown eyes. Sheep love having their heads stroked; best of all they adore having the area underneath their chins tickled.

Even after I had calmed the sheep down and managed to assure it that I didn't mean it any harm it took me over half an hour to release it from its bonds. The brambles were unbreakable and even the Swiss Army Penknife which I always carry with me had a job cutting through the woody tangles. By the time the sheep was free my fingers were sore and raw and even in the dim moonlight I could see that my hands were bleeding quite badly. It was impossible to get the sheep back through to the field from which it had come so I trampled down a path back out of the brambles and then coaxed and pushed and pulled the liberated sheep onto the path leading up to our field where, although it hesitated for a moment at the sight of Ben, it trotted after me quite happily.

At the top of our field our four sheep came out of their stable when they heard me coming. They stared at the newcomer as though it was an alien and the newcomer stared back at them like a new girl starting a strange school. I introduced them to one another and by the time I had fetched a bundle of hay and a couple of handfuls of sheep pellets the five animals seemed to have accepted one another. I left them all sleeping together in the stable and with Ben padding along silently behind me I went into the house, dumped my clothes on the kitchen floor, explained to Patsy what had happened, bathed the blood and mud off my hands, arms and legs and, exhausted but content, collapsed into bed.

As I lay my head down on the pillow I remembered that just before I had left him that evening Dr Brownlow had asked me whether I'd thought of a subject for my second book yet. I had told him that I had no idea at all what I was going to write next, but as I drifted off to sleep I began to have the beginnings of an idea for a book which I knew I would enjoy writing.

*   *   *

CHAPTER TWELVE

First thing the following morning I rang Colin Jackson who rents the field from which the sheep I had rescued must have wandered. I knew that if I didn't ring him early he would have gone out to work in the fields and I probably wouldn't be able to catch him until the evening.

'I think I've got one of your ewes in my stable,' I told him. I explained what had happened. Colin said he would come round with his trailer to pick the animal up. I told him that he needn't bother coming up to the house but that he could just drive straight into the field from the lane. He didn't thank me and I didn't expect him to. People in Bilbury give and receive kindnesses with great ease. Villagers help one another because life is hard and helping your neighbours when they are in trouble is the way that generations of country folk have learned to survive the cruel vicissitudes of country life.

Town dwellers who come to Bilbury Grange sometimes remark on how lonely it must be and how desolate and isolated they feel. I never feel that at all in Bilbury though I do, I confess, feel lonely and alone if I have to go to London or any other big city. There is plenty of space in Bilbury but that's a different thing altogether; space has nothing to do with loneliness.

I put the telephone down, walked across the bedroom and drew back the curtains. The sun was shining. It was a thin, rather watery spring sunshine but it was sunshine nevertheless and it was good to see this additional clear reminder that winter was over. The winter seemed to have lasted a long time and it had been a hard one.

'What on earth happened to your clothes?' asked Patsy, clambering out of bed, coming over to the window to see what I was looking at and catching sight of my torn jacket and trousers. 'And where on earth did all this blood come from?' she asked, quite horrified.

I reminded her about the sheep I had rescued.

'But I didn't know you'd been bleeding so much!'

'Just scratches.' I showed her my hands and arms. 'They'll heal.'

'I wish I could say the same about your trousers!' said Patsy, poking her hand through a long tear.

'Can you mend them?'

'I can mend them,' said Patsy. 'But they'll look mended.'

'That's O.K.!' I grinned. 'Maybe I'll start a new fashion.'

We went downstairs and had breakfast and then I spent the rest of the morning working on an outline for the book I'd decided I wanted to write. I had been told so many stories since I had moved to Bilbury that I decided to try and write a novel about an imaginary village in Devon. I would, I thought, fill it with the adventures of a series of robust and humorous characters. I wondered if I would be able to create a character as full of life as Thumper Robinson!

*   *   *

Just before lunch Tanya telephoned from London.

'Have you sent me that photograph yet?' she asked.

'Photograph?'

'You were going to send me a picture of yourself. For newspapers and magazines.'

'Sorry!' I said. 'I forgot. I'll try and find one. I think I've got one of me in fancy dress when I was a medical student. Do you think that will be O.K.? You can probably cut off most of the headdress.'

Tanya sighed. 'Headdress?'

'I went as an Indian brave.'

'I'm afraid that doesn't sound very suitable. 'The Observer want to print a picture of you to accompany their review of your book.'

'Well, it could have been worse! Nigel Popplethwaite went as a Zulu and was covered from head to toe in boot polish. It took him a week to get it all off.'

'Haven't you got a decent portrait shot?' asked Tanya.

'I'm afraid not,' I confessed.

'I don't suppose you're coming up to London today or tomorrow?'

'No.'

Tanya sighed again. She seemed to sigh a lot when she spoke to me. 'I'll send a photographer,' she said. 'Will tomorrow morning be O.K.?'

I said that it would be fine.

'Make sure you wear something smart but casual,' said Tanya firmly.

I said I had just the outfit.

*   *   *

My morning's work hadn't gone too badly. I had thrown most of it away but I had kept a few good ideas and, by and large, was quite pleased with the way things were going. I had planned to carry on working on my book outline that afternoon but when Thumper came round to ask Miss Hargreaves to go round to her cottage with him I allowed myself to be persuaded to accompany them. I had discovered that although working at home has many advantages it has one huge disadvantage: it is all too easy to allow yourself to be distracted by something more interesting than work. Friends wandering idly by will catch me sitting at my desk and say things like: 'Oh I'm glad you're not doing anything important. Have you seen the gorse on the moors recently? It looks really beautiful today.'

The three of us, plus Ben, climbed into the cab of Thumper's truck and set off for Miss Hargreaves' cottage where work had been continuing at quite a spectacular pace since the night of the storm.

'We could rebuild the cottage so that it looks just the same as it was before the storm,' explained Thumper, picking his way carefully between a huge pile of freshly delivered building sand and an impressive looking stack of freshly cut timber. 'But stronger!' he added with a grin.

Miss Hargreaves looked at him rather sharply. 'That's how I want it, Robert,' she said. She was the only person I had ever met who called Thumper by his real name. Even Annie, his wife, called him Thumper.

'But while we're working on it we could make a few improve-

147

ments if you like,' said Thumper. 'It won't take us much longer or cost much more money,' he added quickly.

'What sort of improvements?' asked Miss Hargreaves, extremely doubtfully. It wasn't difficult to tell that she was a woman who was not enthusiastic about change. She was the only person I knew who still did all her writing with a bottle of blue ink and a simple nib pen. Every other year the children at the school pooled their pocket money and bought her a ball point pen or a fountain pen and each time she said 'thank you' very nicely and then put the new fangled gadget away in a drawer. Generations of children had failed to persuade her that progress was here to stay.

'Well we could build a little porch onto the front, extend your kitchen at the back, put another bedroom in your loft and add an indoor lavatory,' said Thumper.

Miss Hargreaves stared at him. 'Certainly not!' she said indignantly. 'An indoor lavatory!' she repeated, as though Thumper had suggested building a bordello or a ten pin bowling alley onto the side of her cottage.

'Don't you want to think about it?' asked Thumper, who was clearly rather disappointed.

'I've thought about it!' snapped Miss Hargreaves. 'What do I want an indoor lavatory for?'

'Well it'll save you getting quite so chilly if you need to make an urgent call at night!' said Thumper, looking rather embarrassed. I'd never seen Thumper look even remotely embarrassed before.

'I've never had one indoors,' said Miss Hargreaves. She looked at me. 'There's one in the flat at his house,' she said, nodding in my direction. 'But I don't like it. It's not natural or healthy.' She walked briskly back to Thumper's truck, climbed in and sat down. She was clearly waiting to be taken back to Bilbury Grange.

'See if you can persuade her,' whispered Thumper. 'It seems a pity not to make a decent job of it.'

'I doubt if she'll listen to me,' I whispered back.

'What are you two whispering about?' shouted Miss Hargreaves.

'Nothing, Miss Hargreaves!' we both lied. Even though Miss

Hargreaves had not been my teacher I found myself feeling as guilty as Thumper looked.

*   *   *

After Thumper had dropped Miss Hargreaves, Ben and I off at Bilbury Grange, Ben and I popped out into the field to make sure that our four sheep were happy and well. I always visited them at least once, usually twice and sometimes three times a day to make sure that they had plenty of clean straw and fresh drinking water. If the weather was wet I fed them sheep pellets and hay. They always ran for shelter the moment it started to rain for although they didn't mind the wind they hated getting soaked.

The sheep were all out in the field and they were absolutely fine but I didn't need to risk drowsiness by counting them to see that there were five rather than four of them. The solitary sheep that I had rescued the night before was still there. It looked very much at home and Lizzie, Petula, Cynthia and Sarah-Louise all seemed quite at ease with it. I shared out the digestive biscuits which I had in my pocket. After a moment's hesitation the newcomer decided that she too liked digestive biscuits. She was still nervous about Ben but clearly took comfort from the fact that her four new friends weren't in the slightest bit worried about her.

When I had swept the concrete terrace outside the stable and refilled the sheeps' water bowl I walked back to the house and telephoned Colin Jackson. His wife Rosie, who had been brought up in Liverpool and had come to North Devon to work as a barmaid at a holiday camp, answered the phone in her quite unaltered Liverpool accent. I liked Rosie a lot. She and Colin had met at a pub in Ilfracombe and had married within a month. Now, just a few years later, she looked every inch a farmer's wife. She had a huge, soft bosom and rosy cheeks and invariably wore a cheerfully coloured, old fashioned print pinafore. She had a wonderful complexion, completely free of wrinkles or lines.

I was lucky, Rosie told me, after inviting Patsy and I to go round for Sunday lunch. Her husband had just arrived back at the house for his tea.

149

'I don't mind but I've still got your sheep,' I reminded him. 'Have you forgotten it?'

'I picked her up this morning,' replied Colin, tersely. 'Not half an hour after you called.'

'Well, five minutes ago she was in my field,' I told him. 'She must have fought her way through the brambles and come back again.'

Colin sighed. 'I'll pick her up as soon as I've finished my tea,' he said.

*　　*　　*

CHAPTER THIRTEEN

'I knew I should have brought hair and make up with me,' said the photographer gloomily. He was about thirty years old, five foot ten inches tall and so thin that if he had been standing sideways he would have been all but invisible. He stood, hands on hips, and stared at me in clear despair. He was wearing a plain white polo necked shirt, a pale grey silk suit and a floor length coat that was made of something so flimsy that even in the stillness of the living room it seemed to float on the air whenever he turned around.

'Hair and make up?' I said, frowning. 'What do you mean?'

'Someone to do your hair and someone to do your make up, my love,' said the photographer. He sighed. It was a deep sigh, a sigh from the heart. He was clearly a troubled and unhappy man. 'I should have brought wardrobe too,' he added. He stepped forward a pace, reached out and toyed ruefully with a lock of my untameable hair. 'Someone to dress you,' he explained. I was glad Thumper wasn't around to listen to any of this. The photographer stared dolefully at my stained and tattered sports jacket. Patsy had done a good job of mending it and it looked fine to me. It had pockets and kept me warm and I could think of no more to ask of a jacket. 'Are you sure you haven't got anything else you could wear?' he asked, plaintively. 'A suit, perhaps? Maybe something you wear on Sundays?'

'This is all there is,' I told him for the fourth time. I was getting just a little bit fed up of people telling me that my clothes were old and out of fashion. 'Don't think of the jacket as being out of fashion,' I told him, trying to cheer him up. 'Think of it as a timeless classic.' The photographer tried hard to smile but it looked more like a grimace of pain. 'No offence, dear,' he said. 'But I don't honestly think that jacket was ever in fashion.' He gave me what I think he thought was a smile. 'Don't take it personally.' I thought that this was a remarkably silly thing to say. After all, how else could I take it but personally? It was, after all, my jacket he was talking about.

He stepped back a couple of paces, lowered his head to one side like a thoughtful budgerigar about to perform his party piece, and stroked his smooth, pink chin with the thumb and forefinger of his right hand. He tilted his head the other way. 'George, darling,' he said, speaking to his assistant, 'I want you to bring in every light we've got.' He turned back to me. 'I'm going to shoot you in your shirt sleeves,' he said, giving this modest statement a profundity that I did not feel it entirely merited.

'Just my shirt?' I asked, surprised.

'Just the shirt.'

'Er ... no trousers?'

'Darling, I don't care whether you wear trousers or not though to be perfectly honest I wouldn't advise you to take them off with George around. I'm only shooting you from the chest up.'

'Oh.' I said. I looked down. 'Shall I keep my tie on?'

The photographer closed his eyes as though in pain. 'No,' he said, after a long moment. 'You can lose the tie.' He paused. 'And when I say 'lose the tie' I do mean that you can 'lose the tie'.'

I looked down at it. My Aunt Matilda had bought it for me on my fourteenth birthday and I had always rather liked it. It had so many colours in it that it seemed to go with just about anything. On the other hand, if you looked at it from another point of view then I suppose it was equally true that it didn't really go with anything. I removed my tie, rolled it up and put into my jacket pocket, removed my jacket and unfastened my top shirt button. I felt much more comfortable without a jacket and tie.

'Right!' I said, folding my arms, sitting up straight and smiling.

The photographer frowned.

'Ready when you are,' I said.

The photographer glared at me but didn't answer. He

walked off into a corner of the room and stared out of the window.

'I should go and get yourself a coffee,' whispered George, the assistant, who was busy sitting up a battery of floodlights. He had a lisp which I suspect he had deliberately accentuated. I could imagine him standing alone for hours practising his lisp. 'It'll be hours before he's ready for you.'

I quietly thanked him, tiptoed noiselessly out of the room and left them to it.

Escaping from the lunacy in the house I wandered down to the vegetable garden to have a word with Mr Parfitt about our entering the Bilbury Village Produce Show, a village extravaganza which was being organised as part of Revels Week.

*　　*　　*

Miss Phillips and Mrs Blossom had called round to the house the previous evening to tell Patsy and I about the proposed Show.

'I've spoken to quite a few people about it,' said Mrs Blossom, who was clearly rather excited by the whole business. I had poured them both a glass of parsnip wine. 'Apparently the village always used to have a produce show on August Bank Holiday.' She had brought with her a large notebook on the front of which she had stuck a label and carefully written the words BILBURY VILLAGE PRODUCE SHOW in large capital letters.

'We're going to have all sorts of categories,' said Miss Phillips. 'Carrots, potatoes, beetroot, tomatoes, lettuce, parsnips ...'

'Broad beans, runner beans, parsley, rhubarb, soft fruits ...' interrupted Mrs Blossom, reading from her note book.

'... strawberries, raspberries, blackberries, blackcurrants, redcurrants...,' explained Miss Phillips in case I wasn't sure what a soft fruit was.

'But we're not just having fruit and vegetables,' said Mrs Blossom.

'Fruit cake, fairy cakes, rock buns, sponge cake ... ' said Miss Phillips.

'... with jam and with cream,' interrupted Mrs Blossom.

Miss Phillips looked at her, rather sharply I thought.

'Sponge cakes with jam and sponge cakes with cream,' said Mrs Blossom. She held up her notebook and turned it so that Miss Phillips could read what was written in it. 'We agreed. Two separate categories.'

Miss Phillips was nodding enthusiastically. 'Yes. Absolutely,' she said. 'Two separate types of sponge cake. Jam and cream. And plain!' she added. 'That's three, isn't it?'

'But it must be home-made jam,' said Mrs Blossom, firmly.

'Oh, yes, the jam must be home-made,' agreed Miss Phillips. 'As must the cream.'

'That's why we had to have two categories of fillings, you see,' Mrs Blossom explained to Patsy and I. 'Not everyone makes their own cream. So the people who make their own jam have a category they can enter.'

'Though I suppose not everyone makes their own jam,' said Miss Phillips, as though this terrible thought had only just occurred to her.

Patsy and I exchanged glances. We were both trying hard not to giggle at the seemingly interminable duologue which was rapidly threatening to turn into a music hall turn. 'We'd love to enter!' said Patsy.

'Oh, would you!' said Miss Phillips.

'That's wonderful!' said Mrs Blossom. She rummaged around in her huge handbag, found a large black fountain pen and wrote our names down in her notebook. 'I'll bring you a category list as soon as they're ready,' she promised. She suddenly acquired a very serious look. 'We're asking people to pay a penny an entry,' she said, rather nervously. 'To help with the expenses. Do you think that will be all right?'

'I'm sure it will be absolutely fine,' I said.

'We'll be charging an entrance fee to the marquee,' said Miss Phillips. 'For the building fund, of course.'

'But we thought we ought to try to be self-supporting just in case anything goes wrong,' said Mrs Blossom. 'We don't want to end up taking money out of the fund, do we?'

'No,' said Patsy. 'Absolutely not!'

'I think charging a penny an entry is an extremely sensible idea,' I said.

Miss Phillips and Mrs Blossom both smiled, first at each other and then at both Patsy and I, and said how very sweet I was and how much they appreciated our support and how thrilled they were that we were going to take part in the Show and how delighted they were that young people like us didn't look down our noses at old fuddy duddys like them and so on and so on and in the end it looked as though they were going to start another duologue and so I poured them another glass of parsnip wine each while Patsy went out to the kitchen to fetch a batch of freshly baked home-made rock cakes.

'Did you make the parsnip wine yourself?' asked Miss Phillips.

I shook my head. 'No. I'm afraid not. Patsy's uncle made it.'

'Her uncle?'

'My uncle Paul. Paul Simpson.'

'I didn't know he was Patsy's uncle!'

'He's her mother's older brother.'

'It's very nice parsnip wine.'

'Thank you. I'll tell him. He'll be pleased.'

'I must call round and get him to enter. We're having wine categories.'

'Isn't he Esther Kennedy's cousin?'

'I don't know,' I said.

'I think he is,' said Miss Phillips. 'He lives next door to that woman who used to breed dalmatians in Ilfracombe doesn't he?'

I said I wasn't sure.

'She had an affair with a man who sold insurance,' said Mrs Blossom firmly. 'She had wonderful red hair.'

'It was a wig,' said Miss Phillips, rather sourly I thought.

'I don't think it was,' said Mrs Blossom.

'Anyway her husband left her and they had to sell the house. Pink house. 1930s but with a late 50s extension. It was a pity. They'd just built the most beautiful gazebo. Do you remember, dear, it had a wonderful weather vane on the roof?'

'It was lovely, wasn't it?' agreed Mrs Blossom. 'Her daughter married a ski instructor didn't she?'

'Did she? I thought that was the Barnard girl.'

'You're right. It was.'

People who claim that the art of conversation is dead have quite clearly never spent an evening in the company of the indomitable Miss Phillips and the inimitable Mrs Blossom.

I had rushed out of the house so quickly that I'd forgotten to put on a sweater and by the time I got to the vegetable garden I was shivering with the cold.

'You'll catch your death like that,' said Mr Parfitt, tut-tutting. 'Come into the greenhouse and I'll find you something warm that you can wrap yourself up in.' He himself had, I noticed, acquired an even more rural look than before. His suit jacket and its last button had parted company and he now had a piece of binder twine wrapped tightly around his waist and knotted rather flamboyantly. He was now wearing an old, battered tweed hat that was several sizes too large for him. I didn't know what had happened to the other hat. He had this one crammed right down over his ears.

'There's a blanket over here,' said Miss Hargreaves. I turned round. I hadn't noticed her before. 'Mr Parfitt has been showing me round the garden,' she said. She looked almost radiant. 'He's done wonders, hasn't he?' She handed me an old blanket which, judging by the hairs which were stuck on it, had been used as a bed by Sophie and Emily. Miss Hargreaves and Mr Parfitt had clearly got to know each other much better since their first meeting at our dinner party.

Using the back of an old seed catalogue order form Mr Parfitt then carefully drew out a plan of our walled vegetable garden. Some of the beds were, of course, already spoken for. The longest, sunniest bed, underneath the south facing long wall was where our soft fruit bushes were planted. In another month or two it would be time to erect the netting over them to protect the fruit from the birds. Four of the centre beds were occupied by old fashioned wood and glass cold frames and those we would use for raising seeds and growing salad vegetables. The bed underneath the short, easterly facing wall was where we grew our rhubarb (thanks to the straw from the sheeps' stable it was already two feet high) and four small beds were filled with strawberry plants.

'I reckon we've got twelve beds to play with,' said Mr Parfitt, completing his plan of the garden and numbering the free beds one to twelve. 'Do you want to go for quality or variety?'

I scratched my head. 'I'm not sure,' I said. 'What's the, er, difference?'

'Do you want to grow three or four beds full of carrots to give yourself a really good chance of winning first prize in the carrots – or do you want a dozen or more different crops so that you can stand a decent chance of getting a prize in several categories?'

'I think we'll go for variety,' I said without hesitation. 'I want to be able to eat the stuff we grow. We'll never get through four beds' worth of carrots!'

Mr Parfitt looked pleased. 'That's the spirit!' he said. 'We'll go for 'Best Exhibitor in Show'!'

'What's that?' I had to ask him.

'Every entrant gets points for all the categories he enters. Whoever ends up with most points wins the overall prize – Best Exhibitor in Show!'

'I'm not even sure that they're having one of those,' I said.

''Course they are!' insisted Mr Parfitt. 'Village shows always have an award for the best overall exhibitor. They couldn't not have one!'

'You'll be bound to win with Mr Parfitt looking after your garden,' whispered Miss Hargreaves confidently. He looked at her and smiled. She smiled back at him and touched his arm lightly.

In the end, under Mr Parfitt's guidance I agreed that, among other things, we would grow peas, beans (broad and runner), potatoes (three varieties of potato that would be ready early in the season), carrots, parsnip, beetroot, spinach, brussels sprouts, broccoli, kale and onions. Mr Parfitt asked me which seed merchant I used. I told him that although I liked to give as much custom as I could to Peter at the village shop we didn't usually buy our seeds there. I explained that Patsy was in charge of seed brochures and had already compared prices from several catalogues.

I then took the old blanket from around my shoulders and put it back in its original place. Before I went back to the house I walked past the sheep's stable to say 'hello' and make sure that all was well.

All was well but once again we had five sheep living with us. The intruder looked thoroughly at home and baaaed as noisily as any of the other four when she saw me. I gave all five a handful of pellets each and knew that I was about to do something that I really didn't want to do but just couldn't avoid doing.

'I thought you'd be out here!' said Patsy.

I looked up, slightly startled. Patsy was standing on the other side of the gate leading into the field. 'The photographer says he's ready for you now.'

'Right,' I said. I'd forgotten about the photographer. 'That sheep is back in our field again.' I pointed to her. She seemed to know I was talking about her and baaaed noisily.

'That's the one that Colin Jackson has fetched back twice?'

'That's the one.'

'She must like it here.'

'I can't send her back a third time, Patsy.'

'You're daft!'

'I know.'

'What are we going to call her?'

'Well, judging by the number of times she's escaped we ought to call her Houdini but Houdini was a man.'

'We'll call her Miss Houdini then.'

'O.K. Do you think Colin Jackson will sell her to us?'

'Oh, he'll huff and he'll puff and he'll go on and on about how valuable she is and how much he could get for her at the market but he'll sell her. She's a nuisance and he'll be glad to get rid of her.'

'We can't really afford her, can we?'

'No. But now that she's sought sanctuary here three times we can't let Colin sell her to the slaughterhouse either.'

I sighed, opened the gate and slipped through. At the rate we were going it wouldn't be long before we had a full sized flock to look after. I stood there for a moment and looked at the five sheep. 'Damned animals,' I muttered, half under my breath, though I didn't mean it, of course.

Patsy looked up at me and grinned. 'Come on,' she said. 'That photographer will be having a fit.' She put her arm around me. 'And you must be freezing cold.' She looked up at me. 'Has anyone ever told you that you're a big softie?'

'Me? A softie? Never.'

The living room looked like a film studio. The photographer and his assistant had arrived in a small minibus and the whole vehicle must have been crammed with lights, reflectors, camera bodies, lenses and all the other expensive paraphernalia without which some professional practitioners of the gentle and relatively simple art of photography do not seem able to function. Curiously, although the intention seemed to be to flood the room with light huge black drapes had been hung over the windows so that absolutely no natural light could enter the room at all. Several huge metal trunks – in which the equipment had presumably arrived – were stacked in a corner of the room. It occurred to me that the equipment scattered around our living room was probably worth more than the whole house. It seemed a lot of trouble for a couple of snaps.

'Crumbs!' I said, looking round. 'Why the blackout?' I asked.

The photographer, who had changed clothes and was now wearing a lilac coloured camisole top with lace edging, a huge white canvas jacket with enormously baggy pockets, a pair of skin tight black jeans and a pair of huge pink basketball boots, waved a hand about airily.

'God's very untrustworthy when it comes to lighting,' he explained. 'One minute he gives you glorious sunshine and then poof,' he waved his arms dramatically to illustrate what he was saying, 'in a flash it's gone and the sky is brooding black.' He leant forward, peering at my shirt. 'What on earth have you been doing?' he demanded.

I looked down. My shirt was covered with cat hairs. They had presumably come from the blanket that Mr Parfitt had given me to fling around my shoulders. 'George! Brush!' shouted the photographer. I then had to stand very still for several minutes while George attempted to brush the cat hairs off my shirt. When the photographer was satisfied he waved a finger to George, who was now fussing with one of the lamps. George, constantly alert, responded to this almost imperceptible gesture as though his employer had cracked a bull whip.

'Stool for the client, please, George!' said the photographer. He glanced at me, tutted and rolled his eyes heavenwards. 'He doesn't know which side his bread is buttered,' he said. He was, it was clear, a master of the cliché.

George left what he was doing, scurried behind a huge umbrella shaped reflector and rummaged around. You wouldn't have thought it would have been possible to lose a stool in one room but for a moment I thought they'd managed it. George emerged a couple of moments later clutching a tall stool with a small black leather seat and long, chromium-plated legs. 'Things are always in the last place you look, aren't they?' he said. His close contact with the photographer had clearly given him an unenviable mastery of the nonsensical cliché. I was tempted to point out that things you think you've lost are always in the last place you look – because when you've found them you stop looking – but I didn't.

'Just here, I think, George,' said the photographer, pointing to a spot on the carpet.

George put the stool down where the photographer had indicated and glanced up to see that all was well. With a slight wave of his left hand, first this way and then that way, the photographer directed the placing of the stool first away from and then back to the spot he had originally indicated.

'I'll go and get lunch started,' said Patsy, still standing in the doorway. 'Will you both be staying for lunch?' she asked our two visitors.

For some inexplicable reason the photographer seemed overcome by this uncomplicated offer of hospitality. He put his hands together as though praying, lowered his voice and delivered a small speech about how kind we were and how touched he was and how wonderful he thought it was that people in the country still made their visitors feel so welcome.

'It's just home-made vegetable soup,' said Patsy. 'And home-made bread,' she added. She rather wisely disappeared before the photographer could launch himself into yet another eulogy about country cooking.

Deprived of this opportunity the photographer turned to George. 'What's the time?' he asked the infinitely patient assistant. I could see that he himself was wearing an expensive Rolex on his left wrist but it was presumably easier and less exhausting to get George to look at his watch than to raise his arm and look at his own.

'Twelve fifteen,' replied George, after studying his own less expensive timepiece.

This news seemed to startle and upset the photographer. He clapped his hands, looked as though he was about to have a nervous breakdown and then made a great effort to control himself. 'Come on!' he said, though I wasn't sure whether the encouragement was directed at me, George or himself.

George positioned one of the cameras, looked through the viewfinder and then politely asked me if I would be kind enough to sit on the stool. I sat on the stool. When George was content with what he could see he backed away. The photographer then moved in, bent down and looked through the viewfinder himself. After a brief glance he stood up, sniffed thoughtfully and then nodded. George moved back in and pressed a button top of the camera. There was a click and a whirring noise and a photograph emerged from the back of the camera. The two of them studied it carefully and then George brought it over to me so that I could look at it. It was a picture of me in my shirtsleeves sitting on a stool. The photograph made me look very bored and so the camera had managed to capture my feelings very effectively. I said I thought it looked fine. George said he thought it was a tremendously powerful and evocative shot. He then changed something on the camera, looked up to the photographer for permission, and pressed the button again. This time no photograph emerged from the back of the camera.

After half an hour of this I was bored rigid. 'I think that last one was fantastic,' I said, getting down off the stool. My left leg was lucky, it had gone to sleep. 'Lunch will be ready,' I said.

George looked shocked and turned immediately towards the photographer. 'You can't go yet!' the photographer cried.

'Patsy will be cross if we keep her waiting,' I warned him, quite untruthfully. The threat proved extremely effective. He followed me to the kitchen as meekly as a sheep will follow its shepherd. George followed behind like a lamb trailing behind its mother.

After lunch I managed to cut the photo session short by telling the photographer and his assistant that I had to clean out the sheep's stable. I said that they could photograph me up to my knees in dirty straw if they wanted to but I wasn't in the slightest bit surprised or disappointed when they both declared that since they had a long journey back home they thought they had better start packing up.

After they had gone I rang Colin Jackson and arranged to buy the sheep which had decided to come and live with us.

*   *   *

CHAPTER FOURTEEN

After my first, and I thought rather abortive, appearance on television, I had not expected to receive any more invitations to pollute the nation's airwaves with my own peculiar brand of delicate anarchy. But, strangely, the invitations to appear on chat shows, news programmes and magazine programmes had come in far more quickly than even Tanya had expected. What I hadn't realised was that both television and radio producers are constantly looking for new faces and voices with which to entertain their viewers and listeners. The demand for new guests, new topics and even moderately interesting subjects for discussion is constant. I was first flattered into thinking that the tremendous interest that was being shown in me and my book had been inspired by my personality and the value of the words I had written. Only later did I realise that the enthusiasm was general rather than particular and that I would have attracted as much (and possibly more) interest if I had written a book describing the history of lace making on the Norfolk Broads.

In addition to the invitations to appear on television and radio (most of which I managed to avoid) the following few weeks also brought a steady trickle of invitations to speak at literary luncheons and womens' institutes. There were even one or two invitations to sit in bookshops and to sign copies of my book.

I have never believed in the philosophy that one should try everything once. It has always seemed to me that this is a approach which is destined to produce much unhappiness, regret and indigestion. But I was just as inexperienced in saying 'no' to invitations of this type as I was in accepting and fulfilling them.

My first invitation to speak in public came one evening. Patsy took the call and handed me the telephone.

'It's a Mrs Periwinkle,' she whispered, politely holding her hand over the mouthpiece so that the subject of this introduction would not hear herself being announced. I tried, unsuccessfully, to think who Mrs Periwinkle could be. In the days when I had practised as a family doctor I was quite accustomed to receiving telephone calls from complete strangers (and then, within seconds, asking them the most intimate of questions) but since my retirement my natural English reserve had reclaimed its place.

'I'm sorry to bother you, doctor,' said Mrs Periwinkle. 'You don't know me but I'm joint secretary of the Little Tidbury On Sea Branch of the British Literary Guild. Your publisher gave me your telephone number.'

I said 'hello' and told her, as one does in these circumstances, that it was nice it was to hear from her. The British Literary Guild, in case you haven't heard of it, is a huge national organisation. They have branches in just about every town and village in the country and members regularly meet to discuss, dissect and, presumably sometimes even enjoy, modern and classical works of literature.

'We have a meeting every third Tuesday,' said Mrs Periwinkle. 'And one of our most popular themes for speakers is 'My First Book'. Your name was put forward by several of our members last week and we're hoping that we might be able to ink you in for one evening soon.' She put a lot of emphasis on the word 'ink'.

'That's very kind of you,' I said. 'Er ... where is Little Tidbury On Sea?' I asked. I'm not sure why I asked this, though I suppose that I must have been subconsciously aware of the fact that she had rung to invite me to do something that I didn't want to do and so it might have simply been a delaying tactic.

She told me. Any hopes of being able to explain that I lived in a remote village of Devon and would, with regret, have to decline her invitation evaporated when she explained in some detail that Little Tidbury On Sea was no more than forty miles away from Bilbury. I was surprised to discover that, despite its name, the village was at least twenty miles away from the coast and over thirty miles away from its namesake, Tidbury On Sea.

I should not have been surprised. Places in Devon often have misleading and unrealistic names. The village next to Bilbury is called Kentisbury Town but has a total human population of about fifty. The village of Greater Munton is much smaller than the village of Lesser Munton. And the village of South Boreham is directly north of North Boreham.

'Ah!' I said, when she had told me the location of Little Tidbury On Sea.

'Can I put you down for one evening this month?' she asked.

I know now that I should have said almost anything other than what I did say. I should have told her that I was emigrating to Lithuania or suffering from an infectious disease. I should have been honest, risked offending her, and explained that the very thought of public speaking always made me feel so ill that I was never able to fulfil my engagements. I should have explained that I would rather have major surgery than speak in public. It isn't just the twenty or thirty minutes standing up in front of an audience which I dread but the sleepless nights beforehand.

But I didn't tell the truth. I made an excuse. I said I was committed on Tuesdays. It wasn't really a lie. I'm committed to sitting in front of the fire on Tuesdays.

But, if there is one thing that is guaranteed to backfire it is using a feeble and dishonest excuse in order to try and get out of doing something you don't want to do.

And, because I felt guilty about almost lying and because I felt that I ought to have said 'yes' I then proceeded to dig my own grave. 'What a pity,' I said. 'I'd have loved to come and any other day would have been fine. But Tuesdays are just impossible, I'm afraid.'

I had, in my ignorance and innocence, completely failed to make any allowance for the fact that with the possible exception of politicians, club secretaries are the most ruthless and least generous of all beings. Few of them ever wanted to be club secretary but now that they are their main ambition in life is to fill their quota of speakers as quickly as they possibly can. They don't care whether the speakers they book are competent or even capable of speaking the right language. They have no compassion for the shy and retiring. Their aim is simply to get names written into the club diary – preferably in ink.

'Oh dear,' said Mrs Periwinkle, malevolently lulling me into a false sense of security. 'Well, never mind,' she said. And she paused before pulling the pin out of the hand grenade she'd skilfully tucked down the front of my trousers. 'I'll have a word with one or two of the committee members and see if we can rearrange one of our meetings to fit in with you. Shall we say next Wednesday?'

I was sunk. I had wandered up a creek and found myself without a canoe. I had climbed a tree and found myself stuck without a ladder. I was hoist by my own petard. I had shot myself in the foot with astonishing accuracy. Trying hard not to sound as glum as I felt I said that would be very kind of her. We exchanged final pleasantries and then I put down the telephone.

I had, however, learned my lesson, though I was to discover that avoiding public speaking can be even more difficult than you might imagine. Sometimes you have to be quite unbelievably blunt. When the next invitation came, asking me to speak at a literary dinner somewhere in the north of England, I simply thanked the caller and told him that I was terrible at public speaking.

'Oh, don't worry about that,' said the person who had invited me to speak. 'Most of our speakers are pretty rough. In fact some of them are bloody awful. The people who come to our dinners are used to that. To be honest our dinners are just a bit of an opportunity to get out and meet some friends.'

I hadn't expected this. 'I'm sorry,' I said. 'But I really hate public speaking. I don't like leaving home and I get very nervous for days – weeks – beforehand.' Just talking about public speaking was making me feel nervous.

'Oh, I'm just the same,' said the caller cheerfully. 'And you know, the funny thing is that it never gets any easier! We usually have three speakers. Would you like to be on first? I always find I prefer to speak first so that I don't have time to get too nervous!'

'I'm afraid I'd rather not speak at all,' I told him. 'But thank you very much for inviting me,' I added.

'You'll have to get used to it,' insisted the caller. 'Publishers like their authors to speak at dinners and luncheons.'

'Public speaking really isn't my scene,' I apologised. 'Sorry.'

'We'll put you up in a very nice boarding house and your publisher will pay your travelling expenses so you won't be out of pocket.'

'No, thank you.'

There was a pause. When the caller spoke again his voice had changed. 'You're saying 'no'?' He sounded very put out.

'I'm afraid so.'

'Well, don't expect us to put your book on our recommended list for the local public library!' he snapped, slamming down the telephone.

*   *   *

Planning for the Revels Week was continuing so fast that I was beginning to find it difficult to remember exactly what had been organised. The Revels had acquired a momentum of their own and I think most people in the village had more or less forgotten that the original idea had been simply to raise some money to pay for repairing the school cottage. Fund raising may have been the original reason for bringing back the Revels but it was certainly no longer the sole reason for the enthusiasm in the village. Many of the events being organised seemed unlikely to raise any money at all but this didn't seem to discourage people in the slightest. I suspected the truth was that the Revels had added a rare air of excitement and anticipation to the village. Even more importantly, perhaps, they had brought an already close village even closer.

One of the things I had always liked about Bilbury was the fact that the villagers regarded one another as being members of a community. The Revels had strengthened the already powerful community spirit that I so admired and I felt proud and privileged to be regarded as a villager.

In some parts of Devon you have to live in the area for decades before you're regarded as 'local'. A friend of mine who had lived in a cottage in Cornwall for thirty years told me gloomily that he reckoned that if his children stayed in the village then there was a real possibility that their grandchildren might be accepted as 'locals'. In Bilbury you were regarded as being a 'local' if you wanted to be a 'local'. The key was not the length of time that you'd lived there but the enthusiasm with which you lived there. Many of the villagers had themselves moved to Bilbury after living in other parts of the country and they valued the feeling of belonging which the village gave. After all, as Dr Brownlow once said, it is possible for someone to have been in a village for decades and yet to have no love either for the village itself or its inhabitants. He pointed out that a newcomer who contributes to village life is of far more value to the village community than an old resident who constantly yearns to be somewhere else.

It was in the spirit of togetherness that the villagers living around the Bilbury village green had, with varying degrees of enthusiasm, painted their houses with the paint that Peter Marshall had provided. Although there had been some initial dissent most of them had eventually admitted that pink, though it might perhaps not have been their first choice, wasn't too bad a colour after all. Those who remained unconvinced of the appeal of the colour were enormously cheered when the first rainstorm completely washed the paint away. It was only then that Thumper Robinson noticed that the paint which Peter had provided was quite clearly marked 'water soluble' and 'unsuitable for exterior use'.

Patsy and I had both been press ganged by the wife of Bilbury's new vicar into helping with a special midsummer night's revue. Having made it quite clear that I would not accept any role which involved any sort of public appearance I found myself appointed assistant stage manager while Patsy rather reluctantly found herself a slightly nervous member of the 'Bilbury Ladies Amateur Cancan And Exotic Dancing Troupe'. The title of what was generally agreed to be the first Bilbury dance team was admittedly rather a mouthful but it was the result of a democratic compromise between those members of the Committee who wanted the dancers to be known as 'The Buxom Bilbury Beauties' and those who felt that 'The Bilbury Belles' was more appropriate.

When Bilbury's previous vicar had unexpectedly been promoted and moved away to tend to a flock in an altogether grander and more elegant environment the villagers had awaited the appointment of a new spiritual saviour with some trepidation. The villagers had found their previous spiritual saviour rather unbending and had regarded his hardline approach to subjects such as poaching to be a little out of touch with reality.

Technically, Bilbury hasn't actually had a vicar of its own for many years. For as long as most people can remember the village has shared a clergyman with five other small, local parishes.

The Bilbury parsonage, a grand, nineteenth century building with eight bedrooms, two turrets and a swimming pool, has for several years been owned by a mysterious businessman who has only ever been seen twice in the village. On both occasions he landed by helicopter, stayed for a night and disappeared the next morning. In his absence the former parsonage is kept warm and waterproof by a couple from London who do all their shopping at a supermarket in Taunton and have probably not exchanged more than half a dozen words with anyone in the village in the five years of their residence.

The new vicar, Ernest Riddle, had come late to the church. He had worked as an accountant for twenty years before switching careers and becoming a guardian of souls rather than balance sheets. He was short, probably no more than five feet four inches tall, plump, weighing twelve stones or even slightly more, and enormously jovial. It had, he told me, always been a dream of his to acquire custody of a country parish. He was thrilled that his dream had come true. His wife, Delilah, who looked more like a fashion model than a country vicar's wife, a post normally recognised as being ideally suited to a woman built for jam and chutney making, was a decade his junior and had been a well known athlete under her maiden name. She had, she told us, enjoyed an interest in amateur theatricals since she'd been a girl. She regarded the Revels as an opportunity not to be missed.

*   *   *

All too soon it was Wednesday and I was heading for Little Tidbury on Sea with the notes for my speech in my inside jacket pocket and my ordinance survey map of North Devon opened out on the car seat beside me.

I had spent hours agonising over what to say. Should I write a formal speech and read it? Should I simply make a few brief notes and ad lib my speech?

I toyed with the idea of talking about how much of a struggle it had been to turn several reams of copy paper into a book but dismissed that notion as pretentious. Talking about the theme of the book – the cruel greed of the pharmaceutical industry and the naivety of the medical profession – seemed too pompous and earnest. I would have liked to have made it a funny speech but I simply didn't have the confidence. I thought about talking about the technical problems of writing a book but I thought that everyone else who had ever spoken on the subject of 'My First Book' would be bound to have explored that particularly territory. I thought about detailing my bizarre and sometimes seemingly unreal confrontations with the professionals of the publishing industry but decided that that would be too esoteric. I was attracted by the idea of talking about my experiences in television but I didn't really have enough material. In the end I had abandoned all these formal notions, and decided simply to make a few general notes which fitted the theme and to adapt the content and form of my speech according to the audience.

The meeting was due to be held in the church hall and I parked, as I had been told to do, in a tiny car park behind the church. A large white board at the far end of the car park bore two wind and rain battered posters. Both posters carried messages in screaming, fluorescent, orange letters. One said: 'Be Generous To Your Fellow Man And The Lord Will Be Generous To You'. The other said: 'Forgive Those Who Have Sinned Against You And You Will Be Blessed.' Above this a large hand painted sign saying 'NO PARKING – TRESPASSERS WILL BE PROSECUTED' had been nailed to the noticeboard. I locked the car, checked that I had my notes in my inside jacket pocket, and walked round to the side of the church hall.

The door to the church hall was open, as I had been told it would be, but except for a couple of dozen tubular steel stacking chairs the hall itself was empty. I stood there for a moment and then called out: 'Is anyone there?' No one came and no one answered my call so I walked a few paces further into the room and repeated the question. This time a middle aged woman in a floral pinafore responded by poking her head and upper body through a hatchway which I hadn't even noticed before. She asked me if I'd come for the meeting. I said I had and introduced myself. The woman introduced herself as Mrs Kennedy, the society's treasurer, thanked me for coming and asked if I was any good at mending kettles. I said I didn't think so but that I would take a look.

Generally speaking, I know as much about kettles as I do about the economic influences of nuclear power on third world countries but it was pretty clear to me that this particular kettle had boiled it's last teapot full of water. It was one of the old fashioned sorts of kettle that sits on the top of a stove and someone had clearly left it to boil dry. It had a rather large hole in its blackened bottom.

I showed Mrs Kennedy the hole. 'I'm afraid I don't think there's much you can do for this,' I told her sadly.

'Well we can't manage without our kettle,' said Mrs Kennedy firmly. 'Let's pop round to Mrs Alladyce's to see if she's got a spare.'

Obediently, I followed her out of the church hall, waited while she locked the door with a huge, rusty, iron key and then followed her across the road, down a little alleyway and in through the back door of a tiny terraced house. She walked with the shuffling gait of a woman who is a martyr to her feet. English women of a certain age and breeding are always martyrs to their feet.

Mrs Alladyce, clearly the occupier of the house, was in her living room doing her ironing while listening to the radio. She looked up as we entered. 'I was just coming over, Mrs Kennedy,' she said. 'I thought I'd just have time to finish off my ironing and listen to the end of my play.' She spoke of it as though the play had been specially broadcast for her.

'Don't let us disturb you,' whispered Mrs Kennedy. 'Have you got a spare kettle we can borrow?'

'In the kitchen,' replied Mrs Alladyce, in what I suspect she thought was her own version of a whisper. It was a whisper that would have carried two miles in a storm. 'Cupboard under the sink. My Geoffrey bought me one of those electric jobs last Christmas. But I kept my old faithful just in case.'

'Geoffrey's her son,' whispered Mrs Kennedy, as we tiptoed out of the living room, along the corridor, past the door through which we had entered and into the kitchen. Back in the living room we could hear the radio play to which Mrs Alladyce was listening come to a thrilling climax. 'He's a chartered surveyor,' Mrs Kennedy added, and I assumed that she was referring to Mrs Alladyce's son, Geoffrey. I tried to forget this little titbit of information but my brain probably stored it away somewhere safe anyway. I've always noticed that the more irrelevant a piece of information the more likely I am to remember it. In a year's time I would forget where I had parked the car but remember that Mrs Alladyce's son Geoffrey was a chartered surveyor.

Mrs Kennedy bent down, opened the cupboard underneath Mrs Alladyce's sink, removed a small silverish kettle which had a whistling nozzle on its spout, and then closed the cupboard and stood up.

'Thank you, Mrs Alladyce!' she called out as we left. 'Much obliged!' She lowered her voice. 'Remarkable woman,' she added, sotte voce. 'She's got four sons and terrible veins. One of them was very nearly a Parliamentary Candidate for Preston North.' I assumed that she was referring to one of the sons rather than her veins and murmured something suitably non committal and inconsequential. It occurred to me to wonder of whom she was proudest: the son who was a chartered surveyor or the son who had very nearly been a Parliamentary Candidate for Preston North.

When we got back to the church hall there were two people waiting outside. One introduced herself as Mrs Periwinkle, the woman who had invited me to Little Tidbury on Sea. She had bright blue hair, wore spectacles with hugely ornate frames and carried a music case which she clutched to her bosom as though afraid that someone might try to steal it from her. The other woman was tall, and heavy set and wore a short black, pencil skirt and a bright pink sweater. She was heavily made up, had shoulder length, curly blonde hair, wore white, lacy gloves and carried a large, blue, plastic handbag.

'It looks like being one of our quiet evenings,' said Mrs Periwinkle, as we all trooped inside the church hall. Mrs Kennedy disappeared into the kitchen with her kettle and the other woman, who hadn't spoken and to whom I had not been introduced, sat herself down on the front row. Mrs Periwinkle walked briskly across to the side of the hall and brought a small beige topped folding card table across to the middle of the room. I stepped forward, took the table from her and, with some difficulty, erected it. Mrs Periwinkle smiled at me. I moved a couple of chairs round to the other side of the table, so that they were facing the audience of stacking chairs.

'Er . . . how many people usually turn up?' I asked, hesitantly.

'Sometimes, on a very good night, we've had as many as eighteen,' said Mrs Periwinkle, proudly. 'But that was for a very special speaker. Usually we get eight or nine.'

I swallowed. It had never occurred to me that the audience might be so small. I realised that I found the prospect of speaking to a small audience far more intimidating than the idea of addressing a large audience. I suddenly remembered the first time I had spoken in public – at an anti-vivisection meeting in Barnstaple. My throat felt very dry and when Mrs Kennedy thrust a cup of tea into my hand I accepted it gratefully.

'Of course Mr and Mrs Jilkes are away on holiday,' said Mrs Periwinkle. 'And they always bring Miss Llewellyn with them. She has a gammy knee and can't walk far. So that's three who won't be coming. Could we have a water jug and a couple of glasses, Mrs Kennedy?'

'And poor old Mr Bedford is in hospital,' added Mrs Kennedy, over her shoulder as she scurried off towards the kitchen to fetch the water jug and glasses.

'Is he? I didn't know that. Oh, the poor dear? What's the trouble? It's not his liver again, is it?' called Mrs Periwinkle.

'I don't think so. I think he's been having trouble with his, you know, down below . . . ,' Embarrassed, Mrs Kennedy's voice tailed off. She waved a hand around airily.

'Ah!' said Mrs Periwinkle, quickly. 'Well I hope he gets better soon. He always brings Mrs Lawson and Miss Innes so that's another three who won't be coming. I must send him a card. Is he in the Exeter General?'

'Yes, I think so.'

'Do you know which ward he's in?'

Mrs Kennedy scurried back, carrying a water jug in one hand and clutching two unbreakable glasses in the other.

'Mens' surgical I expect,' said Mrs Kennedy.

'He's on the Arthur Thomas Ward Ward,' said a gruff voice.

I looked around to see who had spoken. There was no one

there except the blonde woman with the blue handbag. She smiled at me. She had lipstick on her teeth. There was something odd about her but I couldn't quite make up my mind what it was. She still had her gloves on. Her unusually deep voice made me think that she might perhaps have a thyroid problem. I wondered whether or not I should ask her if she'd visited her doctor. Her gruff voice might be explained by a underfunctioning thyroid gland which thyroid tablets would cure. I wondered if the blonde curls might be a wig. Another symptom of hypothyroidism is hair loss.

'Arthur Thomas,' said Mrs Periwinkle. 'I'll send him a card tomorrow. I always keep one or two in. They never have much choice at the shop do they?'

'I think it's gone down hill since Elsie and Robbie left. I'm sure those new people mean well but they just don't seem the right sort of folk to be running a village shop. She's far too brassy for my taste.'

'Arthur Thomas Ward,' said the gruff voiced, blonde-haired woman with the blue handbag.

Mrs Periwinkle and Mrs Kennedy both looked at her and frowned. 'Yes, dear,' said Mrs Periwinkle. 'Arthur Thomas.' She turned to me. 'This is Josephine,' she said. I said 'hello' to Josephine and Josephine said 'hello' back and smiled at me again. I remembered that women with hypothyroidism also suffered from dry, rough skin. That could explain why Josephine hadn't removed her gloves.

'No,' said Josephine. 'The ward is called Arthur Thomas Ward Ward. It's named after someone called Arthur Thomas Ward.'

'Well,' said Mrs Periwinkle, as though this was just another example of bureaucracy gone mad. 'That's very confusing!'

Josephine looked rather apologetic, as though it was her fault that the hospital authorities had chosen to name the ward in such a manner. I felt sorry for her and decided that I would try to get her alone for a moment so that I could suggest that she seek medical help. I was now quite convinced that she had a thyroid problem.

'Would you like a biscuit, doctor?'

I turned round. Mrs Kennedy had produced a tin of mixed

biscuits. I hesitated for a moment, realised I was hungry and took a bourbon cream.

'Take two,' she said, waggling the tin under my nose.

I wanted to but politeness won. I smiled, shook my head and raised a hand as my 'no'.

'More tea?'

'No, thank you.'

'I'm afraid it doesn't look as if your audience is going to get any bigger,' said Mrs Periwinkle. She somehow managed to make it clear that if the audience was small it was entirely my fault. 'Would you like to start?' She noticed that the blonde with the blue handbag had disappeared. 'When Josephine get's back,' she said. 'She must have gone to powder her nose.'

'Right!' I said. 'I'll just, er, pop to the, er ... '

'The little boys' room is over there on the left,' said Mrs Periwinkle, pointing to the left of the stage.

When I opened the door and saw Josephine standing in front of the porcelain I thought I must have gone into the wrong room. But another glance assured me that I hadn't. She had her skirt pulled up to her waist and was doing exactly what I had gone there to do.

'Hello!' she said, quite unflustered and completely unembarrassed. 'I'm really looking forward to hearing your talk. I'm writing a book myself.' I couldn't help noticing that the backs of her hands were covered in thick black hair. I understood why the gloves were necessary.

'Oh!' I managed to croak. I took my place beside her and tried not to make a big thing out of the fact that I was sharing a urinal with a large bossomed stranger wearing stockings and suspenders and high heeled shoes. 'What about?' I asked her.

'It's a sort of autobiography, really,' said Josephine. 'I thought I'd call it 'From Joe to Josephine'.'

I said what a good title I thought that was. Josephine then finished what she was doing, readjusted her dress (there was a curiously appropriate 'Gentlemen Please Adjust Your Dress' sign on the wall above the washbasin), washed her hands and put her gloves on. A few moments later I followed her back into the main hall. I admired her confidence and her courage enormously and suddenly I didn't feel nervous.

'How did it go?' asked Patsy, when I got back to Bilbury Grange later that evening. Ben leapt up to welcome me home. I had left her behind though I suppose I could have taken her with me. She hated being left behind.

'I think it went quite well,' I replied, rubbing Ben behind the ears.

'Was it a good audience?'

'Oh, yes. They were very good.'

'What sort of people were they? Mostly women?'

'Mostly women,' I agreed. I hesitated. 'Largely,' I added.

'What did you talk to them about?'

'I kept it very informal,' I said, rather vaguely. 'Just talked about drugs and doctors and books and publishers.'

'Did you tell them about the new book you're writing?'

'No. I didn't want to talk about it yet.'

'How many people were there?'

'Oh, not too many. It was quite a compact and friendly audience. But they asked quite a few questions. There was a woman there who was writing a book of her own. She asked a lot of questions.'

'How many people do you think there were, then?'

I hesitated.

'Roughly?'

'Three,' I admitted, ruefully. 'But Mr and Mrs Jilkes were on holiday and Mr Bedford is in hospital,' I added, as an explanation.

'Ah,' said Patsy.

I thought for a moment. 'Do you think I ought to send him a card?' I asked her.

Patsy frowned. 'Who?'

'Mr Bedford. He's in the Arthur Thomas Ward Ward at Exeter General.'

Patsy shook her head. 'I don't think so,' she said. 'If you start sending cards to all the people who weren't there it'll cost a fortune in stamps.'

'You didn't ask me why I'd said he was in the Arthur Thomas Ward Ward,' I complained. 'Two Wards!' I added, unnecessarily.

Patsy looked puzzled. 'Why should I have done?'

'The man they named the ward after was called Ward,' I explained, anxious to share the feeble joke.

'Yes, I know,' said Patsy. 'He was a friend of my father's.'

'Oh.' I said, rather disappointed. I felt rather cheated.

*   *   *

CHAPTER FIFTEEN

I had to look twice to make sure it was him. But it was. Peter Marshall was wearing a bottle green jacket covered with sequins and a huge floppy pink bow tie. His hair was slicked down with hair cream. The effect was slightly spoilt by the fact that he was wearing rather baggy brown corduroy trousers but from the waist up he looked magnificent. 'For this next trick I need a member of the audience,' he said, stepping forward, towards the edge of the stage, and peered out to where Delilah Riddle was sitting. 'It's a card trick,' he whispered, as though unwilling to break the spell which his presence on stage had created. 'I need someone out of the audience to pick a card.'

'Do you want them to come up onto the stage with you?' the vicar's wife asked him.

'I think so,' said Peter. He thought about it and then nodded firmly. 'Yes, definitely,' he said. I couldn't take my eyes off him. I had never thought of Peter Marshall as a magician.

'Then we'll need some steps,' said Delilah. She called to me. 'Do you know if there are any steps we can use at the front of the stage?' she asked. 'Peter needs a member of the audience to go up onto the stage and we can't expect people to clamber up a three foot high stage dressed in their best clothes.'

'I'll go and see what I can find.' I carefully balanced the paint brush I was using to paint one of the fake stone pillars at the edge of the stage on the side of the paint pot and hurried backstage in search of steps. I rather enjoyed being assistant stage manager. I didn't have to think or make any decisions at all. People gave me simple tasks to do and I had to try and finish them as quickly as I could. It was all delightfully simple and free of frustration or responsibility.

Backstage, ten or twelve people were crammed into a space

the size of an ordinary bathroom. They were all busy doing things and trying to keep quiet. Patchy Fogg was oiling something that looked like and, indeed, was half a bicycle. Frank, from the Duck and Puddle, had his eyes closed and, was silently practising his monologue. I could tell what he was doing because his lips were moving. Miss Johnson, my former receptionist, was sewing sequins onto a pair of grey flannels (this, I realised, explained why Peter's stage ensemble was so unbalanced). The Hewitt children (all three of them) were trying to practice their tap dancing but had taken their shoes off so that they didn't make a noise. There was, inevitably, a fair degree of chaos.

'Psst! You can't go in there!' whispered Thumper, as I tried the doorknob leading to the Bilbury Village Hall's tiny washroom and only back stage lavatory. Thumper, whom Delilah had wisely appointed as stage manager, was spraying a huge sheet of hardboard with silver paint from an aerosol can. I leapt back as though the doorknob had been connected to the mains electricity.

'Why not?' I hissed back. We were in the middle of our first and only dress rehearsal and I no longer knew what to expect.

'The girls are in there changing,' explained Thumper.

'Oh. I'm looking for some steps. Have you seen them?'

'Try the store cupboard.' Thumper cursed quietly as his spray can stopped spraying. He shook it, pressed the nozzle and then, when nothing would come out, shook it again. 'Listen to that,' he said, holding the can near to my ear and shaking it. 'It's half full,' he said. 'But it won't spray.'

'Frustrating, isn't it?' I agreed. 'I hate that. I always feel cheated when the propellant runs out before the stuff it's supposed to be propelling.' I opened the door to the store cupboard and slid inside.

The store cupboard, like most store cupboards in village halls, was jammed from floor to ceiling with broken chairs, used light bulbs, bristleless brooms, old cardboard boxes and buckets with holes in them. They had presumably all been kept on the grounds that they might one day turn out to be useful. What those who had kept them had failed to understand was that a use is only ever found for such items the day after they have been eventually thrown away.

I learnt some time ago that the one sure way to find the lock which an apparently useless key opens is to throw the key away.

For four years during my medical school training I carried around with me a small piece of metal which looked as though it ought to have an important role to play in my life. It was round, about the size of an old, pre-decimalisation penny, and had two funny little prongs sticking out of one side. I had absolutely no idea what it was for but in each flat or hospital bedroom which I occupied I found it a safe corner in a dressing table drawer. I lost books, socks, pens, shirts, notebooks and bicycles but I never mislaid that little piece of metal because although I couldn't for the life of me remember what it was for I felt sure that it had a very important purpose.

I finally threw it away just six weeks before I qualified. I was having my annual spring clean and I looked at this little piece of metal, turning it first this way and then that way, and could still see no possible use for it. I decided that I had been looking after a piece of scrap metal. And so I threw it into the dustbin along with the old Christmas cards, the used batteries, the inkless ballpoint pens, the odd socks and the old train tickets.

The very next morning my watch stopped. I took it to a local jeweller. He studied it for twenty minutes then handed it back to me. It was, he said, an unusual make which could only be opened with a special key. 'What does this special key look like?' I asked him.

He carefully described the piece of metal I had thrown away. 'It's round, about the size of an old penny,' he said. 'You know, the ones we used to have before decimalisation. And it has two tiny little prongs sticking out of the side. The manufacturers always used to put one in the box in which the watch came.' I rushed back home but for the first time in a generation the dustbin men had arrived early and had spilt nothing.

During the following week I visited every jeweller in the town. They all knew exactly what I needed but none of them had one. 'Those little metal keys are like gold dust,' said one jeweller. 'I've been trying to get one for years but everyone with one of their watches has thrown their key away. If you ever find one I'll pay you £20 for it.' I ended up having to buy a new watch. I didn't throw the watch away, of course. I put it in a drawer because I knew that the day I threw it out would be the day before I would meet someone who had one of the funny little pieces of metal.

In addition to the legless chairs, the bald brooms and the leaky buckets the cupboard contained a solid looking set of heavy wooden steps which looked as though they would fit neatly onto the front of the stage. (Since that was where they had come from in the first place this was not particularly surprising). I carefully moved away a couple of chairs and a bucket and then half dragged and half lifted the steps out through the cupboard door. As I did so the aerosol can which Thumper had been hitting with a huge metal wrench split into two, making a noise like a hand grenade as it did so. Paint flew all over the room, splattering everyone and everything with silver flecks. The tension in the room meant that this un-expected incident produced much squealing and loud com-plaining. The door to the lavatory/changing room flew open and Kay's head and shoulders appeared. She looked around, tutted loudly, and then swiftly closed the door again.

'Whoops!' said Thumper, his chest, face and arms covered in silver paint. (Since this is an accurate and honest account of life in Bilbury I feel honour bound to admit that the word he actually used was not 'Whoops!').

'What the hell did you do that for?' spluttered Frank, inter-rupted in mid monologue. 'I've forgotten where I was now.'

'I was just trying to get the bloody paint out of the can,' explained Thumper. 'I'd nearly finished! I only needed another couple of squirts.'

'I'll have to go right back to the beginning,' said Frank.

The door to the main hall suddenly burst open and Delilah Riddle burst in. Her face was crimson. 'Ssshhhh!' she hissed. 'We're trying to rehearse out here!' She stared at Thumper, at Frank and then one by one at everyone else. 'Why are you all covered in silver paint?' she asked. She wore half moon spec-tacles for close work and whenever she spoke to anyone she lowered her head a little so that she could look over the top of the lenses. It made her look like a very superior school mistress.

'We had a bit of an accident with a faulty aerosol,' explained a quick thinking Patchy Fogg. We all nodded and murmured and tried hard not to giggle. I couldn't help thinking that it was all rather like being back at school. Thumper, the naughty boy we were protecting, opened his mouth to say something but then thought better of it and closed it again.

'I've found those steps you wanted!' I said, anxious to change the subject.

'Oh wonderful!' said Mrs Riddle. She looked at the steps, still half in and half out of the store room, with an artistically critical eye. 'They look perfect!' she said, and clapped her hands together in front of her chest. It made her look as though she was praying. 'Would you bring them out here so that we can see exactly what they look like?'

Thumper and Patchy helped me move the steps out into the main body of the hall where Peter Marshall, still on stage, was pacing up and down rather nervously.

'You lot go away now you've done that!' he shouted to us from the stage, when we had maneuvered the steps into position. 'I don't want you watching. You'll make me nervous.'

'Come on, Peter!' said Patchy. 'Show us a trick or two.'

'I want to see you switch price labels on a tin of tomatoes,' said Thumper. This was rather a sore point with Peter at the time. A customer who was camping in one of Colin Jackson's fields had accused Peter of putting higher priced labels onto some of the goods she had selected. Peter, clearly angry at this barb, hurled a pink, stuffed rabbit at Thumper's head. It missed by less than a foot.

'Come on, now!' said Miss Riddle. 'Good heavens!' She frowned at us as though she had never seen such behaviour before.

'Are you doing your trick with a tax return?' Patchy asked Peter. This was another cruel jibe for it had been rumoured for a month or so that the Inland Revenue had begun investigating our local shopkeeper. However, Peter's reputation for hanging onto his money and deflecting criticism was such that the general feeling in the village was that the tax inspectors would give up first. Patchy ducked as what looked like a waste paper basket span through the air where his head had been a few moments earlier.

'Stop it!' said Mrs Riddle, sharply. She peered over the top of her spectacles. 'What on earth is going on?' she demanded. 'You're behaving like children!'

'Sorry, Mrs Riddle,' muttered Patchy and Thumper.

'I'm surprised at you, doctor,' said Mrs Riddle.

'Sorry, Mrs Riddle,' I said.

The three us went round to the back of the stage again. We spent the next hour cleaning silver paint off everyone and everything.

*　　*　　*

CHAPTER SIXTEEN

The moment I awoke I knew that something important was happening but for a few happy seconds I couldn't remember what it was. I lay there, enjoying those seconds of disorientated peace which lie between sleep and waking, watching the early rays of sunshine filtering through a narrow gap in the curtains and realising with a light heart that another glorious summer's day lay ahead. And then I remembered.

It was the day of the Old Bilburians first cricket match. The Bilbury Revels were truly taking over the summer.

The peaceful anticipation of another warm, summer's day was banished instantly. Why, I wondered, had we so stead-fastly and defiantly refused to practise? Sitting in the Duck and Puddle it had all seemed a bit of a joke. But with the start of our first match now just hours away our failure to practise seemed foolhardy to say the least. I hadn't played cricket since I'd been at school and even then I hadn't played much of it. The only thing I could remember with any certainty was that cricket balls are extremely hard and that it hurt when they hit you. That fact did not provide me with comfort. A friend of mine who had been hit on the leg by a cricket ball had spent the rest of the summer limping around on crutches. I tried to remember when I'd last seen him.

'What's the matter?' asked Patsy, sleepily. She had only just woken and hadn't even opened her eyes but she knew that something was wrong.

'It's the first cricket match today,' I told her glumly. 'I don't think Roger Toohy ever fully recovered from the time when his leg was broken.'

Patsy sat up. 'Who is Roger Toohy?'

'Someone I was at school with.'

Patsy frowned. 'How did he break his leg?'

'He was hit by a cricket ball. He was fielding at silly mid on. We didn't used to wear shin pads in those days. I don't think any of us had ever seen a shin pad.'

'Well don't do any silly fielding!' said Patsy brightly. She kissed me on the cheek, climbed out of bed and pulled back the curtains. Sunshine flooded the room and Sophie and Emily, lying at the bottom of the bed, both yawned and shook their heads. Ben, lying across my feet, opened an eye and looked at me reproachfully as I tried to struggle out of bed.

'What does the sky look like?' I asked, leaden hearted.

'Bright blue!' replied Patsy instantly. 'There isn't a cloud in sight.'

'You don't think by any chance that it might rain later?'

'There isn't the remotest possibility of one raindrop falling today,' she said cheerfully. Her optimistic weather forecast was not born of malice. I think she'd just mistaken my hope for fear and was trying to cheer me up. It had been a glorious summer; one of the best I could ever remember. The days were long and warm and peaceful and when it rained it usually rained at night. Sometimes I thought that instead of living in Bilbury I was living in Camelot.

But I was not looking forward to our first cricket match.

Glumly, I clambered out of bed wondering which of my limbs would, by evening, be encased in plaster. The more I thought about it the more certain I was that Roger Toohy had never been able to walk properly at all after his accident. I liked my legs the way they were. I wandered over to the window and looked out at a world full of bright colours and singing birds. Flowers were bursting into bloom and Patsy was right: the day promised long, glorious hours of summer sunshine. Idly I allowed my gaze to drift across the shrubbery and towards our large front lawn – it looked like a cricket pitch. In my mind I could see Roger Toohy, gaunt and grey-faced, sitting in a wheelchair.

A summer day's glorious sunshine spoilt by the prospect of cricket balls being fired at my person. I sighed. 'Let's go and get some breakfast.' Ben, Sophie and Emily, eager for their break-fasts too, all raced for the door when they saw me heading in that direction.

I don't know who first started that nonsense about condemned men eating hearty breakfasts. I think it's nonsense. I could hardly eat anything. Patsy cooked freshly picked field mushrooms, scrambled eggs from her mother's hens and served them up on toasted home-made bread. Normally I would have wolfed everything down and would have probably asked for seconds too but although I recognised that it smelt good I just didn't feel hungry. I picked unenthusiastically at the food on my plate. I couldn't help thinking that if I was hit by a cricket ball and needed surgery and a general anaesthetic then it would be best if I hadn't had anything to eat at all.

'Come on,' sighed Patsy eventually. 'Leave that. Go for a walk round the garden. You'll feel better.'

*   *   *

I found Mr Parfitt already at work in the vegetable garden. He was busy feeding the ground around the raspberry canes with home-made liquid fertiliser. We had two varieties of liquid fertiliser with which to boost our crop production. One variety, allegedly rich in iron, had been prepared by putting armfuls of nettles into a tin bath full of water and leaving them to rot. The other variety, the type which my sense of smell told me that Mr Parfitt was using, was rich in nitrogen and had been prepared by putting dirty wool clippings into a water butt and leaving them there for a few months. When Patsy's father had shaved our sheep he had sold the main fleeces to the wool merchants on our behalf but he had left the grubbier bits of fleece – the bits taken from the non-eating ends of our four sheep – and explained to me that we could use it first for making liquid manure and then, afterwards, for stuffing into cushions.

Patsy was right. After half an hour in the garden I felt much better.

*   *   *

Our first match, against an enthusiastic team of cricketers who had travelled down from the Midlands, was due to start at noon and it had been agreed that our team would meet in the bar at the Duck and Puddle at eleven o'clock. This was not because any member of the Old Bilburians thought that we needed an hour to get ourselves ready or because any of us anticipated taking part in serious discussions about team tactics but more, I suspect, because Thumper and the rest of the team seemed to think that if they had an hour's drinking behind them when the match started then they would play better.

I was in at least four minds about this. Part of me felt that it would be wise to remain sober and alert when taking part in a sporting encounter during which a solid piece of leather wrapped cork might well be travelling in the direction of my head at anything up to eighty or ninety miles an hour. Part of me felt that the anaesthetic quality of alcohol might prove useful were I to find myself unable to get out of the way in time. Part of me felt that even if I didn't play any better after a few drinks then I would at least think I was playing better and that since sports psychologists now seem to believe that sporting success is as much mental as physical then the extra confidence that the alcohol might give me would probably be invaluable. And part of me believed that if I began the game as tight as a drum then I wouldn't have to worry about the other three parts of me.

'Do you want another?' asked Thumper, pointing to my glass.

I looked at him and hiccuped. 'Beg your pardon,' I said; the phrase serving both as an apology for the hiccup and as an indication that I hadn't heard Thumper's comment.

'Another beer?'

I screwed up my eyes and tried to concentrate. 'How many have I had?' I glanced out of the window and saw a blurred version of Gilly, the landlady, walking past. She was carrying a huge blurry, cardboard box. I waved but she didn't see me.

'You must get these windows cleaned,' I told Frank. I decided that the problem was that they were still covered with salt from the last storm.

Frank looked across at me and frowned. 'Why?' he asked.

I didn't know why so I couldn't answer.

Thumper, who had been thinking, suddenly spoke. 'Four, I think,' he said.

I looked at him. 'Four what?'

'I think you've had four.' He thought a little longer and corrected himself. 'No, five,' he said.

I shook my head and then winced. I don't know why this

should be but alcohol always seems to have a far more fierce-some effect when drunk before lunch. When I was a medical student I could put away four or five pints of beer in an evening, balance a beermat on my chin and sing twelve verses of Eskimo Nell without showing any signs of inebriation. But I had long ago noticed that if consumed before twelve noon the same amount of alcohol seemed to have a devastating effect. Some day a team of scientists with nothing better to do should look into this phenomenon. 'I don't think I'd better have any more, thank you,' I said. I spoke slowly and clearly, not wanting anyone to think that I had had too much to drink, and then looked across at the bar. Frank, the landlord, seemed to be having trouble in focusing his body.

'Are you all right?' asked Thumper, solicitously.

'Yes. Tell Frank he's all blurred.'

'Frank, the doc says you're all blurred.'

'That's all right,' cried Frank, remarkably cheerfully for one so blurred. 'Tell the doc he's all blurred too.'

Thumper, who was standing next to me, passed on this information as though he were an essential relay station without whom intra Duck and Puddle communications would have been impossible. 'Oh good,' I said, for some reason relieved and cheered by this news. I was still puzzled by the fact that on my journey to the Duck and Puddle I had seen an apparently endless procession of energetic looking men in track suits jogging earnestly along the road.

I was about to comment on this bizarre occurrence when the door to the bar opened and Peter Marshall (also looking rather blurred) appeared. He was closely followed by a cluster of blurred but extremely athletic looking men. I immediately recognised them as the men I'd seen jogging through the lanes. They were all dressed in dazzling white shirts and equally dazzling white flannels and their white, studded cricket boots made a clatter as they marched across the red and black tiled floor at the entrance to the Duck and Puddle bar. The swarm of newcomers all had red faces and damp hair and had that clean and godly look that people have when thy have just finished exercising and have showered away their sweat. Even though I had probably had a little bit too much to drink I realised that unless these cricketers had been stranded in our village through some unfortunate mechanical mishap this was our opposition.

'They look a bit keen,' murmured Thumper.

This was an understatement of quite heroic proportions. The opposition looked very keen and professional. If the match had been decided on appearances we would have lost there and then. They even smelt more professional than we did. Our lot smelt of stale tobacco, beer and sheep dip. They smelt of oil of wintergreen and massage oil.

Only three members of the Bilbury team wore anything that could be described as being either remotely white or sporty. Dr Brownlow was by far our smartest player. He wore the cricket trousers and shirt which he had worn when he had played for his university second eleven team in his early twenties. Both trousers and shirt were a rich Devon clotted cream colour rather than white and although they had probably once fitted him to perfection they were now what a tailor might politely describe as a little bit on the tight side. Unable to fasten the zip at the front Dr Brownlow had secured his privacy and guarded against unpleasant draughts and accusations of indecency with the aid of two large safety pins. The shirt, bought for a man with a thinner, more youthful chest was stretched to the limits. Around his neck Dr Brownlow had casually tied the sleeves of his college sweater.

Patchy Fogg wore a brand new plain white shirt that still had the original creases in it (and, as Patchy discovered a little later still had one or two pins in it too) and from the waist upwards he looked every bit a cricketer. Unfortunately, his bottom half was draped in a pair of faded blue jeans and so that part of him didn't look quite so much a cricketer.

Third in our list of sartorial leaders, and most imaginatively dressed of our fashion trend setters for the international sports scene, came Ernie McBride, Kay's husband, the locally famous tractor engineer from Ilfracombe. Ernie wore a pair of baggy, knee length pale khaki tennis shorts, a flowered Hawaiian shirt, (the predominant colours of which were orange and green) and a pair of brown, artificial leather strap on sandals. The effect of this otherwise potentially acceptable ensemble was rather spoilt by the pair of fluorescent pink socks which Ernie wore beneath his sandals. Until his marriage to Kay the much loved

Ernie had lived at home with his mother who had always bought his clothes for him. She had never grown out of the habit of buying his clothes a size too large so that he could grow into them and this meant that he had a permanently creased, slightly unkempt, baggy look and so, according to the fashion of the day, he either looked extremely fashionable or quite out of touch with reality.

'Do you think your players would like to get themselves a drink?' Peter asked their captain, a dour faced fellow whose trousers were held up with a club tie and whose upper lip was decorated with the thinnest moustache I have ever seen. He was just over six feet tall, looked as though he weighed around fourteen stone and was probably the shortest man and lightest man on their team. Still in his early thirties he was probably also the oldest. I couldn't help thinking of the amateur football side from Exeter which had gone to Italy on a five day tour and had accidentally got themselves booked for a match against Turin A.C., Rome B.D. or one of the other famous professional sides. It was a historic mismatch. The Italian professionals had scored 36 goals in the first half of the match. By then everyone realised that a mistake had been made. The professionals played the second half of the match with half a team and still won by the impressive total of 42 goals to five.

The captain nodded. 'I expect they would. They've only just got back from a five mile run round the village.' He craned his neck and spoke to his colleagues. 'Would you like drinks, lads?'

There was a deep throated, masculine murmur of approval.

On the other side of the bar Frank, anticipating a flurry of his favourite activity, beamed, flexed his right arm and grasped the handle that would enable him to draw twelve pints of foaming best Devon bitter.

The captain leant across the bar. 'Twelve lemonades, please,' he said to Frank. 'But individual bills, please,' he added.

Frank's smile disappeared as quickly as it had come.

'We have crisps, I think,' said Peter, anxious to drum up a little more trade. 'Should any of your players feel they need to replenish their salt levels.'

'I don't think so, thank you,' said the visitors' captain. 'Our nutritionist doesn't allow us to eat junk food.'

Hearing this Thumper and I exchanged horrified glances. I

suddenly felt cold. The effects of the alcohol seemed to have worn off rather quickly.

'I think I'll have another drink,' I muttered to Thumper. 'Some of the opposition aren't looking quite as blurred as they did.'

Peter Marshall, however, was not in the slightest bit shaken by the fact that our opposition had their own nutritionist.

'Oh, our expert chap feels that crisps make an excellent pre-match snack,' he replied, without any hesitation. 'Full of iron and magnesium – as well as salt.'

I felt proud of him.

*   *   *

'Have you seen Harry Burrows?' asked Patchy Fogg, a few moments later. We were all standing outside the front door of the Duck and Puddle, watching in awe as our opponents went through a series of warm up exercises. As huge muscles stretched and relaxed and stretched again and tendons were toned and retoned the air was filled with annoyingly wholesome grunts and earnest sounding groans. On the other side of the road the village green, the arena for our forthcoming sporting encounter, waited patiently and silently for the dramas to come.

Josh Wilkins, our elderly and arthritic captain, leant heavily on his stick and wheezed uncomfortably as his lungs breathed in draughts of rich, fresh air.

'He was in the bar when I arrived,' I answered Patchy.

Harry Burrows, bank clerk, keen gardener, fisherman and father of six, was number five on our batting order and joyfully free of ambition. Now in his late forties, Harry had lost count of the number of times he had been offered promotion by the bank for which he worked. 'He could have been managing his own branch by now,' Dr Brownlow once told me. Harry steadfastly turned down all offers of promotion because moving up the career ladder would have meant moving to another area. 'Why should I leave my friends, sell my house, abandon my garden and move to a part of the country I know nothing about to take on a job with extra responsibility?' he asked. 'I've got a house, a car, a steady job with a pension and twenty miles of free sea fishing within half an hours drive. Why do they think I would want to go and live in Manchester, Fulham or Swindon?' Had Harry been married to a woman who wanted to be married to a man of greater substance then this philosophy might have led to many arguments and much unhappiness. But since Enid, Harry's wife, was equally content with her life everything in his garden was lovely.

'If I did that much exercise before a match I'd need to lie down for an hour,' murmured Dr Brownlow, nodding towards the opposition, still earnestly performing their warm up exercises. He sighed. 'It makes me feel tired just to look at them.' Dr Brownlow's trousers and shirt were so tight that when he moved he did so as though he was wearing armour.

'Harry and Kevin were supposed to roll the pitch,' said Patchy. 'But I don't think they have.'

Kevin Pettigrew was an electrician by trade but wasn't terribly good at it. 'I was O.K. until they invented electricity,' he once admitted. 'Then it all got a bit too complicated for me.' A series of unfortunate accidents means that these days he earns his living as a car park attendant. He is notoriously unreliable though he has a mellow, laid back manner which it makes it difficult for anyone to get cross with him. At the first sign of criticism he always apologises profusely and asks what he can do to put right that which he has done wrong. It is difficult to continue to feel cross with someone who is obviously contrite and his readiness to admit his mistakes invariably takes the wind out of his would be critics. His broadly based lack of talent and skill is supplemented by an affection for rum.

Patchy pointed towards the centre of the green where the two sets of stumps were already standing waiting. The roller, huge, heavy and brown with rust, lay abandoned in the middle of the wicket. When I looked at it closely I felt sure that I could see a leg sticking out of one side of it. I knew that when last I had seen it the roller had been quite devoid of legs.

Slightly alarmed, but not wanting to alarm anyone else unnecessarily, I walked fairly briskly out to the middle of the pitch and peered around the roller expecting the worst. The possibility of some sort of emergency had sobered me up. Patchy followed me. I'm sure that Dr Brownlow would have come too but he found walking difficult. What we saw wasn't the worst, but it was pretty close. Harry and Kevin were sitting on the ground with a bottle of dark, Navy rum in between them. When I looked closer I could see that the bottle was empty. I didn't need to look any closer to know where the rum had gone.

'Iss werry, hic, heavy!' said Kevin, pointing over his shoulder at the roller he was leaning against.

'We had a little drink to give us strength,' explained Harry. 'Rum's supposed to give you strength,' he said. 'Did you know that? It's full of iron. Absolutely full of iron. It's got more iron in it than spinch ... sppin ... spinch ... spinstuff ... that green stuff that Popeye eats ... you know what I mean.' Suddenly everyone in our team was an expert on minerals. I hadn't been aware of this and although I was not entirely sure of the reliability of the information I nevertheless thanked Harry and showed what I hoped was suitably earnest appreciation.

'Have you got enough strength to get up?' asked Patchy. 'The match is about to start!'

Harry thought about this for a moment and then shook his head. 'No,' he said. 'Can't stand up.' He turned to Kevin. 'We tried that, didn't we?'

Kevin nodded. 'We need more rum,' he said. 'We ran out. If we had more rum we'd be able to stand up.'

'The last thing you need is more rum,' I told him.

Kevin looked up at Patchy and I. 'Have we let you down?' he asked, suddenly but convincingly contrite.

'Yes!' said Patchy, bending down and pulling Kevin to his feet. I did the same with Harry. I had the worst job because Harry was several stones heavier than Kevin.

'I'm very solly!' said Kevin, who genuinely looked it. 'I wouldn't have let you down for the world. What can I do to put it right?' His mouth happened to be close to my face when he spoke. I instinctively pulled away from the rum fumes and nearly dropped Harry.

'We need to keep these two away from naked flames,' said Patchy. 'Let's lean them up against the oak.' He nodded towards a huge old tree which stands about twenty yards away from the wicket at square leg. The two of us then half carried and half dragged Kevin and Harry to the base of the trunk and left them sitting up against the tree. I noticed that Kevin had instinctively picked up the empty rum bottle and taken it with

193

him. He clutched it to his chest the way a child will clutch a favourite teddy bear.

'We'll be all right in a couple of minutes,' said Kevin, quite unrealistically.

'Be absolutely fine in a couple of minutes,' insisted Harry. He tried to get up but quickly abandoned this idea.

Patchy and I finished rolling the wicket and pushed the roller to the edge of the village green. We then walked back to the Duck and Puddle forecourt.

'I'm afraid that two of our players have been taken ill,' I announced.

'Oh dear!' said our opponents' captain. 'Nothing serious, I hope?'

'They'll be O.K.,' I told him.

'One of our players is a qualified first aider,' said the captain. 'Would you like him to have a look at them?'

'That's very kind of you,' I said. 'But I'm a doctor.'

The visitor raised an eyebrow, as though he found this difficult to believe. I suppose you couldn't blame him. He was probably used to doctors who looked like doctors.

I turned away from him and spoke to Peter Marshall. 'Have they tossed yet?' I whispered.

Peter shook his head.

'We're two men short,' I told him. I quickly explained about Harry and Kevin.

'We're three men short,' said Peter.

I stared at him and frowned.

'Colin Jackson was supposed to be batting at number three,' he reminded me. He sighed. 'His wife rang twenty minutes ago. A cow trod on his foot.'

'Can't he play on one leg?'

'You know Colin,' said Peter. 'He's gone to bed. He thinks he'll die if he walks on it.'

'We can't play with eight men! They'd slaughter us if we played with twenty two men!'

'Good luck you chaps!' cried a cheerful female voice.

We both turned and looked. Kay McBride, the district nurse, had stopped her car outside the pub and was waving to us.

Peter looked at me and I looked at him and then Peter looked back at Kay. 'Park your car!' he shouted. 'You're playing.'

Kay stared at him and laughed. 'Don't be daft!' she said.

'We need you!' I told her. Peter and I walked across to her and explained what had happened.

'But I've never played cricket!'

'It doesn't matter.'

'Do they let women play?'

'They do now.'

'Who's your captain?' asked the visiting captain. He looked at his watch. 'Shouldn't we toss and get on with it? My chaps are all warmed up and ready to go.'

'Is it better for us to bat first or field first?' I asked Peter.

'How soon will Harry and Kevin be fit to play?'

'Wednesday, I should think,' I told him, gloomily. I thought about it for a moment. 'They might be able to stand up for the second innings,' I said.

'Then I'll tell Josh we have to field,' said Peter, walking briskly over towards our captain. 'That's O.K. because that's what we normally do anyway.'

'Wouldn't we be better off batting first?' I asked Peter a couple of minutes later as we strolled onto the field behind Josh.

'When we bat there's a chance that we'll all be out in half an hour,' explained Peter. 'In which case we'll be batting two men short if we bat now. If we bat second then we should have eleven players. Besides,' he added, 'Harry and Kevin can field lying down but they have to stand up to bat.'

I was deeply impressed with Peter's logic and strongly suspected that these were not problems that were dealt with in any detail in standard cricket coaching manuals.

*　　*　　*

I think it is fair to say that our opponents were not quite prepared for combat with the Old Bilburians Cricket Club. As their opening batsmen (tall, broad, immaculately attired and carrying bats which were still new enough to show individual marks where contact had been made with the ball) walked out to the wicket I could see that there were things about our team which surprised them.

It was, for example, probably the first time they had seen a wicket keeper sitting in a deck chair.

Josh, our captain, suffers terribly with his arthritis and though he is mentally alert for his age, and bravely regards the deterioration in his visual and auditory capacities as an inevitable consequence of advancing years, we had agreed among ourselves that he could not possibly be expected to stand for a day's cricket. Between overs Thumper and I carried Josh and the deck chair from one end of the pitch to the other.

It may well have been the first time they had seen a fielder (Harry) sitting with his back to a tree, just a few yards away from the wicket. It was probably the first time they had seen a fielder lying on his side at mid on. This was Kevin, who had been carefully positioned to stop any straight on drives. And it was almost certainly the first time they had seen a buxom district nurse, still attired in her full uniform, fielding at third man with her dress tucked into her knickers.

They stood together in the middle of the wicket and looked around them in quiet amazement. And then, after exchanging a brief word or two, one of them walked up the wicket and spoke to the vicar, who was umpiring for us. Our other umpire hadn't turned up so the vicar had to stand at both ends (though not at once).

'Are that man's hands tied together?' he asked the vicar, nodding towards Harry.

The vicar followed the batsman's gaze, peered at Harry, turned back and nodded. 'Yes, I think you're right.' At Thumper's suggestion we had used a length of binder twine to tie Harry's hands together into a catching position. We had used another piece of string, looped around his neck, to hold his hands a few inches away from his chest in a perfect catching position.

The batsman frowned. 'Is that allowed?' he asked.

The vicar thought for a moment. 'I don't think it's not allowed,' he said. 'I don't think I've ever seen anything in the laws about it. Have you?'

The batsman had to admit that he too had never seen anything in the laws forbidding the tying together of a fielder's hands.

'What about the deckchair?' he asked. 'Is that allowed?'

The vicar thought carefully again. 'I don't think there's a

problem,' he said. 'As long as the wicket keeper doesn't use the deckchair to assist him in making a dismissal.'

Josh had wisely decided that Thumper would open the bowling for us. This was not a difficult decision to make for when those of us who could move had gathered around Josh to discuss the team's tactics only Thumper Robinson and Patchy Fogg had admitted to any bowling experience. Since Patchy claimed to bowl either leg breaks or off breaks ('but definitely something slow') it was felt that he should be introduced into the Bilbury attack a little later on in the innings. What this meant in practice was that he would be bowling the second over.

'Play!' cried the umpire, when the opposition's opening batsman had finally settled down, taken guard, flattened a molehill which he seemed to think might interfere with play and removed the heads, stalks and leaves from a large dandelion plant growing in the crease.

Thumper, who had been carefully marking out his run up and was by now almost out of earshot put a hand to his ear to indicate that he wasn't quite sure whether or not he could start bowling.

'PLAY!' yelled the vicar.

Thumper smiled, waved and began his approach to the wicket. He ran as fast as he could for about thirty or forty yards, and then started to slow down. By the time he was about ten yards away from the delivery crease he was panting heavily and sweating profusely. By the time he was ready to deliver the ball he had slowed to a gentle walking pace.

The opposition batsman was clearly deceived by the pace and flight of Thumper's first ball. He had probably been misled by Thumper's enthusiastic run up and had not expected a slow, looping full toss. He changed his planned backward defensive stroke into a full blooded drive but still overestimated the speed of the ball and had completed his stroke by the time the ball finally arrived. As the ball hit him in the groin he sank noiselessly but gracefully to the ground. The vicar, the other batsman and I rushed forward to see if we could help. Dr Brownlow, moving as quickly as his clothes would let him, joined us a moment or two later. Thumper, looking slightly guilty and embarrassed, walked a third of the way down the wicket as though planning to apologise, realised that this was not what was normally expected of a fiercesome opening bowler and stayed where he was.

Even though he was wearing the usual protection the batsman was in no fit state to continue. Patchy Fogg and I helped him off the pitch and handed him over to his colleagues who were sitting, looking slightly stunned, on a row of benches at the edge of the village green. As we lowered him to the ground he groaned loudly. 'Listen, friend,' said Patchy to the injured batsman, 'the only thing you can count on in this life is that some terrible things will happen to you. There may be some good things. But you can guarantee that there will be bad things. This was one of the bad things.' He beamed at the bemused batsman. 'But look on the bright side,' he finished, 'this is one of the bad things that you haven't got to worry about happening because it's already happened.'

The batsman frowned and looked at his colleagues. They looked as puzzled as he did.

'Am I right in thinking that one of your fielders has got his hands tied together?' the opposition captain asked us.

I told him that he was, indeed, quite right about this.

'Is this allowed? Is there anything in the laws about it?'

'I don't think there's anything in the laws about tying together a fielder's hands,' I said. 'Harry's a bit tired,' I added, in explanation.

'Ah!' said the opposition captain. 'And the deckchair?'

'Josh has terrible arthritis,' I explained. 'He finds it more comfortable to field in a deckchair.'

'I've never seen anything like it,' said the opposition captain, shaking his head.

'No,' I agreed. 'I suppose not.'

'Is that a woman you've got fielding at third man?'

'Yes,' I agreed. I thought about it for a moment. 'I suppose we ought to say that she's at third woman!' I said.

'Your captain didn't mention that you were playing a mixed side.'

'It's not a very mixed side,' I said. 'Kay's our only female player. She wouldn't have been playing at all but Colin Jackson had his foot trodden on by a cow. She's married to Ernie,' I said. 'The chap in shorts.' I pointed to Ernie. The opposition number three batsman finished fastening on his pads and started off towards the crease. 'I'd better get back,' I said, apologetically. 'I don't want them to start without me.'

* * *

By lunch our opponents had scored 128 runs and had used up exactly half of their allocation of 40 overs. And although one of their batsmen had had to retire hurt they still hadn't lost any wickets. The two batsmen were clearly wary and unwilling to take risks. I suspect that this was simply because they were wary about being dismissed cheaply by such a poor side. In any team sport good sides are at a tremendous disadvantage when playing poor sides. A good side can hardly take much pride in a win when the opposition is of low quality but their self esteem and self respect can take quite a battering if they lose.

The remainder of Thumper's first over had been something of a disaster. The replacement batsman had shown very little respect for Thumper's bowling and had hit him for two fours and a six. If it hadn't been for Patchy Fogg's bowling the opposition score would have been even more impressive. Patchy's main advantage was that no one had any idea what he was bowling. He didn't know. We didn't know. And the opposition batsmen certainly didn't know. Sometimes the ball would turn prodigiously to the left. Sometimes it would turn an equally impressive amount to the right. Sometimes it would leap up into the air. Sometimes it would land and shoot forwards along the ground. And most of the time it wouldn't turn or do anything exceptional at all. The two batsmen could see that Patchy had no idea what he was doing and this intimidated them enormously for they were both terrified of being dismissed by a bowler who had no control at all over the ball. Both batsmen were dismissed immediately after lunch and in both cases the dismissals were neither expected nor predictable. Nor, for that matter were they explicable or believable.

When watching the credits rolling at the end of a movie I have often wondered whether it is really necessary to list so many people. Occasionally, at the end of an epic, the list goes on and on for so long that it seems as if it would have been quicker to have listed all the people in California who weren't involved.

After the first of our two unexpected dismissals, the first glorious post-prandial success, I felt that cricket scorers ought to follow the movie makers' example and spread the credit around a little more. The scorebook will for ever show that H.Ainsworth was bowled by P.Fogg and caught by T.Robinson but this bald and sketchy outline of the truth does not in any way begin to tell the true story. This dismissal was, perhaps like no other dismissal in cricket, a genuine team effort and I was proud to have played a part in it.

Before lunch, Ainsworth, the hugely muscled assistant manager of an estate agents' shop, had batted carefully and wisely and had accumulated 47 runs without taking any chances whatsoever. During the luncheon interval he had clearly been advised by his team captain to push the scoring rate along a little and when he returned to the crease, full of pork pie, egg salad and thickly cut home-made bread spread with creamy, hand-churned butter he walked down the wicket to Thumper's first delivery and played a shot that seemed guaranteed to turn the ball into some sort of intergalactic object.

Unfortunately for Ainsworth the ball didn't come off the middle of the bat but hit the edge and instead of clearing the village green, the road, the cottages on the other side of the road and the gardens behind the cottages on the other side of the road (as it would have surely done if it had been hit cleanly) it skied upwards, almost out of sight.

It was Dr Brownlow who first realised that the ball was going to come down into the branches of the oak tree at square leg. He called out to tell us all this and so deserves credit in the scorer's book for conceiving Mr Ainsworth's dismissal. Credit for inspiring the execution of the dismissal must go to Frank Parsons, the corpulent, genial landlord of the Duck and Puddle for it was he who had the presence of mind to lead us into action with a shout of: 'Let's try and catch it!'.

For hours after the match there was much discussion about the legality of this dismissal. Our visitors claimed, without rancour, that the ball was 'dead' when it first hit the tree and that what happened to it thereafter was of no relevance to the match. We claimed (and, importantly, our claim was supported by the umpire) that the tree was merely a local hazard which had, in practice, made the catching of the ball considerably more difficult than it would have been had the tree not been there. Since no one had a copy of the laws of cricket the umpire's decision was adopted.

At the time of the incident, of course, no one was very concerned about the laws of cricket. Encouraged by Frank's vocal enthusiasm all those who could move (Kevin was still fielding prone, Harry was still sitting with his back to the tree with his hands tied into a catching position and although Josh did try to get up he didn't manage to escape from his deck chair until it was too late for him to take an active part in the Ainsworth dismissal) hurried up to the base of the oak tree and stood around, looking upwards, waiting for the ball to appear. We could hear it crashing through the branches but for what seemed like an hour or so we couldn't see anything at all.

It was Patchy Fogg who saw it first, and for this he deserves a large chunk of the credit for what happened next. Without his alert advice the ball might well have come crashing down to the ground before any of us could spot it. 'There it is!' he cried, pointing upwards.

We all followed his outstretched arm and looked up. Frank, Kay McBride, Dr Brownlow and I, who were all standing on the wrong side of the tree, hurried around to join Patchy and Ernie McBride who were standing directly underneath the ball. The two batsmen were racing up and down the wicket as quickly as they could but none of us was concerned with what they were doing. We all knew that this was our first real opportunity to take a wicket. Heads thrown back we all watched carefully as the ball bounced from one branch to another, crashing through leaves and temporarily disappearing and reappearing. It was, I suppose, inevitable that some of us would collide. Frank, Kay and I, all looking upwards and none of us looking where we were going, crashed into each other and seconds later lay sprawled flat on the ground on our backs. Slowed down by his trousers and shirt Dr Brownlow was several yards behind us at the moment of impact. Temporarily distracted, Patchy, Thumper and Ernie all looked down to see what had happened. It was at that inconvenient moment that the ball chose to begin its final, untroubled descent from branch to ground.

Patchy still says that he would have been able to catch the ball if he hadn't been staring at Frank, Kay and I, lying flat on our backs on the ground. Ernie and Thumper both think that the ball's final ricochet off the lowest branch of the tree was so unpredictable that no one would have been able to catch it. Regardless of this disagreement Kay and I both claim that our part in the dismissal was crucial; we argue that if we hadn't bumped into him Frank wouldn't have ended up flat on his back and the ball would have probably just landed on the grass. Frank insists that he and not Thumper should have been credited with the catch since it was he who managed to get in the way of the ball. None of this matters, of course, because what happened was that with a strange, half thuddy, half squelchy sort of sound the ball landed on Frank's abdomen.

For a brief moment it stayed where it was. Frank's shirt had burst open with his fall, revealing his large, pink (and surprisingly hairless) abdomen and the cricket ball looked for all the world like a cherry bobbing around on a bowl of pink blancmange.

'It's going to roll off!' cried Ernie, playing his own small but crucial part in the Ainsworth dismissal.

And so it was Thumper, diving to his left, who caught the ball as it started to roll off Frank's abdomen.

In the end, as I have already reported, the dismissal went down in the score book as H.Ainsworth bowled P.Fogg and caught T.Robinson but that simple shorthand goes nowhere near enough towards explaining the full story of the quite remarkable Ainsworth dismissal.

Gilly Parsons brought out drinks as we recovered from the excitement. One of the visiting batsmen said that he had never before seen a woman carry so many full pint glasses without spilling a drop. Much to the horror of Frank and Thumper the other batsman told us that on the grounds where he usually played it was more usual for 'drinks' to consist of glasses of orange squash.

*   *   *

In the end the visitors didn't score as many runs as we had at first feared. Much to our own surprise and delight the Ainsworth dismissal turned out to be the stimulus that inspired us to become something of a team. At the same time this incident seemed to have a very demoralising effect on our opponents. They rather seemed to regard it as a sign that the fates were conspiring against them.

There were, of course, one or two more highlights and memorable moments in their innings.

After the miserable Ainsworth had left the field trailing his bat, muttering curses about trees and threatening to do things with a chainsaw that would bring tears to any arborphile's eyes he was briskly replaced by his team captain, a man who had not up until that point impressed me as being the sort of fellow who gets a lot of laughs out of life. The corners of the fellow's mouth drooped downwards, giving him the permanent appearance of a man who has spent too much of his life sucking lemons. He did not strike me as a man who did anything for fun and he was certainly not amused when his first shot, a sizzling drive which sent the ball hissing across the grass, was stopped from reaching the boundary by the inert form of Kevin Pettigrew. Much to everyone's surprise the semiconscious Kevin had probably been our best fielder. He had certainly saved an enormous number of runs, though the personal cost was a high one and a fortnight later his wife told Patsy that some of the bruises he had acquired in the line of duty were still visible.

'Well, really!' snorted the captain. He stalked down the wicket and glowered at the vicar. 'Is that allowed, umpire?' he demanded, in the tone of a man who is accustomed to having his whims fulfilled and his fancies expedited.

The vicar said that although he realised that it was unusual to have a semicomatose fielder he didn't think he knew of any law which prevented a member of a side fielding the ball while asleep and recumbent. 'As long as he doesn't use any article of clothing to assist him,' added the vicar.

The captain made the mistake of allowing this relatively trivial incident to disturb his composure and he unwisely walked down the wicket and tried to hit the next ball into an adjacent county. Unfortunately, his enthusiasm proved too much for his skill and after completely missing the ball he span round just in time to see Josh, leaning forward in his deckchair, picking up the ball and rolling it back along the ground towards the stumps. I was fielding at slip at the time and had a perfect view. The sight of the captain's face as he watched his bails drop almost noiselessly to the ground was worth almost any amount of ready money. The not inconsiderable, and largely partisan, crowd which had gathered around the edge of the village green showed their appreciation in the traditional way.

In the end, although they reached the very respectable score of 189 runs our opponents would have to agree that they batted disappointingly. As the church clock struck three we had 40 overs in which to score 190 runs to win. No one seriously expected us to be able to do it. But it was a much smaller target than we had at one time feared that we would face.

*   *   *

CHAPTER SEVENTEEN

While Thumper, Peter, Patchy, Kay and the rest of us sat on the grass quenching our thirsts and appetites with tankards of beer and plates of crusty sandwiches our opponents began to prepare for their stint in the field. Their injured player, the opening batsman who had received a blow in the groin, seemed keen to resume his involvement in the match. He still looked a little pale and rather groggy but, when questioned by his captain, insisted that he was fit enough to bowl. This was not a view with which I had much sympathy when I watched him warming up. He turned out to be one of those infuriatingly talented individuals who opens both the batting and the bowling; a fast bowler with a mission to maim.

'I don't fancy my chances against him,' I muttered to Dr Brownlow, as we lay sprawled on the grass watching this huge sporting hooligan burst out of convalescence, speed through recuperation and arrive at top flight fitness, all in the space of about fifteen minutes. I have never wished anyone ill but I wouldn't have minded if he had decided to spend a little longer getting better.

Dr Brownlow leant a little in my direction. 'Pop to my car and get my bag, will you?' He grimaced. 'I'd go myself but I want to delay having to get up for as long as possible.'

I grinned at him, got up, strolled over to his elderly Rolls Royce which was parked in front of the Duck and Puddle, opened the front door and took out his black, leather medical bag. It was some time since Dr Brownlow had practised medicine but he still kept his black bag in the car in case of emergencies. And I'd never seen him lock his car or hear him complain that anything had been stolen. Crime was not a problem which figured high on our list of anxieties. There had been an incident the previous summer which worried us all when Frank, the publican, noticed that a spare gallon can of petrol had disappeared from his garage (actually the can itself hadn't disappeared – but the petrol had) and for a while there was some concern in the village that we might have been contaminated by the twentieth century crime wave which seems to have swept the nation. And then Frank received a letter from Manchester which contained a generous cheque and an explanation. The petrol had, it seemed, been taken by a holiday-maker who had set off from Ilfracombe early one Saturday morning in an attempt to beat the holiday rush. He had not realised that the local garages would not be open at that time of night and during his search for a petrol station had driven round and round getting more and more lost. Eventually he had spluttered to a halt a hundred yards away from the Duck and Puddle and rather than wake anyone up had simply helped himself to Frank's petrol. We were all mightily relieved when we discovered that we did not have a major criminal living in our midst.

'What do you suggest we do?' I asked, putting his bag down beside him and lowering myself back down onto the grass. 'If you fill a couple of syringes with a decent tranquilliser I could probably put him out of action before he manages to kill me!'

Dr Brownlow, who was rummaging through his bag, just grunted. 'This will do!' he said at long last, producing a piece of official looking paper.

'What on earth is that?' I asked, peering over his shoulder.

'It's an S.B. form,' explained Dr Brownlow. 'I had these printed years ago.' He handed me the form. Underneath a very impressive looking crest and a dozen words in Latin were printed the following words:

I . . . . of . . . .do hereby declare that I have rejected the medical advice of Dr . . . . . .
. . . .

Furthermore, I understand that by rejecting his advice I am putting my health at risk. I take full responsibility for my actions.
Signed . . . .
Witnessed by . . . .

I looked at Dr Brownlow and frowned. 'How's this going to help us?' I asked him.

'Help me up and then watch,' said Dr Brownlow, holding up a hand so that I could pull him to his feet.

I followed him as he marched stiffly over to where the fast bowler was busy practising his scowl.

'I'm Dr Brownlow,' said Dr Brownlow. He put his black bag down on the grass and then formally introduced me. 'How are you feeling?' he asked the fast bowler solicitously.

The fast bowler stopped and thought about his answer for a moment. 'I'm all right!' he said gruffly.

'May I examine you?' asked Dr Brownlow.

The fast bowler blinked. 'What for?'

'To make sure that you're fit to play,' he said.

The fast bowler turned and looked around for his captain. 'Captain!' he called. 'These doctors want to examine me. Is it all right?'

The captain came scurrying over.

'I just thought I'd give your chap the once over,' explained Dr Brownlow, giving the captain what he called his ten guinea smile.

'That's very decent of you,' said the captain, succumbing entirely to Dr Brownlow's admirable bedside manner.

'Not at all,' said Dr Brownlow. He stood on tip toes, reached up and peered into the fast bowler's eyes. Satisfied with that he lowered himself back down onto the ground. 'Open your mouth!' The fast bowler did exactly as he was told.

'Multiply 234 by 56,' said Dr Brownlow briskly.

The fast bowler stared at him. 'Yer what?'

Dr Brownlow repeated the instruction. 'It's a mental agility test,' he explained. 'Designed to make sure that you aren't suffering from any delayed effects.'

The fast bowler frowned and scratched his head. 'I dunno.'

'Never mind,' said Dr Brownlow. 'Don't worry about it.' He smiled. 'You're doing fine,' he said, somehow managing to give the fast bowler the impression that he wasn't doing fine at all.

'Touch your left ear with your right forefinger.'

The fast bowler lifted his left arm, lowered it, raised his right arm, thought for a moment, touched his right ear with his left thumb, touched his nose with his right forefinger and went very red.

'I've never been any good at this sort of stuff,' he said, rather crossly. Beads of perspiration were beginning to form on his brow.

'I think you ought to sit out the rest of the match,' said Dr Brownlow. 'We'll find a substitute to field for you.'

The fast bowler stared at Dr Brownlow as though he'd suggested that he retire from the game and take up ballet dancing instead. He stood up straight, squared his shoulders and stuck out his not insignificant chin.

'I'm gunna play!' he said defiantly.

Dr Brownlow let out a little sigh, took one of his forms from his bag and handed it to the giant. 'Then you must sign this,' he said.

'Wot's that?'

'Just a form confirming that you've rejected my advice and chosen to risk your health by continuing to play,' said Dr Brownlow.

The fast bowler blanched but took the form that Dr Brownlow held out. He studied it, thought about it for a moment and then, with some visible reluctance, took the pen that Dr Brownlow offered, filled in the form and then scrawled his signature in the appropriate place.

'I'll give him thirty minutes at most,' whispered Dr Brownlow as we walked back to his Rolls to deposit his black bag. 'Every time either he passes near you ask him if he's still feeling all right. Tell everyone else to do the same.'

I didn't think our huge opponent would crack so easily but I was prepared to give it a try. 'What does S.B. mean?' I asked him, as we walked back onto the village green.

'S.B.?'

'You said the forms were S.B. forms.'

'Ah,' smiled Dr Brownlow. He leant towards me, conspiratorially. 'S.B. stands for silly beggar,' he told me. 'I had the forms printed for silly beggars who won't listen to good advice.'

Just then Peter Marshall approached us and handed me a cricket pad. 'Since you're opening the batting you'd better put this on,' he said. He turned to Dr Brownlow. 'Do you think Kevin and Harry are fit to play?' he asked.

'Can they stand up?' asked Dr Brownlow.

'Just about,' said Peter.

'Then they're fit to play,' said Dr Brownlow. 'I'm going to get myself another beer. Do either of you want one?'

'No, thanks,' I said. 'Not just before I bat.' I turned to Peter. 'Where's the other one?'

'Yes, please. I'll have a pint,' replied Peter. He frowned. 'Other one what?'

'Pad.' I held up the pad he'd given me. 'You've only given me one.'

'Josh has got the other one,' explained Peter. 'You've got one each.'

I looked at the single pad and sighed. It was grey and flimsy. 'Which leg am I supposed to put it on?'

'Up to you, doc!' said Peter. 'Do you bat right handed?'

'Yes. I think so.' I took up a practise batting stance. 'Yes.'

'Then put the pad on your left leg. That's the one that is most likely to be hit. They're good pads. I got them from Mrs Winterbottom. They used to belong to her husband.'

'He was over 80 when he died and he'd been bed ridden for years. He probably hadn't played cricket since the last war!'

'A pad's a pad!' said Peter. 'What's wrong with them?'

'These are antiques!' I told him. 'We should be auctioning them not playing in them!'

Peter looked concerned and bent down to examine the pad I was preparing to put on. 'Well, just make sure you don't damage it,' he said. 'I'll take them into one of the antique dealers in South Molton next week.' He looked thoughtful. 'Maybe you should put it on your other leg?'

I stared at him.

'So that it won't be so likely to get hit by the ball,' he explained.

I ignored him and sighed. 'We don't have to share a bat, do we?' I asked, buckling my solitary pad onto my left leg. The leather straps were dry and cracked and the buckles were rusty.

'Of course not!' said Peter. 'I bought two brand new ones. I'll get them.' He hurried off and returned a few moments later clutching a pair of those cheap, rather flimsy cricket bats that are sold for beach cricket and made for use with old tennis balls. Josh followed him over.

I took one of the bats from Peter and stared at it. 'We can't play with those!' I protested. 'They're far too small and they've got no springing. I thought you said you were going to get proper bats!' I twirled the bat around. 'These are made of balsa wood!' I turned the bat around. It carried a sticker on the back. The sticker said: 'Foreign Made'. There was a price label for three shillings and sixpence.

'They're proper bats!' insisted Peter. 'Look!' he said, reaching out, turning round the bat I was holding and pointing to the front of it. 'Look at that!'

I looked at the front of the bat. In black print it said: 'W.G.Grace Special.'

'There you are!' said Peter. 'W.G.Grace! He was a proper cricketer!'

I sighed, took one of the bats from him and turned to Josh. 'Come on,' I said. 'Let's get it over with.'

*　　*　　*

Apart from his arthritis, his bad chest, his angina, his bad hearing, his poor eyesight and his prostate trouble Josh Wilkins was in pretty good health for a man of his advanced years. He still had a terrific sense of humour, although jokes and witticisms sometimes had to be slowly explained to him several times before he could benefit fully from every nuance, and he never tired of telling people that on a recent visit to the chiropodist he had been assured that he had feet that would have looked good on a man of seventy. However, it was probably not unfair to say that Josh was rather a long way past his prime as a sportsman.

As we walked out to the wicket together I had to keep stopping so that he could catch up with me and by the time we finally arrived at our destination he was wheezing badly and using his rather small cricket bat as an impromptu walking stick.

'Glad you could both make it,' said the opposition captain, when we finally arrived. I thought it was rather unnecessarily sarcastic of him. 'We were getting worried that we would have to start without you.'

At the other end of his twenty yard run up the fast bowler glared at us all. 'Can I start?' he called to the umpire. The vicar held up a hand while I walked down the wicket to defend my stumps. I took guard, as I'd seen the professionals do, looked around the village green to check on the positions of the fielders, adjusted my pad, twirled my little bat, which felt absurdly flimsy, swallowed hard and then nodded to the vicar to let him know that I was as ready as I was going to get.

Peter said afterwards that I must have damaged the bat in some way while I was walking out to the wicket. 'It was in perfectly good condition when I handed it over to you,' he insisted. 'You must have leant on it, or banged it against the ground.' I still maintain that the problem was that the bat was too flimsy for proper cricket and that a well made bat would have withstood all such traumas without ill effect.

I suppose that from a distance what happened must have all seemed rather funny. But from where I was standing it didn't seem funny at all. I didn't see the ball after it left the fast bowler's hand until it hit my bat. And then there was chaos. Cries of 'Catch it!' were interspersed with cries of 'Watch out!' When I looked down I found that although I was still holding the handle of a bat the handle had no blade attached to it. I discovered afterwards that when the ball had hit the bat the latter had instantly broken and while the ball had flown off in one direction the best part of the bat had flown off in another direction. The good news was that no one was hurt by the piece of airborne cricket bat. The even better news was that the fielders were so distracted by what had happened that none of them managed to catch the ball.

After that the opposition had little option but to lend us their bats. It was either that or abandon the match.

*   *   *

By the end of the third over we had scored 22 runs (mostly extras) and lost three wickets. The match looked almost finished. Josh had been our first victim. The second ball I had received had slid off the face of my bat (without either my knowledge or consent I confess) and had squirted down to long leg at a tremendous pace. Seeing the ball disappear across the grass and realising that there were no fielders in the area I had immediately looked down the wicket, yelled 'Run!' and started off for the other crease. I don't think Josh heard me because he didn't move straight away but he soon realised what was happening when he saw me tearing down the pitch towards

211

him. When I arrived at his end of the wicket he had made very little progress and still had about twenty yards to go to reach safety. I checked the position of the fielder who was chasing the ball and decided that we would have plenty of time to make it so I dropped my borrowed bat on the ground, took Josh's arm and started to walk with him back in the direction from which I had come. When I had escorted him to the batting crease, and made sure that he was fairly stable and not likely to topple onto his wicket, I scampered back up the pitch as quickly as I could.

Although I had effectively run two and walked one and the scorebook would only register a single I was still quite pleased with myself for masterminding what had turned out to be fairly complicated exercise in logistics.

Then, just as I was relaxing a little and thinking of the century that would be mine if I could just get those other 99 runs, I heard a huge cry from Josh's end of the wicket. I turned round just in time to see him walking slowly back up the pitch towards me and pointing to the bat which lay on the ground at my feet.

'I forgot my bat!' he shouted to me.

'You've got yours! I shouted. He was using it as a walking stick.

When they ran him out he was a third of the way down the wicket. They nearly ran me out at the same time because I had started down the pitch to try to explain to him that the bat he could see was the one I was using whereas the stick he was using to help him walk up the pitch to fetch his bat was, in fact, his bat.

When I saw that it was too late to save him I turned round and just got back into my crease in time. Josh was quite sporting about it. He said that he needed to go to the lavatory anyway. All things considered we were pretty well resigned to the fact that it was just a matter of time before we lost, though to be honest I think we all felt that we had put up a better show than anyone might have expected.

*   *   *

After our third wicket fell Kay McBride came out to bat. During the interval she had gone back to her cottage to change and to put on something more appropriate for the occasion and was wearing a breathtakingly short, white tennis skirt and a diaphanous white blouse which was clearly a couple of sizes too small for her. The opposition certainly found it extremely difficult to concentrate. When Kay bent down into her batting stance the fielders behind her found themselves staring at the tops of her stockings and a foot of white thigh while the fielders in front of her found themselves gazing into an apparently bottomless cleavage. I don't know whether it was because they were distracted by these unexpected visions of rural loveliness or because they didn't want her stay at the wicket to be too short lived but the fielders did not react particularly quickly when Kay was at the crease.

The humourless fast bowler was not amused by what he clearly regarded as indefensible sloppiness and when the second catch was put down he got very angry and said some very hurtful things. He was putting his heart and soul into his bowling and I suppose he felt a little let down.

*　　*　　*

Dr Brownlow had forecast that their fast bowler would not stay on the pitch for more than half an hour and I decided that this was the moment to start taking advantage of the seeds of doubt which Dr Brownlow had sown. I wandered a little closer to the angry fast bowler. 'You shouldn't get so excited!' I warned him, gently. 'If your blood pressure goes up too high you could be in real trouble.'

He looked at me with eyes that could burn holes in armour plating. 'What do you mean?' he demanded, scowling.

I sucked half a litre of air in through my teeth, let it out slowly and shook my head knowingly. 'I don't want to say any more,' I said. I paused and bravely looked him in the eye. 'But just tell me immediately if you get a headache.'

The fast bowler stared at me and frowned. 'What sort of headache?'

'Any sort of headache.'

He looked at me and frowned. 'Why?'

I shook my head. 'I don't want to say any more,' I said. 'You signed one of Dr Brownlow's S.B. forms and so it's really nothing to do with me.' I regarded this abuse of my professional position as justified since if the fast bowler continued to bowl one of us would probably be severely injured. Apart from a bat and a single pad each we had nothing to protect us from the ball. I felt that getting him out of the way could be regarded as a valuable form of preventive medicine.

Three balls later the fast bowler stopped in mid run up and held his forehead. His captain and I wandered up to him. 'What's up?' asked the captain.

'I don't feel well,' complained the fast bowler. 'I've got a bit of a headache.'

'Probably just a bit too much sun,' said the captain. 'I'll send for an aspirin.' He turned and waved towards the boundary.

'Maybe I ought to go and lie down for a while, captain,' said the fast bowler. He swallowed and mopped at his brow. His captain did not think this was a good idea. He force fed the fast bowler with a glass of water in which two aspirin tablets had been dissolved and told him not to be such a sissy. The bowler sent down two rather medium pace deliveries which Kay McBride succeeded in deflecting into the outfield. We ran two off the first and the second went for four.

'Is there anyone we should telephone, you know, in case...,' I asked him when he next walked past me.

The fast bowler stopped and stared at me.

'You're a very brave man,' I told him quietly. 'Not many people would put their team before their health.'

He bowled just one more ball and then walked off the field clutching his head. When his captain remonstrated with him he started to cry and talk about his children.

*   *   *

Without their fearsome opening bowler the visitors turned out to be a very ordinary side. What is more the loss of their star player seemed to weaken their spirit and remove much of their confidence. The substitute they fielded as a replacement turned out to be their twelfth man, a flimsy looking fellow who obviously hadn't expected to be called upon to play and turned out to be an individual of a nervous disposition. His presence did not do much for the morale of our visitors.

The twelfth man's credibility was finally destroyed when he missed a catch which was such a sitter that Ernie McBride, who

214

had hit the ball, had already given up hope and left the crease. Ernie had to scurry back in order to avoid being run out.

We had never been in the slightest bit worried by the prospect of losing. It had, after all, been our original intention to let all our opponents win so that they would happily spend more money on buying rounds of drinks for one another (and for us).

But by teatime, when we had scored a quite remarkable 77 runs for a modest five wickets, something strange had started to happen: we had, for the very first time, begun to think of not losing. There were two reasons for this. First, our opponents had given absolutely no indication that they were likely to start spending money if they won. They were a rather miserable bunch. And second, as our innings progressed we noticed a distinct change in their attitude. They began to make sneering, uncomplimentary remarks. They called all our scoring shots 'lucky'. They criticised our pitch. They complained about having a tree on the playing area. And they made loud, rude remarks about our attire. We still had over 100 runs to score in order to win, and none of us thought of winning as a realistic possibility, but we felt that if we could last out the remaining 20 overs of our innings then we would have won a modest, moral victory. One thing gave us hope that we might be able to do this: it was getting dark.

Although the match had started at twelve noon, and should have finished while it was still light, there had been a considerable number of unexpected delays. Having Josh as wicket keeper had meant that our opponents' innings had taken rather longer to complete than anyone had expected (we would have been happy to carry him seated in the deckchair but sometimes he had insisted on moving from one end to the other under his own steam). Injuries on the field had taken up quite a lot of time and luncheon had dragged on for an additional, unscheduled three quarters of an hour. As we resumed the match after tea the sun was already beginning to set and it was clear that it would be quite dark by the time the match was completed. Under normal circumstances it is generally thought that the batting side are most disadvantaged by playing in poor light. But these were not normal circumstances and we all felt that the darker it got the greater our advantage would be.

I had been given out leg before wicket just before tea (it

would be unnecessarily immodest of me not to record that I scored 23 runs though dishonest of me not to confess that only three of them came from deliberate strokes, the rest were more a result of the ball hitting the bat than the bat hitting the ball) and so, it was Ernie McBride and Dr Brownlow who strode out onto the pitch to resume our innings.

Dr Brownlow was lucky to survive the first ball he received. Inspired, perhaps, by memories of a dim and distant playing career, he greeted his first delivery for nearly half a century by swinging his bat around his body at waist height. Remarkably and unexpectedly the bat and the ball collided in mid air and the latter, being the smaller and more mobile of the two, flew sharply upwards and then began a slow descent that would have taken it straight into the hands of a nearby fielder.

At least, it would have taken it into the fielder's hands if he had been ready for it. But he was too busy dancing around and generally doing a rather good impression of an African tribal rain dancer to pay any attention to the ball.

Those of us sitting or standing watching at the boundary's edge were confused by what we saw. At first we thought that the fielder must have been stung by a bee or a wasp. Only a few moments later, when Dr Brownlow strolled rather guiltily to the boundary in search of safety pins, did we discover that the unfortunate fielder had, in fact, been hit by one of Dr Brownlow's shirt buttons. The effort of making such an athletic manoeuvre had proved too much for Dr Brownlow's elderly shirt and buttons had flown off in several random directions. As luck would have it the only fielder who was struck by one of these button bullets was the only one who had been in a position to catch the ball.

Dr Brownlow clearly regarded this escape as a sign from the gods that they were inclined to look favourably upon his batsmanship. He swung at every other ball he received and by the end of two overs had scored an astonishing 26 runs, 24 of them in boundaries. We thought that the fact that he didn't throw his bat at every ball he received meant that he was choosing the balls to attack but in fact he admitted later that on those occasions when he had not thrown his bat at the ball he had been merely recovering his breath and energy.

By the time the gods decided that Dr Brownlow had been

blessed enough he had been joined at the wicket by Frank Parsons and had helped to take our score to a quite remarkable 136 and his own personal score to a team best 42.

Frank only lasted three balls before being run out and Peter Marshall, who had followed him, lasted another over before being caught at the wicket. When Thumper Robinson, our number 11 batsman, strode out to the wicket to join Patchy Fogg, we had nine overs left and were just 45 runs short of our opponents' total. It didn't look as if we could win and it didn't look as if we would be likely to still be batting when we ran out of overs, but we were on top of the world. As Frank pointed out, we had almost become a cricket team.

What hope there was came from the fact that it was now almost pitch black and our opponents were having a terrible time keeping track of the ball. If Thumper and Patchy had been more skilled as batsmen then the fielders would have been able to judge the direction of the ball by watching their bodies and bats. But although both were playing well neither of them were particularly successful at controlling the direction of the ball. A firm, straight drive which should have sent the ball whizzing towards mid on or mid off would instead send the ball flying over the slips, soaring past square leg or bouncing into the covers. It is more difficult to field competently in the dark when even the batsman has absolutely no idea where the ball will go when it has been hit.

Things moved even further in our favour when the visitors lost their vice captain, who thought himself a real tough guy, in a collision with our oak tree, which didn't think of itself as anything very much but which turned out to be considerably tougher than the vice captain.

The vice captain had been running flat out after one of Thumper's drives and had run straight into the side of the tree. He regained consciousness quite soon after the collision but Dr Brownlow and I both felt that he needed to be X rayed at Barnstaple hospital and seen by a dentist. We picked up as many of his teeth as we could find, popped them into a plastic container full of milk and told him to give them to the doctors as soon as he arrived at the hospital.

By half past nine that evening the unthinkable had happened and the impossible had nearly happened: we needed just eleven runs to win and we had just six balls in which to score them. Thumper Robinson and Patchy Fogg were playing like giants and the fielding side was in total disarray.

But although we didn't get the runs we needed we went out fairly gloriously. Thumper walked down the pitch to drive the opposition bowler straight back over his head. He missed. The wicket keeper caught the ball and, without fuss, removed the bails. We had been dismissed just eleven runs short of the opposition's total.

Our opponents were so relieved about their win that they abandoned their puritanical training regime and bought alcohol with such enthusiasm that even Frank started smiling his approval. It was a cricket match worth remembering. The only pity is that most of the players had so much to drink that the following morning they could not remember whether they'd been playing cricket, croquet or ping pong.

* * *

CHAPTER EIGHTEEN

With just half an hour to go before the curtain went up on the Bilbury Revue even Thumper and I were as excited and jittery as seven year olds on Christmas Eve – and we weren't performing.

Mrs Riddle had insisted that everyone in any way involved with the revue should be at the village hall at least two hours before the show was due to begin. 'I don't want to be pacing about wondering where you are,' she told us all at the pre-performance briefing.

'And no calling in at the pub for a quick one!' she had added, sternly, and although I think she probably thought the use of the phrase 'quick one' made her look worldly-wise it did, in fact, show that she had little conception of what went on at the Duck and Puddle. I don't think any local had ever gone into Frank and Gilly's pub for a 'quick one'. If she'd really wanted to appear knowing she should have forbidden us all to go into the pub for a 'slow three or four'.

Mrs Riddle had insisted that alcohol would not be allowed backstage but had not allowed for the ingenuity of the hard drinking locals. Frank Parsons, the publican, had filled a two litre vacuum flask with hot mulled wine and had thrown half a dozen carrot slices into the brew so that anyone glancing at the mixture would assume that it was some sort of vegetable soup. Patchy Fogg had filled a Coca Cola bottle with Vodka and blackcurrant. Peter Marshall had hidden a pewter hip flask full of brandy in one of the secret pockets inside his jacket. And Thumper Robinson had stashed a bottle of red wine and a bottle of whisky behind a beam high above the stage.

'How big is the audience?' Patsy asked me, in a whisper. It was the fifth or sixth time she had asked the same question. Like the other members of the 'Bilbury Ladies Amateur Cancan and Exotic Dancing Troupe' Patsy had been dressed and fully made up for several hours. The Troupe's stage gear consisted of matching, pale pink swimming costumes (bought at what Peter Marshall insisted was cost price from the village shop), fishnet tights (most definitely not bought from Peter Marshall's shop since Peter had only recently recognised the invention of the ordinary silk stocking and would never have even contemplated the notion of selling such an indelicately natured article of female apparel), multi-petticoated cancan skirts (hired at enormous expense from a theatrical outfitters in Bristol) and exotic head- dresses (individually built by Kay McBride with materials supplied by Anthea Yarnold whose husband owned the 'Happy Chickens Lay Nicer Eggs' chicken farm just outside Bideford). Like the other five members of the troupe – Kay McBride, Anne Thwaites (Thumper Robinson's girlfriend), Gilly Parsons, landlady of the Duck and Puddle, Deidre Mulberry and Elspeth Nutcomb – Patsy was preserving her modesty and her body temperature for as long as possible by wearing a dressing gown over her costume.

Gingerly, I opened the door out into the main part of the hall and peered through the tiny gap that appeared between the hinge end of the door and the doorframe. I was getting quite good as this.

'It's nearly half full,' I told Patsy. I looked at my watch. 'And there's still twenty minutes to go!'

Patsy turned. 'Nearly half full!' she hissed to Kay, who was standing just behind her. Kay turned to pass the information on to those standing behind her and decided to economise on words. 'Nearly full!' I heard her whisper. Not surprisingly, this good news brought a murmur of approval from the other members of the Revue; most of whom had been ready to go on stage for at least an hour and were now beginning to feel rather fretful.

Mrs Riddle's requirement that they be at the village hall two hours before the curtain went up might have saved her from worry but it hadn't helped the performers. The greatest and most popular worry seemed to be that although all the tickets had been sold no one would turn up to watch the performance. Financially, the revue was already a great success. But to the performers, waiting back stage, the financial success of the event was not something which they regarded as a priority. For most, if not all of them, this was their first adventure in the world of show business and they were all looking forward to their moments of glory.

'I hope the weather stays nice,' said Anne Thwaites. 'If it rains people won't want to come out.'

'Well, I hope it's not too nice,' said Elspeth Nutcomb. 'If it's a lovely sunny evening people won't want to come and sit in a stuffy old village hall, will they?' Elspeth runs an animal sanctuary and years of frustration and disappointment have lined her face. In her spare time she is married to an insurance underwriter. He works in London during the week and comes home only at weekends. Surprisingly, they both seem happy with this arrangement.

'But surely they'll come if they've paid!' argued Deidre Mulberry, a divorcee with two children who thinks that accepting state help or alimony would be a sign of defeat and weakness, who keeps herself and children fed and clothed on what she earns by working as an occasional relief barmaid at the Duck and Puddle and who regards waste as the most heinous crime of all. Deidre cannot afford the bus fare into Barnstaple and so has to do all her shopping in the village. Because she can't afford Peter Marshall's prices she only ever buys stale bread and fruit and vegetables which are slightly past their best.

I borrowed a chipped china cup from the store cupboard, persuaded Frank to fill it with mulled wine from his flask, and passed the warming brew around the Revue members.

'Everything's going to be absolutely fine!' I promised them, without justification, as they sipped at Frank's wine. 'The audience will be marvellous and you'll be brilliant!'

Like all performers they accepted this fulsome praise without hesitation and settled down to try and relax. It was at least a minute and a half before Patsy asked me to check again on the size of the audience.

*　　*　　*

The waiting went on for so long that when the time came for the show to start no one was ready.

'Good luck, everybody!' said Mrs Riddle, after looking at

her watch so often that Frank had warned her that if she looked at it again it would wear out. She spoke in one of her now famous backstage whispers. I think she thought she was whispering but even when whispering her voice carried so well that villagers in Combe Martin would have had no difficulty in hearing her. Mrs Riddle herself was due to introduce the show and act as the compere. She was dressed in a pair of black tights and a black leotard, a white dress shirt, a black bow tie, a black tail coat and a pair of black, high heeled shoes. She wore a top hat on her head and carried a black, ebony walking cane.

'Oh, is it time for the show?' squeaked Miss Phillips. She sounded surprised, as though she and all the others had all gathered backstage for some other purpose entirely. She and Mrs Blossom were due to close the first half of the concert with a duet on the piano but they were still arguing about what to play. Mrs Blossom wanted to play something by Chopin whereas Miss Phillips had made no secret of the fact that she rather favoured a composition by Liszt.

'Oh, I must just spend a penny!' cried Kay McBride, darting into the ladies changing room and bolting the door behind her.

There was a chorus of 'me too's and 'me next's from the other female performers who, in true English fashion, quickly formed a neat queue. It wasn't a straight queue – there wasn't room – but everyone instinctively seemed to know who they followed. The male performers did not have to queue. Their lavatory was behind a hedge just outside the back door.

'Give it until quarter past,' suggested Thumper calmly to a suddenly distraught Mrs Riddle. He took his hand away from the switch with which he had been planning to extinguish the house lights and gave Mrs Riddle a comforting pat on the shoulder.

'People are still coming in!' I added. I watched as Patsy's parents took their seats. Patsy's father was wearing his Sunday best suit and had even shaved for the occasion. As for Patsy's mother, well it took me a few moments to recognise her. For a while I couldn't work out why she looked so different. Finally, I realised that it was the first time since our wedding that I had seen her without a pinafore on.

Looking around the audience it wasn't difficult to tell the locals from the visitors. The locals all wore their best clothes.

The men were pulling uncomfortably at shirt collars and ties and wriggling their shoulders in suits that were a size or two too small for them. Normally unkempt hair had been brushed, combed and cajoled into place with the aid of hair gel or water and feet which were accustomed to roaming free in wellington boots were universally imprisoned in once fashionable but hardly worn leather shoes. The women had all helped one another do their hair. And they all wore summer dresses that reminded me of clothes my mother had worn when I'd been a boy. Even the younger women wore slightly out of date clothes.

This final quarter of an hour didn't seem to last anywhere near fifteen minutes.

'Lights out, please, Thumper!' whispered Mrs Riddle.

Since they heard this at exactly the same moment as Thumper the audience fell silent a split second before the house lights went out.

'Curtain!' she whispered.

'Good luck! I whispered back, as I pulled on the rope which would open the curtain on my side of the stage. I watched Thumper's hand signals so that we could draw our curtains at the same time. We had practised this several times and were quite proud of our skill in this regard. Too late I remembered that Mrs Riddle had told us all that we weren't allowed to say 'Good luck!' to one another because it was considered unlucky in theatrical circles. 'Break a leg!' I added, remembering the old theatre saying that she had taught us, just a second or so too late.

Mrs Riddle had gone and was standing in the centre of the stage long before Thumper and I had finished opening the curtains. I thought the stage looked terrific. The silver painted hardboard reflected the light from the four Ford Cortina head-lamps which Thumper had fitted up as spotlights and the two artificial apple trees on either side of the stage gave the whole stage a suitably rural, albeit perhaps rather surrealistic, aspect. The children at the village school had, under Miss Hargreaves' expert tuition and supervision, made the leaves out of green crepe paper and the fruit out of clotted cream cartons, half of which had been painted red and half of which had been painted green. The piano which Mrs Blossom and Miss Phillips would use for their recital was at this stage disguised as a rock. At least it was supposed to be a rock but the grey paint which Thumper and I had used to cover the cardboard edifice which surrounded the piano looked rather white in the bright spotlights and during the interval there was much curiosity among the audience about the reason for the iceberg on the stage. It was, I gather, generally thought that it was considered to be an ironic reference to the North Devon weather.

'First of all I'd like to thank you for coming along to our first annual Revue,' began Mrs Riddle, startling those of us who had thought that this Revue was a one off production. She wore her hat at a rakish angle, leant on her cane as she spoke and radiated confidence. I'd never seen her look so calm or so comfortable. 'As you all know tonight's performance is for a wonderful cause and if you haven't done so already I hope you'll all buy programmes from two lovely young attendants.' Mrs Riddle waved a hand towards Jackie and Dawn Peters, fifteen year old twins who actually lived in Parracombe but who, when they had heard about the Revue, had come rushing over to offer their help. 'During the interval,' she went on, 'you'll be able to buy tea and scones at the back of the hall.'

She paused for a moment. 'And now, let the show commence!' she cried, waving her arms about enthusiastically. 'Our first performer is someone most of you know very well, though you might not have been aware that he had a hidden talent as a monologist!'

Someone nudged my elbow. I turned my head. It was Frank. 'Hold this for me!' he hissed, handing me his now almost empty vacuum flask.

'Ladies and gentlemen,' continued Mrs Riddle. 'Please welcome your local publican: Frank Parsons!' She took off her top hat and held it and her cane at arms length. There was a roar of approval from the audience which confirmed Frank's popularity and Mrs Riddle's good sense in choosing him to open the show.

At the dress rehearsal Frank had sped through his monologue (an old music hall favourite about a girl and a boy, a dog, a rowing boat and the girl's mother) so quickly that he hadn't been on stage for more than a minute or so and, therefore, my second job, after opening the curtains, was to remind him not to speak too quickly. I did this by simply muttering: 'Slow!' to him as he was about to stride out onto the stage.

The result was something of a modest misunderstanding for while Mrs Riddle strode daintily into the wings Frank moved much less daintily, and painfully slowly, towards the centre of the stage. For some reason he seemed to think that in addition to walking slowly he had to face the audience as he walked and this gave him a distinctive and rather crab like gait.

After arriving at the small chalk cross which marked the centre of the stage he stood there for a moment or two just peering into the darkness. For a moment I feared that he had forgotten his lines. But he hadn't. He was simply doing his best to obey the instruction he had been given. Miss Johnson, the Revue's official wardrobe mistress, had chosen to dress him in Austrian lederhosen, complete with a green chiffon blouse with bouffant sleeves and a pair of long grey socks borrowed from Patchy Fogg, who had once been a boy scout. Frank had at first been reluctant to dress in such a flamboyant manner but somehow Mrs Riddle and Miss Johnson had managed to persuade him that making a complete and utter fool of himself was an unavoidable part of show business. I had asked Miss Johnson why she'd chosen the Austrian national costume of lederhosen for Frank, a traditional English publican who was, after all, reciting a nineteenth century Victorian monologue. She had explained that she's found them in a pile of old clothing donated to the last church jumble sale. When I pointed out that although this was an answer it wasn't really an explanation she had just smiled rather sweetly and told me that she thought someone ought to wear them and that they fitted Frank almost perfectly. There had been much discussion about whether or not Frank should shave his legs but it was quite clear that the final decision had come down against shaving.

I suspect that when Mrs Riddle had said she she wanted him to deliver his monologue more slowly she had meant that she wanted him to deliver the whole thing at a steadier pace. This was not, however, the way that Frank interpreted the instruction. He delivered each line as rapidly as he had done during the rehearsal but at the end of each line he paused for what seemed to be a good chunk of eternity, though it was probably no more than half a minute at a time. It is true that this had the effect of slowing down the overall pace at which the monologue was delivered but it also had the effect of rather disrupting the flow of the story. By the time he began a new line the audience had largely forgotten what the previous line had been about.

Still, none of this mattered for the audience hadn't come to listen to a rather dated monologue they'd come to watch Frank deliver it. And when he finally finished they cheered and clapped enthusiastically. I hadn't heard such cheering since I'd been at school and a visiting speaker had given us all an extra half day's holiday. This wasn't the sort of polite clapping sound you get when people clap their hands as if they are praying, or tap the fingers of one hand on the palm of the other; this was the much louder sort of clapping you get when people slam their palms together and produce great resounding, echoing claps.

Frank had been nervous beforehand but when he heard the audience's response he didn't want to leave the stage. He would have probably still been there if Mrs Riddle hadn't marched out, thanked him and escorted him back into the wings. I drew the curtains and was proud to be the first to shake Frank by the hand. He was perspiring heavily but beaming broadly and looked justifiably pleased with himself.

After that tremendous start the concert went swimmingly. Patchy Fogg rode his monocycle round and round in circles for twelve and a half minutes. The audience got a little restless after the first minute, and to be perfectly honest I rather think that some of them might have expected Patchy to do more than just ride his monocycle round and round in rather erratic circles, but they were far too polite to do anything but applaud him enthusiastically when he finally got dizzy and crashed into the cardboard rock (or iceberg) which was disguising the piano. This was not an evening for criticism. Besides, everyone had to admit that Patchy had cleaned and greased his machine assiduously and it positively sparkled in the glare of the Ford Cortina headlamps.

The Hewitt children did their tap dancing routine (and although I have never been an aficionado of tap dancing even I had to admit that it sounded much better and looked far more impressive when they did it with their shoes on than it had when they had practised in their stockinged feet) and seemed not in the slightest bit distracted by the fact that throughout their performance their father danced around in front of the stage taking photographs.

(Mr Hewitt, by profession a sewage consultant, had appointed himself our official photographer and had come to the Revue equipped with two boxes of flashbulbs and six rolls of 36 exposure film. A week after the concert he got his films back from the developer and proudly displayed the results on the walls of the village hall. Of the 216 pictures he took 187 were of his tap dancing children. There were some in the village who felt that as official photographer Mr Hewitt had provided a rather unbalanced historical record of the evening. This view was held most strongly by those members of the troupe who did not appear at all in any of Mr Hewitt's photographs.)

After the Hewitt children came the vicar.

Mr Riddle had been planning to juggle with three old tennis balls which Miss Johnson had painted red, green and yellow, but the day before the concert he injured himself when the church bell rope on which he was pulling snapped back rather suddenly and unexpectedly. Bravely insisting that the show must go on, he ignored his sprained wrist and performed half his juggling act with enviable panache. He couldn't manage three balls with one arm in a sling, of course, and there had been a serious discussion before he went on stage about which ball he should leave out of his act. He originally planned to leave the yellow ball behind and to juggle with the red and green balls but Miss Johnson said she thought that the yellow and the green would look best and that he should leave the red ball behind. Mrs Riddle said she thought that red and yellow would look rather nice together and that he should allow the green ball to 'rest'. In the end the vicar, Mrs Riddle and Miss Johnson had decided on a compromise. And so for the first two minutes of his spot the vicar juggled with the red and green balls; for the second two minutes he juggled with the red and yellow balls; and for the finale he brought back the green ball and rested the red ball.

'What did you think of the vicar's act?' I asked Patsy's father after the show.

'I've never seen a one armed juggler before,' my father in law replied, laconically. 'So I haven't anything to compare it with. But the balls were very pretty.'

And I don't think anyone would have disagreed with him. There was back stage controversy too before Miss Phillips and Mrs Blossom went on to bring the first Act to a close. They had been arguing about which piece to play for days and with just minutes to go their argument did not seem any closer to resolution. After the vicar had left the stage and Thumper and I had closed the curtains he and I rushed out to remove the piano's disguise and to push the instrument into the centre of the stage. We then added two piano stools and exited rapidly. At this point I realised that Miss Phillips and Mrs Blossom, who were on my side of the stage, were still arguing about what to play. Mrs Blossom still wanted to play the Chopin. Miss Phillips still insisted that they should play the Liszt. I was tempted to tell them that I didn't think that anyone would know the difference and that the audience would probably prefer a Russ Conway tune anyway. I looked across at Thumper and then at Mrs Riddle. She seemed surprisingly calm as she gave Thumper and I the signal to open the curtains. Then, as the curtains drew (smoothly) back she strode out onto the stage and announced that Miss Phillips and Mrs Blossom would close the first Act by playing a piece by Brahms. As she came off the stage she smiled sweetly at the two duelling pianists. They glowered at her but had little option but to go on and play something by Brahms. This they duly did.

*   *   *

During the interval while Mrs Hewitt (mother of the Hewitt children and wife of their doting father) and Jackie and Dawn Peters from Parracombe fulfilled Mrs Riddle's promise and sold scones and tea at the back of the hall we all huddled together behind the stage and told each other how wonderfully well we thought it was going.

The performers who had performed had relaxed a little and were desperate to hear how well they'd done. I was quickly to discover that people who have been on stage will believe anything you tell them – as long as it is complimentary. There was more performing going on back stage than there had been on stage.

'How was I?' asked the normally urbane Patchy Fogg. 'Do you think they liked it?'

'You were terrific. They loved you.'

'Do you really think so? That's very kind of you. You're not just saying that, are you?'

'No, of course not!' I replied.

'You would tell me the truth wouldn't you?'

'Yes, of course!' I lied.

Frank sidled over to me. His flask had been emptied long ago but he had sent Miss Johnson back to the Duck and Puddle for a refill and he was now half way through the second quart of his special recipe mulled wine.

'What did you think?'

'I think the whole show is going very well,' I replied, knowing very well that he didn't want to know what I thought about the whole show.

'Er, what did you, er, think about, er, my, er, little bit?'

'Oh, *your* bit?'

'Er, yes. What did you think?'

I put my hand on his shoulder. He visibly blanched, expecting the worst.

'I thought you were sensational, Frank.'

His face lit up. And then a slightly worried look appeared. 'You're not just saying that?'

I tried to look hurt that he should even think this of me. 'Of course not! You were absolutely fantastic. Couldn't you tell? The audience loved you.' I stared down at his hairy legs and knobbly knees. 'Aren't you going to get changed?'

'Mrs Riddle wants us to stay in costume for the final curtain,' he told me. I rather thought that he was pleased of this excuse to make sure that the moments of glory lasted as long as possible. He spotted Pauline Peterson, in charge of make up, excused himself and hurried across to ask her to check his rouge, eyeshadow and lipstick. Pauline's first attempt at stage make up had been quietly restrained but Mrs Riddle had persuaded her that in making up a stage artiste the key criterion is not the skill with which the make up is applied but the quantity of powder, paint and lipstick which is applied. Pauline had taken this lesson to heart and had used up two lipsticks already.

The performers who had done their routines might still be

just slightly edgy but they were definitely less tense than those Bilburian performers who hadn't yet been on stage.

Five of the six members of 'The Bilbury Ladies Amateur Cancan And Exotic Dancing Troupe', due to open the second half, were in an absolutely terrible state. Kay McBride kept rushing around telling everyone who would listen (and, for that matter, those who wouldn't) that she'd been to the lavatory at least twenty times. Anne and Patsy were sat huddled together in a corner, shivering despite their dressing gowns. Two of the others, Deidre Mulberry and Elspeth Nutcomb, had not yet re-emerged from the changing room and ladies' cloakroom wherein they had been securely locked for the whole of the first half of the Revue.

Gilly Parsons, the sixth member of 'The Bilbury Ladies Amateur Cancan And Exotic Dancing Troupe', had loyally watched her husband's stage debut from what Mrs Riddle tried to persuade us to call the wings but what the rest of us, through habit rather than stubbornness, still tended to call the side of the stage, and had stayed there to watch the rest of the show. As the only performer to have seen the whole of the first half she was much in demand for approving comments and repeated requests for praise had led her to produce the sort of super-latives for which West End producers would have sacrificed their souls.

'You were out of this world!' I heard her tell Patchy Fogg, the erratic monocyclist, just as Mrs Riddell announced, in her now familiar stage whisper, that it was time for the second half of the show to begin.

*   *   *

I realise that I may be accused of bias but in my view 'The Bilbury Ladies Amateur Cancan And Exotic Dancing Troupe' were truly sensational. I hadn't seen anything like it since Horace Inchmore and I got lost in Amsterdam when we were fourth year medical students.

During the dress rehearsal I had been busy helping Thumper paint the artificial rock (or iceberg) and so I hadn't seen the Troupe in their costumes until they went on stage. Nor had I seen them perform any of their numbers. Patsy hadn't let me see her when she tried on her costume on home. She said that it would be unlucky. I said I thought it was only brides who had to keep their dress secret. Patsy said that the same rule applied to exotic dancers.

Their act began with a traditional heart-stopping cancan number and I was glad of the fact that Dr Brownlow was in the audience for when the six women started kicking their legs and waving their petticoats in the air I became quite genuinely concerned that members of the audience might start collapsing. I rather suspect that if the show hadn't been organised by the vicar's wife who was, ex-officio, president of the Bilbury Wives' Group it might have been banned by the village elders. There was some consternation among the visually less acute members of the audience when, inspired by the fact that they were wearing pink swimming costumes, a whispered rumour started that none of the women were wearing anything underneath their petticoats. Mr Horace Halifax, a retired stockbroker who had seen the cancan performed in Paris in the 1920s, told everyone who would listen to him that cancan dancers never did wear underwear and a little wishful thinking did the rest.

After the cancan the Troupe performed what Kay announced was a rare formation tango and entertained us with a flamenco dance (complete with clicking fingers). They then finished off with another rendition of France's favourite dance.

The enthusiastic applause was accompanied and punctuated by loud cries of approval, most of which seemed to emanate from a group of teenage youths from Ilfracombe. There was no doubt at all that Patsy and the other girls had been the hit of the evening.

Megan Underwood, curiously billed on the programme as 'The Sensational Singing Soprano', was the next act and it was difficult not to feel sorry for her. Following 'The Bilbury Ladies Amateur Cancan And Exotic Dancing Troupe' cannot have been easy.

However, Megan, who once sang professionally in a Welsh pop group called 'The Psychedelic Mushrooms', did not appear to be in the slightest bit overawed by the success of the dancers. Wearing a floor length evening dress in bottle green satin, and accompanied by Mrs Blossom on the piano, she sang three songs, 'Oh Come All Ye Faithful', 'Give Us A Kiss For Christmas' and 'White Christmas', and by the finish she had the audience tapping their feet and humming along with her. Mrs Riddle had tried to persuade her that her choice of songs was hardly appropriate for a mid summer festival but Miss Underwood had at first insisted that these were her favourite tunes and eventually admitted that they were, in fact, the only three songs to which she knew the words.

It was during the first few verses of 'Oh Come All Ye Faithful' that I first realised that there was a problem with the lights.

* * *

The Bilbury Village Hall is normally lit by two 100 watt light bulbs though during a single six month spell a year or two ago, when the Parish Council had badly misjudged its financial commitments and every aspect of community living had been subjected to a fairly vicious economy drive, the hall had actually been lit by nothing more enlightening than two 40 watt light bulbs. Naturally, Mrs Riddle wanted her performers to be lit with rather more enthusiasm than this meagre allotment could provide and so, as I have already explained, Thumper had cleverly lit the stage with four old headlamps powered by a motor car battery. The battery was on the far side of the stage so that Thumper, when not busy closing or opening his half of the curtains, could control the lights by the simple expedient of removing the clip from the battery's positive terminal.

Thumper had expected the battery he had acquired to last throughout the performance but it was clear that his expectations were not going to be fulfilled. I looked across the stage. Thumper was looking back towards me. I looked up at the lights. Thumper looked up at the lights and nodded. Unless the rest of the concert was going to be completed in steadily growing darkness we clearly had to do something. And we had to do it fast. We had to find a new battery and somehow we had to get the new battery across to Thumper's side of the stage. The leads from the four lights were tacked to the beams above the stage and only reached as far as the window sill on the far side of the stage. It was on the window sill that the fading battery stood. Thumper's first problem was that he had somehow got to get from his side of the stage to my side of the stage. He couldn't wait until Megan finished her act and he certainly couldn't just stroll across the stage while she was singing. He looked up, looked across at me and smiled, and then, with a casual shrug, using window, curtains, ropes and everything else he could grab hold of, managed to pull himself up onto the beam above the stage upon which the four fading car headlamps were anchored. He then performed what I can only describe as the most daring and impressive feat of beam walking that I have ever witnessed. Although he was walking in darkness, his path lit only by a feeble glow from the backs of the tethered headlamps, he was clearly visible to the audience and after a moment or two of fairly heavy nudging I think that just about everyone in the room except Megan Underwood was aware of what was going on above her head.

It took Thumper no more than a single verse of 'Oh Come All Ye Faithful' to get across the beam and another verse to clamber down the ropes and curtains and pillar on my side of the stage. He put his hand on my shoulder, grinned at me, and motioned for me to follow him. Loyally, I did so.

A few seconds later we were standing in the small car park outside the back of the village hall. It was a beautiful, balmy evening and although it was after half past nine it was not yet completely dark.

'Whose is that?' demanded Thumper, pointing to a brand new and rather smart looking German car whose owner had ignored the huge notice asking motorists not to block the hall's rear exit with their cars. The car, a large, silver grey, expensive looking model, had been abandoned rather than parked.

I shrugged. I didn't have the faintest idea whose it was.

Thumper poked a stick through the car's radiator grill and fiddled about for a moment or two. A few seconds later the bonnet clicked open.

Thumper and I arrived back in the hall, carrying a replacement car battery, just as Megan Underwood was launching into her final song, a tearful and emotional rendition of the Bing Crosby classic 'White Christmas'. When I heard the words I couldn't help thinking of that terrible night when Miss Hargreaves' cottage had lost its roof and Ben had saved my life. It occurred to me that it was, after all, a rather apt song under the circumstances. The rapidly fading car headlights meant that Megan completed the song in a rather romantic half light.

'I can't carry the battery up by myself,' whispered Thumper. 'So I'll go up and let down a piece of rope and you then tie the battery to the end of the rope. I'll pull the battery up, carry it across the beam, lower it down the other side and connect the lights. Simple!'

It sounded simple.

But as they always do when they sound that simple things went wrong right from the start.

To begin with I couldn't find anywhere on the battery to fasten the rope. I had to borrow Miss Johnson's capacious handbag, tie the handbag to the rope, put the battery in the bag and then get Thumper to haul up the bag and the battery. Then, when he had got the bag and the battery in his arms Thumper nearly fell off the beam and almost dropped the battery down onto the stage. It would have missed Megan's head but it would have almost certainly spoilt her big finale. He put the bag and the battery down on the beam and tied the rope with which he had hauled them up firmly around his waist. I wondered at the wisdom of this for it seemed to me that it meant that if he dropped the battery he would fall with it. I didn't fancy the idea of being promoted to full stage manager with such little experience.

It was only when Megan curtsied to the audience and they applauded that it occurred to me that since she was finishing her spot we needed to draw the curtains across the stage so that we could get things ready for the next act – billed on the programme as 'Peter Marshall's Astonishing Conjuring Tricks'! At the same moment it also rather belatedly occurred to me that if we were drawing the curtains then Thumper didn't need to risk life and limb carrying the heavy car battery across a narrow beam twelve feet above the stage.

Sadly, however, this thought did not occur to Thumper.

I looked up and tried to catch his eye but it was far too late for he had already begun to make his way along the beam. The audience, spotting him, were quickly distracted from what was going on in front of them on the stage and their applause for the 'Sensational Singing Soprano' faded away as their hands reached up to cover their mouths. Thumper was rapidly becoming the evening's main attraction.

'I love the way Thumper has dimmed the lights!' whispered

Mrs Riddle behind me. I turned round. The vicar's wife, top hat in hand, was smiling at me. 'Marvellously evocative!' she murmured. 'How did he do it?'

I opened my mouth to explain but the vicar's wife noticed that Megan had come running off into the wings, leaving the stage quite deserted. 'Shouldn't you draw the curtains?' she asked me, in a throaty whisper which probably resulted in citizens from Ilfracombe to Lynton leaping up from their armchairs and drawing their curtains.

I said that I would happily draw my curtain but that we would have to wait for Thumper to cross the stage before his curtain could be drawn.

Mrs Riddle looked puzzled.

I pointed upwards, at the wobbling figure of our stage manager.

'What on earth is he carrying?' asked Mrs Riddle.

'A car battery,' I replied.

'It looks more like a handbag!'

'Well, the car battery is in the handbag. The handbag belongs to Miss Johnson.'

'Ah!' said Mrs Riddle, as though this made it all clear and it was the most natural thing in the world for a stage manager to be doing. She frowned and thought about what I'd said for a moment or two. 'Why?' she asked.

I explained about the floodlights.

'Aha!' said Mrs Riddle.

'Shall I draw my curtain?' I asked.

'No,' said Mrs Riddle, vehemently shaking her head. 'We'll have to wait until Thumper can draw his curtain as well.' She turned round, reached out and caught hold of Megan Underwood by the arm. 'Go back on!' she hissed. 'Do an encore!'

Megan, who was already accepting congratulations from Anne and Kay of 'The Bilbury Ladies Amateur Cancan And Exotic Dancing Troupe' looked thoroughly startled. 'An encore?'

'Sing another song!'

'But they've stopped clapping!'

'It doesn't matter!' insisted Mrs Riddle. 'Just go out there and sing something else.'

Confused but obedient Megan headed back out onto the

stage but stopped after two or three paces and turned back, bumping into Mrs Blossom, who was trotting back towards the piano. 'I don't know any more songs,' said Megan anxiously.

'Do 'White Christmas' again! They loved that one.'

I looked up. Thumper had reached the far end of the beam and was gingerly lowering the car battery down onto the bar. Now that this additional piece of entertainment was almost over the audience was getting restless.

And so, while Thumper first lowered the bag and the battery down to the ground and then clambered down after them Mrs Blossom and Megan Underwood launched into another rousing version of 'White Christmas'. The audience, slightly surprised but quite uncomplaining, hummed along with, or almost with, the tune. Half way through the song the spot lights went out for a moment and then came back on again, much brighter, as Thumper swapped the batteries over. When it looked as though Megan was about to finish her encore Thumper and I both drew our curtains so speedily that the unfortunate soprano suddenly found herself singing the last few seconds of her final note to an extensive but unresponsive patch of curtain material. As she staggered off stage exhausted Thumper walked across carrying the completely dead battery. He put it down on the floor on my side of the stage and winked at me. 'Pop that into the car we took the other one from, would you?'

*   *   *

It took Thumper and I a couple of minutes to get everything ready for Peter's magic act. As we hurried around turning the piano back into a rock and dragging surprisingly heavy equipment into position Peter scurried about hiding playing cards, eggs, stuffed rabbits and other bits and pieces of magical miscellanea around the stage.

'Where did you get all this stuff from?' I had asked Peter before the dress rehearsal, as I had helped him carry his disappearing lady cabinet onto the stage.

'I bought it all at an auction,' he had told me. 'It was very cheap.'

'Were there any instructions with it?'

Peter shook his head. 'I still haven't worked out how to use it all yet,' he confessed. 'I can make the stuffed bunny disappear but I don't always get the same one back again.'

I had asked him how long he'd had it all but he said he couldn't really remember. He said he was pretty sure that he thought he'd probably bought it sometime during the sixties, though it could have been during the fifties. I hadn't pressed him for a more precise answer. I found his answer strangely satisfying. I have always found it immensely dispiriting when I find someone who can tell me exactly what they were doing for lunch on March 22nd 1968.

Eventually, with everything in place, Thumper and I told Peter that we hoped he broke a leg and then we left him to face his audience.

Things went wrong right from the start.

Encouraged and advised by Mrs Riddle, Peter had decided to begin his act with the card trick which required the participation of a member of the audience. 'It'll get them interested, make them feel they're part of the act,' she had told him.

And so as the curtains drew back Peter was standing at the front of the stage with a pack of cards in his hand and a huge, patently false smile on his face. His black hair was slicked down with copious quantities of grease and he wore the sequin studded bottle green jacket and the floppy bow tie which I had first seen him wearing at the dress rehearsal and the sequin starred grey flannels which Miss Johnson had been working on when Thumper had had his accident with the silver paint. The trousers still had a streak of silver paint across the back of one leg. Most impressive of all, however, was the fact that Peter had put in his best teeth especially for the occasion. Having been bought from a house auction in Bideford and made for a seventy year old woman with an overhanging bite these did not fit particularly well but they were unstained and reflected the bright lights perfectly.

Mrs Riddle's idea had been that Peter would stand at the front of the stage and invite a member of the audience to join him and take a card from the pack he was holding. What Mrs Riddle hadn't allowed for was the fact that most of the people in the audience knew Peter and were genuinely worried that if they went up on stage under the pretext of selecting a card they would end up buying a wooden handle for a garden rake, a two gallon drum of tractor oil or a sack of only very slightly mouldy dog biscuits. None of these purchases would, they knew, be in any way dependent upon whether or not they owned a garden rake with a broken handle, a tractor or a dog. Peter's ability to sell out of date or entirely worthless commodities to people who wouldn't have needed them even if they had been brand new, best quality and bottom price was the subject of gossip and rumour throughout the West Country, and had been for several decades.

When the audience showed that they were reluctant to wander up onto the stage Peter decided that if the mountain wasn't going to come to the prophet then the prophet would have to swallow his pride and make the first move. So he jumped down off the stage and onto the wooden steps which I had found in the store cupboard and which we had carefully pushed into position the day before.

Afterwards Peter claimed that the steps collapsed because the wood was rotten. Thumper and I both claimed that it was his fault for jumping down onto them far too heavily. 'They were only wooden steps,' insisted Thumper, without even a hint of a smile. 'You have to treat wood with respect.'

'What stupid fool put those old steps in front of the stage?' demanded Patsy's father afterwards. 'They were thrown out years ago. They're riddled with woodworm.' I bought him a large drink at the Duck and Puddle and swore him to silence.

Whatever the cause the consequence was that Peter went crashing into a pile of splintered firewood, the playing cards were scattered far and wide and I suddenly felt terribly guilty for telling him that I hoped he broke his leg. For a brief moment I had an awful thought that he might have done just that.

Peter made a brave attempt to shrug the fall off as part of the act but his nonchalance was not convincing. Once the audience could see that he was not hurt their shock quickly turned into sniggers and their sniggers then duly grew into laughter. That was really when Peter lost control and he never looked like getting back in charge again after that. Red-faced and breathing heavily he spent a few moments scrabbling around in the wreckage of the steps looking for the playing cards which he had dropped before he abandoned this and climbed back upon the stage to resume his act.

But he had, not surprisingly I suppose, lost his confidence and after that terrible beginning things went rapidly downhill. The pink rabbits wouldn't disappear, the chiffon scarves came out of the back of his neck in a large, messy clump and the invisible glass shelf fell out of the bottom of his bottomless bucket and shattered on the stage.

Things got worse when he reached what was supposed to be the penultimate high point of his act – the sawing of the lady in half.

The glamorous but nervous eighteen year old chemist's assistant from Barnstaple had run out of the back of the hall in her swimming costume and a pair of borrowed six inch high heeled shoes less than ten minutes before she was due to make her stage debut and poor old Miss Johnson, my former receptionist, was press-ganged into acting as substitute. Unfortunately, Miss Johnson was rather broader beamed and less supple than the chemist's assistant and she couldn't pull her legs into the top half of the box. Her screams and waving arms alerted Peter to the fact that things weren't going quite right and he abandoned this trick before any permanent damage was done.

Peter's final trick, his pièce de resistance, was a disappearing lady trick which involved the use of a wardrobe shaped piece of equipment which had a false back and a trap door in the bottom. When performed properly the trick involved getting a pretty young woman to walk into the wardrobe and then apparently stand quite still while the magician thrust sharp swords through parts of her body. The woman would, of course, be standing in the back half of the wardrobe, well away from the swords, and for the finale she would disappear down through the trap door in the bottom of the wardrobe and through a matching trap door in the stage so that she could startle, amaze and astonish the audience by reappearing from the side of the stage.

Peter's problem was that the village hall stage didn't have a trap door and neither the vicar nor the Village Hall Committee would give us permission to make one. They said it would be a possible health hazard to visiting dignitaries but Thumper and I decided that what they really meant was that it would be a dignity hazard and that no local politician would dare stand on the stage lest some local prankster should be tempted to crawl underneath the stage and open the trapdoor.

So Peter had persuaded Jackie and Dawn Peters, the twins from Parracombe, to help him with the trick. The idea was that Jackie, dressed in a pale blue swimming costume, a pair of her mother's tights and a pair of borrowed high heeled shoes, would climb into the wardrobe, wriggle through into the back section and stay there until the end of the show. Then, at the appropriate signal from Peter, Dawn, dressed in a similarly coloured swimming costume, another pair of tights and another pair of borrowed high heeled shoes, would amaze everyone by running up the centre of the hall.

It wasn't Peter's fault that this apparently simple trick went wrong.

Dawn, standing waiting at the back of the hall had started to shiver (though it was thought later that this was more likely to be a result of nerves than the temperature) and had borrowed a bright red, knee length anorak from her friend Cheryl. In all the excitement she forgot to take off the anorak when Peter gave her the signal she had been waiting for and she headed up towards the stage.

The audience was, not surprisingly, very confused when, after watching Peter shut a girl wearing a pale blue swimming costume into a wardrobe a girl wearing a red anorak ran up the centre of the hall. They watched, in mystified silence, as Dawn ran up onto the stage and stood alongside Peter in the way they had rehearsed. Dawn even remembered to smile and to hold her arms aloft in the way that Mrs Riddle had taught her. The audience, wondering what was going to happen next, remained silent.

When Peter, furious that even this moment of glory had been denied to him, hissed 'Take that thing off' and Dawn, shocked, started to back away from him the audience began to titter. When Peter, furious now, started to chase a squealing Dawn around the stage in an attempt to remove the red anorak from her and to prove to the audience that even if Dawn was not the very same girl as the one who had been locked in the wardrobe she was a pretty good imitation and that even if a standing ovation would be too much to ask for he was due a few cheers, the titters grew louder. Things got even worse when Jackie, who

240

was still locked in the back section of the wardrobe, and who was alarmed by the squeals which her sister was making, tried to get out, found that she couldn't and suddenly started to panic.

It was then, with Peter chasing the squealing Dawn around the stage and Jackie banging on the inside of the wardrobe and shouting for help, that the replacement car battery, which had been providing the power for the lights, inexplicably and without warning stopped working. The inevitable result was that the entire stage was suddenly plunged into darkness.

And it was at that point that Peter sat down on the stage and started to cry.

It was generally agreed by the company that Mrs Riddle's presence of mind in borrowing a small torch from Patchy Fogg and using it to lead Mrs Blossom out onto the stage and across, round and through the wreckage so that she could round the evening off with something jolly on the piano showed enormous presence of mind.

When they heard the haunting strains of the title tune from 'The Sound of Music' and saw Mrs Blossom, lit only by a small torch beam, enthusiastically banging away at the keys of a piano disguised as a rock (or possibly an iceberg), the audience began to applaud and stamp to their feet and to cheer as though they had never before seen anything quite so funny. Peter's disaster had become the hit of the evening.

*   *   *

CHAPTER NINETEEN

Despite the dramas which had brought the evening to a rather noisy and slightly premature close it was generally agreed that the first night of the first Bilbury Revue had been a resounding success (although there was one member of the audience who did not have a smile on his face when he left – the owner of the vehicle who had unknowingly donated his battery to the cause was not well pleased when his expensive foreign motor car would not start).

Even poor old Peter Marshall, quite exhausted by his ordeal, had quickly regained his enthusiasm when he had found himself surrounded by enthusiastic fans insisting that his comedy magic show was one of the funniest things they had ever seen.

Mrs Riddle was quite prepared to change the nature of her show to satisfy the demands of the public. 'I want you to do everything just the same tomorrow night,' she had told him. 'Don't change a thing!'

Thumper and I were instructed to reconstruct a collapsible staircase and when Dawn and Julie flatly refused to have anything further to do with Peter's act (and were only persuaded to carry on selling scones and tea during the interval when they were promised that Peter would not go anywhere near either of them) Mrs Riddle persuaded Patchy Fogg to dress up in Mrs Blossom's best swimming costume and to agree to be locked in Peter Marshall's wardrobe while Frank from the Duck and Puddle was somehow talked into running up to the stage wearing Mrs Blossom's second best swimming costume. It was agreed that since Patchy and Frank bore absolutely no resemblance to one another the red anorak would not be a necessary prop.

There was never any doubt that the Bilbury Revue was an

enormous financial success. The quite surprisingly substantial income from the modest admission charge had been more than doubled by the income from the sale of scones and cups of tea, from the sale of programmes and from a modest charge made for storing people's summer coats and hats on pegs at the back of the hall. At the end of that first evening Mrs Riddle announced that we had collected a quite magnificent £327.45 towards the Bilbury Village School Cottage Rebuilding Fund.

But despite all the excitement generated by the Revue (and it is, I think, fair to say that the whole village was enthralled by its first venture into show business) life in Bilbury still had to go on.

The following morning, after I'd fed Ben, the cats, the sheep (five of them now, of course) and myself, Patsy and I and Mr Parfitt went down to the vegetable garden to choose the vegetables and flowers that we would enter for the Bilbury Village Produce Show. Miss Hargreaves, carrying a stout basket, came with us to help pick and carry the selected items.

We had been keeping a careful eye on the best of our produce in each category but, inevitably, some of the most promising looking vegetables, fruit and flowers had either gone past their best or had been eaten by slugs or birds. Our only consolation was that all the other entrants would be facing the same frustrations and disappointments.

After we had made our selections for each class I left Patsy, Mr Parfitt and Miss Hargreaves busy in the kitchen getting the entries ready for the Show and I took my pen and notebook down to the summerhouse to do a little more work on the novel I was writing.

I had a room in the house which I used as a study but I found it much easier to work well away from distractions such as the telephone and the doorbell. One or two people I knew in London had telephone answering machines to protect them from irritating or disturbing calls but even if I had been able to afford one of these devices I doubt if I would have been able to buy one without a trip to Bristol, or maybe Exeter. Besides, a telephone answering machine would not have provided me with any protection against casual callers.

Since I had moved to Bilbury I had acquired quite a number

of good friends – people who I trusted, respected and liked a great deal.

When I had been at medical school, or working in hospital as a junior doctor, I had met lots of people but somehow none of those acquaintanceships had gone on to turn into fully fledged friendships. I suppose part of the problem was the fact that at a medical school or in a hospital everyone was always rushing to be somewhere else. And even when there weren't any immediate pressures to be doing something else acquaintanceships were put under tremendous pressure by the demands of personal and professional ambition.

In Bilbury people had time to develop friendships; time to listen to one another and time to share personal hopes and fears and aspirations. Living in a fairly remote village one soon learns to accept that having a roof, a fire, some warm clothes and enough to eat are really the only material essentials for a comfortable life. When I'd lived in a city I had found myself under constant pressure to conform to the city dweller's restless urge to find something better to do and to find somewhere more important or more interesting to be. I never found that lifestyle comfortable or satisfying and I much preferred the simpler life in Bilbury.

Surrounded by friends like Thumper, Patchy, Frank and Gilly and Dr Brownlow I found it comforting to know that Patsy and I were not alone. We were not fighting life by ourselves but as part of a community; a large and loving family. It was reassuring to know that if ever I or Patsy were in trouble we would have friends we would be able to call upon for help. In Bilbury I had learned that real wealth is measured in friendships not in television sets, jewellery, motor cars or expensive clothes.

The only problem was that, as I have already explained, I soon found that working at home and being surrounded by good friends were mutually incompatible. Patsy and I rarely locked our doors (and when we did it was more because we wanted some privacy or some warning of a visitor's arrival than because we were worried about being burgled) and if I was working in the house I would often look up from my desk and find myself staring at a grinning Thumper or Patchy.

The business of writing involves a lot more sitting and doing nothing than actually scribbling things down on bits of paper and my visitor would usually mutter something like: 'Glad you aren't doing anything' or 'Pleased to see you aren't busy' before offering me a chance to do something far more enjoyable than stare at a wall and a ream of blank paper.

So, to protect myself and to prevent myself succumbing to the temptations offered by my friends, I had taken to writing in a small, wooden summer house which we had uncovered in a quiet part of the garden. Surrounded in summer by a sea of glorious poppies the summerhouse provided privacy and peace and although the constantly active birds and frogs and rabbits tended to distract me I did manage to get more work done there than I did in the house. I sat there in a deckchair with my notebook on my knee, a straw hat on my head to shade my eyes and Ben lying at my feet. It wasn't a bad workplace.

The novel was growing at quite a decent rate and I had already filled a notebook and a half but I had hit one problem: the characters seemed to have taken on lives of their own. Although I had made plans for them, and had, when I had started the book, thought I had known what was going to happen, they seemed quite determined to control their own destinies. I had not expected this. Each morning I would start work thinking that I knew what was going to happen next. But within twenty minutes or so I would have to abandon my so carefully plotted story outline and allow the characters (I quickly gave up thinking of them as *my* characters) to take charge of their own lives.

Having had no previous experience of writing fiction I wasn't quite sure whether this was normal or not. At first I was peeved when, one after another, my carefully constructed story lines had to be abandoned and the characters who I thought I had invented ungratefully refused to utter the neatly honed phrases I had devised for them. For a while I fought hard to impose my will. But when I tried to get heavy handed the characters, who had by now established strong personalities of their own, stubbornly refused to cooperate and I began to find myself writing in circles.

When I eventually gave up battling and decided to let the characters speak for themselves and to allow the plot to unfold without any interference from me I found the business of

writing fiction far easier and much less exhausting. The one
enormous and entirely unexpected advantage of allowing the
characters to decide what happened was that instead of the
writing being a struggle I found that I was enjoying it as much
as if someone else had written it and I was reading it.

On the morning after the first night of the Bilbury Revue I
worked for about three hours (the longest length of time I
found I could write without a break) and then went up to the
house to help Patsy finish off her preparations for the Bilbury
Village Produce Show.

*   *   *

Mrs Blossom and Miss Phillips had, in the end, produced a list
of nearly a hundred different entry classes for the Show.

There were five main categories: Vegetables, Flowers, Domestic, Men and Children. Each entry cost one penny and the
first, second and third in each class would receive certificates
(described on the official programme as 'suitable for framing').
The certificates, like the Village Produce Show and Bilbury
Revue programmes had all been printed at cost price by a
jobbing printer in Barnstaple who owed Thumper a favour
(though Thumper would not share with us the truth about how
he had earned the favour).

Apart from the money they collected from the entrance fees
Miss Phillips and Mrs Blossom intended to raise money for the
Bilbury Village School Cottage Rebuilding Fund by charging
visitors 10 pence to enter the marquee, (which Dr Brownlow
had had erected on his front lawn); by selling them pots of tea
and plates of scones liberally laced with clotted cream and
generous dollops of strawberry jam and, at the end of the show,
by auctioning all the entries.

I read through the impressive list of categories that villagers
could enter:

FRUIT and VEGETABLES

potato (white)	*6 in a bowl*
potato (red)	*6 in a bowl*
cabbage	*1 on a plate*
peas (in the pod)	*12 on a plate*
peas (out of the pod)	*from 12 pods in dish*

cauliflower	*1 on a plate*
broad beans	*from 12 pods in a dish*
runner beans	*6 on a plate*
onion	*1 on a plate*
onions	*12 on a string*
turnip	*1 on a plate*
beetroot	*3 on a plate*
carrot	*6 on a plate*
parsnip	*1 on a plate*
radish	*12 on a plate*
celery	*1 head on plate*
melon	*1 on a plate*
tomato	*6 on a plate*
cucumber	*1 on a plate*
lettuce	*1 on a plate*
sweetcorn	*3 cobs on a plate*
parsley	*bunch on a plate*
cress	*bunch on a plate*
water cress	*bunch on a plate*
marrow	*1 on a plate*
pumpkin	*1 on a plate*
rhubarb	*6 sticks on a plate*
apple	*6 on a plate*
pear	*6 on a plate*
strawberries (cultivated)	*a dish*
strawberries (wild)	*a dish*
gooseberries	*a dish*
blackcurrants	*a dish*
redcurrants	*a dish*
cherries	*a dish*
logan berries	*a dish*
raspberries	*a dish*
blackberries	*a dish*

FLOWERS

potted plant
cactus in a pot
fuchsias in a pot
vase of 12 poppies

vase containing 2 each of 6 different annuals
vase containing 2 each of 6 different perennials
vase of 12 chrysanthemums
vase containing a single rose
vase of 12 red roses
vase of 12 white roses
vase of 12 roses (not red or white)
vase of 12 stems of sweet peas
vase of 12 dahlias
hanging basket
vase of 3 hydrangea stems
vase of 3 gladioli
flower arrangement
dried flower arrangement

DOMESTIC

pot of strawberry jam
pot of gooseberry jam
pot of blackcurrant jam
pot of blackberry jam
pot of blackberry and apple jam
pot of honey (hard)
pot of honey (runny)
pot of lemon curd
pot of marmalade
pot of chutney
jar of pickled onions
jar of mixed pickles
dish of clotted cream
pound of butter
eggs   *12 in a dish*
loaf of bread   *white*
loaf of bread   *brown*
fruit cake
sponge cake (plain)
sponge cake (filled with jam)
sponge cake (filled with cream)
rock cakes   *6 on a plate*
scones   *6 on a plate*

fairy cakes	*6 on a plate*
gingerbread man	
shortbread	*6 pieces on a plate*
fudge	*dish*
knitted article	

MEN

bottle of white wine	
bottle of red wine	
bottle of beer	
neatest bale of hay	
neatest bale of straw	
rock cakes	*6 on a plate*

CHILDREN

oddest shaped vegetable
longest stick of rhubarb
prettiest wild flowers in a jam jar
longest runner bean
biggest strawberry
greatest number of different objects in a matchbox

*   *   *

In addition to the individual prizes there were five small cups, to be awarded to the overall winners of each category and a very splendid looking Bilbury Produce Show Cup which would, so the programme notes made clear, be awarded to the household which scored the greatest number of points in all the different categories and classes. For the purpose of judging the Show Cup winning a first prize in any class was worth three points, a second prize was worth two points and a third prize was worth one point.

Patsy had chosen to enter all the Vegetable and Fruit classes except for the cauliflower and radish classes (our cauliflowers had, for some inexplicable reason, failed to flourish and all our radishes had been eaten by something), all the Flower classes, except for the cactus in a pot and the various rose classes, and all the Domestic classes except for the clotted cream, the home-made butter, the 12 eggs in a dish and the knitted article classes. Under some duress, and with some trepidation, I had agreed to enter the Men's rock cake class and had spent the previous afternoon doing my best to follow the instructions which Patsy had given me. I managed to rescue half a dozen buns that weren't burnt too badly and these I had put on one side as my entry. I tasted one of the rejects and was glad that I didn't have false teeth fitted for I don't think there is any man-made material which could have cut through one of my rock cakes.

It was twelve fifteen when I arrived back at the house and as I walked through the back door into the kitchen I could hardly believe my eyes. Every flat surface in the kitchen was covered with baskets and boxes full of produce which Patsy, Mr Parfitt and Miss Hargreaves had got ready to take to the Show.

We had a quick snack of scrambled eggs on toast for lunch but had to eat without plates because every plate that we owned had been carefully wrapped in newspaper and packed into a cardboard box so that we could use them for displaying our produce. I very nearly got my fingers rapped with the back of a fork when I almost opened Patsy's best looking pot of home-made chutney.

*   *   *

When we arrived at Dr Brownlow's home it looked as if the whole of the village was already there. Although the Produce Show was by far and away the most important part of the event it wasn't the only thing happening. At a meeting of our committee we had decided to hold a proper old fashioned fête alongside the produce show and so Dr Brownlow's grounds were packed with stalls.

But it was the Produce Show in which Patsy and I were most immediately interested. The huge marquee in which the produce would be displayed and judged, and which had been erected on Dr Brownlow's lawn, already looked like a high quality food store.

I parked as close as I could to the back of the marquee and then helped Patsy and Mr Parfitt and Miss Hargreaves carry all our entries into the tent and place them on the correct trestle table. Even using the large wooden tray we had brought with us it took us seven journeys to carry all the stuff from the car to the marquee. When we'd finished I moved the car into a nearby field which was being used as a car park so that some other entrant could get closer to the marquee.

When I got back I bumped into Miss Phillips.

'Where on earth did you find all these trestle tables?' I asked her, after I'd told her how well I thought that she and Mrs Blossom had played in the Revue. Poor Miss Phillips seemed nervous and very slightly harassed but she looked very elegant and distinguished in a long pale blue dress, a dark blue blazer, a pair of navy blue high heeled shoes, single row of pearls and a flamboyant straw hat with bundles of very realistic looking artificial fruit fastened around its rim.

'A friend of Thumper's let us have them,' whispered Miss Phillips. 'Someone from Ilfracombe who owed him a favour,' she added with what I think was intended to be a wink but which ended up looking rather more like a twitch. I don't know why it is but women rarely seem able to wink properly.

'Good old Thumper!' I said.

'Indeed!' agreed Miss Phillips. 'Where would any of us be without him?'

We exchanged gossip about some of the other entries and I truthfully told her how cool and elegant she looked, and she seemed quite pleased about that and even blushed a little and I thought how beautiful she must have been when she was younger and wondered what wonderfully romantic secrets there were hidden away in her past and then I rushed off to help Patsy who was clearly having a good deal of trouble keeping all her white potatoes on a plate.

'I dropped one,' said Patsy, looking glum. 'I think it's probably all bruised.'

'Put the bruised bit where it won't show,' I suggested.

'Oh, I couldn't do that!' said Patsy. 'Anyway,' she added, examining the potato she had dropped, 'I don't know which is the bruised bit.'

'What have we got left to put out?' I asked her. 'Just the jams, the soft fruits and the flowers,' said Patsy, nodding towards the spot where we'd temporarily deposited all our entries. I walked back across with her, picked up a dish full of strawberries and a dish full of blackberries and headed for the soft fruit display tables.

'Psst!'

I turned round and saw someone I recognised but couldn't name standing right behind me. He was about fifty five years old and despite the heat he was wearing a heavy tweed suit, complete with waistcoat and fob watch. He had a large, rather overgrown moustache, the sort of thing that RAF officers used to wear during the Second World War. I had seen him around in the village quite a lot, usually walking a pair of huge Great Danes but I didn't know him well. He kept himself rather to himself and never patronised the Duck and Puddle.

He came a little closer, leant forwards and whispered. 'I say old chap, I don't suppose you've got any spare blackberries have you?' he asked. His breath smelt of beer and onions.

'I'm afraid these aren't for sale,' I said. 'But I think there is a refreshment tent.'

'I don't want to eat the damned things!' snorted the man with the moustache. He leant closer. 'My damned blackberries haven't ripened,' he added. 'It's far too early in the season for blackberries.' He peered at the plateful of blackberries I was holding. 'I suppose you forced yours?'

I suddenly realised that he meant he wanted to buy some of our blackberries to display as his own. I was quite shocked. 'No.' I told him, firmly. 'But we have a walled garden and so most of our soft fruits tend to ripen a couple of weeks earlier than they otherwise would.'

'I'll give you a fiver for them,' he said, reaching into his jacket pocket as though about to take out his wallet.

'But you can't do that!' I said. 'It wouldn't be fair!'

The man with the moustache stared at me as though I was stark raving mad, scowled, muttered something under his breath, and then turned and stalked away without another word. I continued on my way to the soft fruit stall and put Patsy's strawberries and blackberries on display. There were a couple of dozen dishfuls of strawberries already there but only one other dishful of blackberries.

When we had finished displaying the Bilbury Grange entries Mr Parfitt, accompanied by Miss Hargreaves, took our completed entry form along to Miss Phillips and Patsy and I went for a walk around the other stalls. Although I had known that Dr Brownlow had intended to organise a proper fête I was, nevertheless, extremely impressed by what I saw.

There was a stall where you could get rid of your anger by throwing wooden balls at old china; a treasure hunt where you could try to win a bottle of rum by sticking a small wooden stick into a sandpit; a stall where you could pay 5 pence for three sopping sponges and then throw them at the vicar fixed in wooden stocks and a roll a penny stall where, if you were lucky, you could win a goldfish in a small glass bowl.

There were stalls selling massive slabs of sugary, home-made chocolate fudge, huge black lumps of home-made treacle toffee which had to be cracked into chewable sections with the aid of a small hammer and six flavours of home-made ice cream which tasted so creamy and rich that it was difficult to believe that it was made according to anything like the same sort of recipe as is used to produce the mass market variety. When you've once tried home-made ice cream you are spoilt for life.

There was a stall where you could try your luck at darts, a stall where sharpshooters could show off their proficiency with an air rifle and a stall where you could try to win a huge, cuddly, fluffy, pink monkey by tossing jam pot sealing rings onto coat hooks screwed into a board.

The fête wasn't officially open and none of the stalls were ready for business but I hadn't ever seen anything that so closely matched the mental image I had always had of how traditional English village life ought to be.

*   *   *

'Who's that chap with the moustache?' I asked Patchy, a few minutes later. Our local Member of Parliament, The Right Honourable Justin Fitzwalter-Simmons PC,QC,MP and goodness knows what else, was fumbling with his notes and hopefully about to declare the Bilbury Village Produce Show and Fête well and truly open and the mustachioed man who had tried to buy blackberries from me was standing by himself, leaning on a shooting stick. He had a piece of paper in his hand and he was staring at it moodily. Eventually he thrust the piece of paper into his jacket pocket. He looked very cross about something.

253

'That's the Wing Commander,' said Patchy.

'Wing Commander Who?' I asked.

'Haven't the foggiest,' said Patchy. 'He likes people to call him Wing Commander. He probably hasn't got a name. I think his mum probably called him 'Wing Commander' when he was a lad.'

'He tried to buy some blackberries from me,' I said.

Patchy looked at me. 'Did he?'

'I think he was going to show them and pretend that he'd grown them himself.'

'Of course he was!'

Now it was my turn to look at Patchy. 'Why?' I was honestly shocked to think that anyone in Bilbury would be prepared to cheat to win a certificate suitable for framing.

'He wants to beat the Colonel.'

'The Colonel?' I didn't know the Colonel but I knew of him. He was Bilbury's only other retired military man of distinction. He was in his eighties but still stood as erect as a telegraph pole.

'That's the one! He's over there.' Patchy nodded towards the far end of the marquee. I could just see the Colonel standing talking to Mrs Blossom.

'Why does the Wing Commander want to beat the Colonel?'

Patchy looked at me and shrugged. 'I haven't got the faintest idea,' he said. 'But his gardener told me that he was promised a £20 bonus if they won the Cup.'

'Which cup?'

'The Show Cup, you idiot!'

'Crumbs! I wonder if the Colonel knows what's going on?'

Patchy snorted disdainfully. 'Don't you worry about the Colonel,' he said. 'I bet you a bag of truffles to half a pound of acorns that he's been at the same thing himself.'

There was a smattering of polite applause from the far end of the marquee. The Right Honourable Justin Fitzwalter-Simmons PC,QC,MP had successfully managed to open the fête and everyone was looking very relieved. Our local MP was well known for being slightly forgetful and disorganised. A few weeks earlier he had given the members of the local Womens Institute a half day's holiday and had subsequently congratulated the children of a primary school in Lynton on the consistency of their chutney. I had once asked Frank why the electorate still voted for a man who no longer seemed to be in touch with what was going on in the world. Frank had told me that he thought that was exactly why they did vote for him. 'We've probably got the only parliamentary representative who is incorruptible,' he had explained. 'He's too stupid to get involved in any financial jiggery pokery.' I had had to agree that, given the general ability of parliamentary representatives to get into trouble of one sort or another, these were powerful factors in his favour.

'He tried to get me to sell him some chutney!' muttered a voice I recognised instantly.

I turned round. I'd never seen Thumper looking quite so smart. He was wearing a pair of brand new jeans and a freshly ironed lumberjack shirt. He had even combed his hair. 'Who? Fiztwater-Simmons?'

'No, you clot! The Colonel.'

'The Colonel wanted to buy chutney off you?'

'Yes.'

'But why? You don't make chutney do you?'

'No, I don't. But Anne does. And last year her chutney won first prize in the Shirwell, Kentisbury and East Down Produce Shows.'

'See, I was right! They are both at it!' said Patchy.

'It's a pity really,' said Thumper. 'But one of them is bound to win.'

'They're a pair of mean old devils,' said Patchy. 'Mrs Blossom told me that the Wing Commander tried to get out of paying his penny an entry. He said he wanted a discount because he was entering for so many different classes. Do you know he's even got his gardener's five year old to enter the childrens' category so that he can pick up a few extra points there.'

Patchy muttered something under his breath. It didn't sound very complimentary.

'I bet neither of them bought tickets for the Revue,' said Thumper.

We all stood and silently fumed.

'Maybe we could make a few bob out of them after all,' said Thumper thoughtfully.

Patchy and I both looked at him.

'Wait there a minute,' he said, and darted off in the direction of Mrs Blossom who was talking to two of the three judges. Thumper gently touched her arm and when she turned to look at him he whispered into her ear. She excused herself and they moved to a nearby table where Miss Phillips was busy checking entries. The two judges, I didn't recognise them but knew that they had come from villages thirty or forty miles away, carried on talking to one another. Thumper and Mrs Blossom and Miss Phillips spoke for a few moments and then Miss Phillips bent down and took a thick wad of entry forms from out of a large, brown leather bag at her feet. She carefully flicked through the forms, taking out two and handing them to Thumper. She then handed him two sheets from another pile on the table in front of her. Thumper smiled at both Miss Phillips and Mrs Blossom, hesitated and then gave them both a kiss on the cheek and hurried back to where Patchy and I were standing.

'We've got twenty minutes,' he said. 'The third judge telephoned to say that he'd had some trouble with a mare in foal and would be a bit late. Miss Phillips says she'll continue to accept entries right until the judging starts.'

'What have you got there?' Patchy asked him, nodding towards the four pieces of paper he was holding.

'The Wing Commander's entry,' said Thumper, holding up one piece of paper. 'And the Colonel's entry,' he said, holding up a second form.

'What are the other two?' I asked him.

'Complete entry lists – so that we can see which classes they haven't entered yet!'

'Brilliant!' said Patchy, rubbing his hands together. 'Let's get to work!' He took one of the lists from Thumper and started to compare it with the full list of possible categories and classes.

'Hang on a minute,' I said, genuinely puzzled. 'I don't understand. What are we going to do?' Although I've been living in Bilbury for a while I'm still nowhere near as quick as Thumper or Patchy when it comes to plotting a scam.

'We're going to look through these lists and find out which classes these two haven't entered,' explained Thumper.

'And then we're going to sell them the produce they need to enter the classes they haven't entered!' added Patchy.

256

I thought about what they'd said for a moment. 'But that's not right!' I protested, mildly. 'That's cheating!'

'Listen,' said Patchy, 'one of these two will win anyway. They both cheat. And this way we'll make a few bob for the Fund!'

'How?' I asked. I was obviously having one of my really thick days. Sometimes I feel that both Thumper and Patchy must think I am one of the most innocent people in the world. I'm just glad they are friends of mine! After what happened at the Bilbury Village Produce Show I was more than ever convinced that no city huckster or street trader could beat this pair when it comes to working out a way to take a few pounds from a well-heeled mark.

'By selling them what they need!' explained Thumper. 'Ten pounds for a dish full of luscious blackberries!'

'Twenty pounds for a really good marrow!' said Patchy.

'But where are we going to get the stuff from?' I asked.

'You leave that to me,' said Thumper with a wink. 'You two go and see how much you can get those two old reprobates to pay for the produce they haven't got.' He handed me the other two forms.

'What if they spot what we're doing?' I asked. I looked at the forms he had handed me. One of them had 'Wing Commander' written at the top.

'Try and make sure they do,' said Thumper, with a rather sly laugh. 'If they both realise that the other one is cheating they'll be even more eager to buy what they need!' I studied the two lists. The Wing Commander had entered most of the classes (though none of those under the heading CHILDREN) but still needed blackberries, loganberries, a cucumber, a dried flower arrangement, a pot of gooseberry jam, blackcurrant jam and lemon curd, two pots of honey (runny and hard), a pot of marmalade, a jar of pickled onions and a knitted article. 'I'll be behind the marquee with everything they're likely to need in ten minutes,' Thumper added.

And so with my heart beating fast I walked over to where the Wing Commander was standing. Fortunately, he was still alone. 'Do you still want to buy some blackberries?' I asked. I felt sure that I must be blushing bright red.

The Wing Commander glowered at me. 'It's too late.' he said.

'No, it isn't,' I told him. 'One of the judges has been held up. You can still enter them.'

'How much?'

'F-f-f-f..,' I began. 'Ten pounds,' I said. If I was going to get involved in such chicanery I was damned certain I was going to make it pay.

'Ten pounds!' The Wing Commander glared at me and his bushy eyebrows zoomed inwards. I thought how frightening he must have been to those unfortunate men who were under his command.

I said nothing.

'I'll give you five. Not a penny more.'

I didn't say anything at all, but shrugged and started to walk away.

'All right, ten,' said the Wing Commander quickly.

I turned back. 'It's for a good cause,' I told him.

'What?' he demanded.

'The Bilbury Village School Cottage Rebuilding Fund.'

'Oh, that.' He reached into his coat pocket, took out his wallet and removed a ten pound note. 'Where are the blackberries?'

'I can get you the other things you need,' I whispered. I have to admit that I felt a bit like a street trader selling dirty postcards.

'Pardon?'

'The other things you need – marmalade, honey, gooseberry jam – I can get them all for you.'

The Wing Commander stared at me furtively, and leant closer. I could smell tobacco on his breath. 'All of them?'

I nodded. 'Except for the stuff in the Children's Category – you'd need a child to enter that anyway.'

'But including the knitted article?'

'Including the knitted article.' I had no idea where Thumper was going to obtain a knitted article at such short notice but I had absolute faith in his ability to do so. I would have trusted Thumper to have found bright pink water cress, a carrot in the shape of a heart or a full suit of sterling silver armour. 'How much?' The question came out as a growl.

I did a rapid mental calculation. 'I'll let you have them all for a hundred pounds.'

The Wing Commander made a sound like a horse. 'Don't be absurd, man! I'm not paying that sort of money!'

I shrugged and casually looked over to where Patchy and the Colonel were deep in conversation. The Wing Commander's eyes followed mine.

'What the devil is that crooked, good for nothing up to?' he demanded, suspiciously.

'Who?' I asked, innocently. To be honest I thought he was referring to Patchy and I was about to leap to the defence of my friend (though to be honest I very much doubt if he would have argued with the description).

'That Colonel fellow! What's he up to?'

'Much the same as you,' I told him, rather wickedly.

'Damned cheat!' exploded the Wing Commander.

I looked around. No one seemed to have noticed. 'Ssshhhh!' I warned him.

'A hundred pounds you said?'

'Plus the ten pounds for the blackberries,' I added quickly. I was, I confess, particularly pleased with that touch. When I think back to my first scam I think that that was by far my most glorious moment.

The Wing Commander glared at me. He was furious. But he had little option other than to pay up. His face was bright red with anger when he had finished handing me the notes.

'Where is the stuff?' he demanded, as I rammed the money into my jacket pocket.

I looked at my watch. 'Do you know Thumper Robinson?'

'I know what he looks like. Another damned rogue.'

'He's behind the marquee with everything you need.'

The Wing Commander hurried off without so much as a 'thank you'.

And a few minutes later I watched as the Colonel followed him.

Patchy Fogg, now alone, looked across at me, winked and held up a thumb. I winked back. I felt quite pleased with my first venture into hucksterism. It had, I thought, been rather successful.

Patchy had managed to sell the Colonel a turnip, six tomatoes, three sweetcorn cobs, a bunch of watercress, a dish of wild strawberries, a vase containing 12 poppies, a vase containing three gladioli, a dried flower arrangement, a jar of mixed pickles and, most surprisingly of all, perhaps, a jam jar full of wild flowers (for the CHILDREN category) for the princely but slightly uneven total of £76.45.

'It was all he'd got,' said Patchy, rather apologetically. 'I made him empty out all his pockets and he really didn't have a penny left.' To be perfectly honest, I felt quite pleased about the fact that I'd manage to gouge so much out of the Wing Commander. Between us we had 'acquired' £186.45 for the Rebuilding Fund – though, admittedly, this wasn't all profit for Thumper had had to spend £7.40 to acquire the goods we had sold to the Wing Commander and the Colonel. Still, a £179.05 profit was not to be sneezed at!

Minutes later the third judge arrived, looking very hot and flustered, and after he had had a quick cup of tea the judging and the tension began in earnest.

Mr Parfitt was too excited to go far from the marquee, though he wasn't allowed to stay inside. He said he simply couldn't bear the idea of being anywhere else while the judging went on and so he simply stood outside and watched through the open doorway as the potatoes, and the beans and the carrots he had grown with such loving care and attention were subjected to close scrutiny. Patsy and I both pretended that we weren't particularly bothered about winning any certificates, though I felt sure that all her jams and cakes would win their categories. We had only entered to please Mrs Blossom and Miss Phillips, and to do our bit for the village, but for Mr Parfitt's sake, we both hoped that we managed to get one or two certificates. We thought that our soft fruit was especially good and probably our best bet for winning a certificate or two.

We had grown our vegetables and our fruit under quite a handicap since we didn't use any inorganic fertilisers or chemical insecticides. Instead of using sprays and powders we had relied entirely upon natural fertilisers: manure and straw from the sheeps' stable, kitchen compost and the rather pungent concoction which we made, according to the recipe given to us by Patsy's father, and by soaking armfuls of nettles in an old tin bath for several months. As a result our vegetables and fruit weren't quite as perfectly formed as those which had been grown with artificial aids.

We weren't sure whether the judges would take this fact into account when comparing our produce with that which had been grown with the aid of chemicals, but in the hope that it might perhaps make a small amount of difference Mr Parfitt had carefully written 'organically grown' at the bottom of all our labels.

I didn't much mind whether the judges took any notice or not; I much preferred the taste of naturally grown food and I very much enjoyed knowing that the food I was eating had not been contaminated by possible poisons made far away in factories in Birmingham, Chicago or Hamburg.

By now the fête accompanying the Produce Show was in full swing and the stalls all seemed to be doing a roaring trade. Everywhere you looked people were licking ice creams, chewing fudge and crunching brittle treacle toffee. I couldn't help thinking that a few dentists would probably notice a strong uplift in their business as a result of our village fête. Small children were walking around with balloons clutched in their fists and older children were carrying goldfish in bowls and huge, colourful stuffed toys. Mothers were being harassed and fathers, having emptied their wallets, were now emptying their pockets of loose change. Everyone was having a wonderful time.

Patsy and I bought ice creams and sat on a bench and watched this colourful and ever moving carnival unfolding before our eyes.

* * *

The minute the judging was over Mrs Blossom took down the green ribbon which she had tied across the doorway of the marquee. The removal of the ribbon was a sign that exhibitors, friends and members of the public were once again allowed to enter. Some exhibitors were very casual about it all but Patsy and I stood up the moment we saw the green ribbon being removed. Despite my earlier calmness I realised that I found these last few moments just as exciting and as nerve wracking as waiting for examination results or reviews of my first book.

Even though we had been quite quick off the mark there was a big queue to get back to the marquee and by the time we got in Mr Parfitt had been round half of the exhibits and had an enormous smile on his face. Patsy, who was holding my hand, squeezed my fingers as he approached.

'I've counted three firsts, five seconds and three thirds in the vegetable and fruit category!' said Mr Parfitt, clearly thrilled by this success. 'We've done much better than I dared hope. Our potatoes got first prize in both classes!'

'Congratulations!' I said, reaching out and shaking him by the hand. Mr Parfitt mumbled something about it being our success (meaning Patsy's and mine) but Patsy and I made it clear that we both regarded the vegetable and fruit category as being entirely his responsibility. Miss Hargreaves was beaming as broadly as if she was the one who had won.

When we'd finished congratulating Mr Parfitt (and I had never seen him look so happy) Patsy and I walked around the rest of the marquee to see how our other entries had got on. I was delighted to see that Patsy's jams and cakes had won her no less than four first prizes, two second prizes and two third prizes. We hadn't done quite as well with our flowers but we had won a first for our sweet peas and a second prize for our mixed perennials. And Patsy's dried flower arrangement had won her a second prize too!

Most surprising of all was the discovery that, much to my astonishment and delight, my rock cakes had won third prize! I could hardly believe it! It was my first ever cooking adventure and it had been a success. My feelings of delight were only very slightly modified when I discovered that there had only been four entries for this particular competition. Nothing could change the fact that I now had a certificate (suitable for framing) proving that I was a prize winning chef! I wasn't in the slightest bit bothered by the knowledge that two men in Bilbury could make better rock cakes than I could. All I was interested in was the much more fascinating fact that somewhere in Bilbury there was someone whose rock cakes weren't as good as mine!

*   *   *

We had just completed our tour of the marquee when we heard Mrs Blossom's voice announcing that the winners of the five separate category Cups (for the best overall scores in each of the five categories: fruit and vegetables; flowers; domestic; men and children), and the absolutely magnificent Bilbury Village Produce Show Cup for the household obtaining the greatest number of points, were about to be announced. The marquee was packed; everyone in the village seemed to be there. Since only villagers or people living in the area stood a chance of winning any of the prizes the visiting holiday-makers were still roaming around outside, enjoying the sunshine, the ice cream and the entertainments.

Someone had fixed up a not terribly clear loudspeaker system which only seemed to amplify every other word. Because she was conscious of this fault Mrs Blossom raised her voice to compensate for the occasional lack of loudspeaker support. Unfortunately, the fault in the system meant that all that happened was that the loud, and perfectly audible words became so loud that they were distorted, and therefore inaudible, while the unamplified, and therefore rather inaudible, words remained largely inaudible.

Mr Parfitt, Miss Hargreaves, Patsy and I stood together near the back of the marquee and tried to work out what Mrs Blossom was saying. Everyone else seemed to be having exactly the same problem and so the people who were standing at the front were, in response to constant tapping on their shoulders, turning round every few seconds to pass on the latest bit of news. In this way the news spread slowly around the assembled villagers; the words arriving at the back of the tent some thirty seconds after they had left Mrs Blossom's lips.

Young Nathaniel Bishop won the Children's category, and to absolutely no one's surprise our sheep farming neighbour Colin Jackson won the Men's category. Colin would have been entitled to a recount if he hadn't won the cup in this category for he had won first prize certificates for his red wine, his white wine, his beer, his hay and his straw! (His rock cakes had taken second place). The cup for the greatest number of points in the Flower section was awarded to a highly embarrassed Miss Phillips who tried to turn the cup down but was eventually persuaded to accept what was rightfully hers. The cup for the highest score in the Domestic category was won by Mrs Colin Jackson and although I naturally felt that Patsy should have won I had to admit that Mrs Jackson was not an unworthy winner.

Mrs Blossom had delayed announcing the winner of the Fruit and Vegetable Category until last since it was generally agreed that, of the five categories, this was the blue ribbon event.

When the woman standing in front of me turned round to tell me that she had been told that Mrs Blossom had announced that Bilbury Grange had won this category I didn't really take in what I had been told. I had never expected to hear that we had won anything so important. Indeed, the news was so unexpected that I had turned around and passed it onto the person standing behind me before I realised that it was us – or rather Mr Parfitt – who had won!

When the news finally sank in Mr Parfitt's face was taken over by a huge grin. I honestly do not think I had ever seen anyone look quite so happy. I had the shock of my life when Miss Hargreaves turned, put her arms around him and gave him a big kiss.

But that wasn't the biggest shock.

I think that most of us in the marquee had assumed that either the Wing Commander or the Colonel would have assuredly won the Bilbury Village Produce Show Cup. Even those innocent Bilbury residents who didn't know the amount of cheating that had gone on behind the scenes had assumed that either one or the other of these two former military men would be driving home with the big Cup proudly displayed on the back seat.

Neither of them won.

And when the woman in front turned round and told me that Mrs Blossom had announced that Bilbury Grange had won the big Cup I really didn't believe her. At first I thought I had misheard. Then I thought it was a joke.

But I hadn't misheard. And it wasn't a joke.

We had won.

Apart from a small box of chocolates, which I was awarded for coming second in a church raffle, I had never won anything before. And I'd never felt quite as proud before either. I hugged and kissed Patsy. I shook hands with Mr Parfitt (who had, I think, just the beginnings of a tear in the corner of one eye) and I accepted a bone-crushing hug from Miss Hargreaves, who seemed to tear herself away from Mr Parfitt with some reluctance and whose cheeks were quite definitely very wet with tears. It was all made especially joyous by the fact that apart from the Wing Commander and the Colonel (who both stalked out of the marquee looking very ill tempered) not one person in the village seemed to begrudge us our small success.

Our win made it quite certain that neither Patsy nor I would ever forget the first Bilbury Revels.

*　　*　　*

CHAPTER TWENTY

The unofficial 'put a roof over Miss Hargreaves' head' action committee, more formally known as the Bilbury Village School Cottage Rebuilding Fund, met for the final time a week later at the Duck and Puddle. There were, as usual, the six of us present: myself, Gilly Parsons, Kay McBride, Peter Marshall, Thumper Robinson and Dr Brownlow.

'How's the repair work going, Thumper?' asked Dr Brownlow, our unofficial chairman, when we had all settled ourselves down with our chosen intoxicants.

'Finished!' said Thumper, with some considerable pride. He leant back in his chair and grinned with the solid confidence of a man who knows that he has done a good job. 'Miss Hargreaves can move back in whenever she likes. We put the last coat of paint on this afternoon!'

'That's wonderful news!' said Dr Brownlow. He paused, and his voice fell to a whisper. 'What's the final bill?'

Thumper took a grubby piece of paper out of the back pocket of his jeans, put it down on the table in front of him, smoothed it out and started to read out the figures for timber, paint, labour and other costs.

'Just the total will do, Thumper!' said Dr Brownlow, putting his hand across his eyes, as though he felt the need to hide his face at the moment of truth.

'£9,276.84,' said Thumper, reading out the bottom line.

Slowly, Dr Brownlow took his hand away from his eyes. Gradually a smile appeared. 'And that's everything? Absolutely everything?'

'Every last nail and drop of paint,' said Thumper proudly.

'No hidden labour charges? No timber merchant in Taunton is going to be sending us a bill in six months time?'

'No. That's the lot. And we put a lavatory in for that too.'
Thumper looked at me and grinned. It had been hard work persuading Miss Hargreaves to accept an indoor lavatory.

'That's pretty good, Thumper!' said Dr Brownlow. He looked around the table at the rest of us. We all nodded our agreement. It was very good. Thumper and the others had virtually rebuilt School Cottage. A commercial builder would have undoubtedly charged half as much again.

'Can we pay it?' Dr Brownlow asked Peter Marshall, our treasurer. We had all taken part in numerous events but we had no idea how successful our fund raising had been. We'd been too busy raising money to stop and count it. Just about everyone (apart from the Wing Commander and the Colonel who had, nevertheless, unwittingly made their own contributions) had done something. The Bilbury Morris Dancers had danced their way round North Devon. Miss Venables had given her illustrated talk on the ferns of North Devon seven times. Mrs Oliphant had held an exhibition of her oil paintings in the public library in Barnstaple. Elijah Huttlecombe had been persuaded to give holiday-makers two talks and a short demonstration on charcoal making. We had played four cricket matches (we had lost all four but had acquitted ourselves admirably) and the Bilbury Revue had been performed a total of six times (including one matinée).

Peter shook his head and sucked air in through his broken front teeth. The rest of us waited in an increasingly gloomy silence.

'Come on, Peter!' shouted Gilly, unable to bear the tension any longer.

Slowly, very slowly, a smile spread across Peter's face. 'We raised a total of £10,041.39,' he announced with considerable pride.

If I hadn't been there I wouldn't have believed that six people could have made as much noise. Gilly and Kay both kissed Thumper, and then they both kissed Peter, Dr Brownlow and myself. We all shook hands and congratulated one another.

'Well!' said Dr Brownlow, at last. 'I reckon that means we've got a surplus of . . . '

'£764.55,' said Peter, instantly. 'Minus £24.53 for the paint.'

'Paint?'

'The pink paint. The paint for the cottages around the village green.'

'That all washed off!'

'It wasn't my fault!'

'Yes it was. You can't charge for that.'

'What are we going to do with the money?' asked Gilly.

Peter, who seemed to have accepted Dr Brownlow's ruling on the paint uncharacteristically easily, coughed.

We all looked at him.

'I just wondered,' he said, hesitantly. 'Are we going to have a Revels again next year?' he asked.

We all looked at him.

'Oh no, I don't think so,' said Dr Brownlow. 'It was all a bit too exhausting. And my front lawn is going to take months to recover. We only needed to organise the Revels to raise money for School Cottage.'

'But we could do with renovating the village hall!' said Kay.

'Especially if we're going to perform another Revue!' said Gilly. 'We need better changing facilities.'

'And a proper kitchen!' said Kay.

There was a simple flaw in this argument. Since if we didn't hold a Revels we wouldn't need a Revue, Gilly's claim that we needed better changing facilities if we were going to hold another Revue was hardly an argument in favour of organising another Revels. But I kept quiet.

'It's just that I thought that if we were going to organise another Revels then we could keep the surplus from this year as a sort of float for next year,' said Peter. 'To pay for better costumes ... '

'... and some decent cricket bats!' said Thumper.

'Good thinking, Thumper!' said Dr Brownlow. 'We need some proper bats, Peter. Not that cheap rubbish.'

'And pads!' I added. 'Two for each batsman!'

'And pads!' nodded Dr Brownlow.

And so it was agreed. The Bilbury Revels would become an annual event.

*　　*　　*

'Do you know when Miss Hargreaves is moving back into School Cottage?' Thumper asked me as we got up from the table an hour or two later. 'I'll give you a hand with her stuff, if you like.'

The others, who had heard his question, looked and waited.

'I think she wants to wait until next Saturday afternoon,' I said.

'Oh!' said Thumper, clearly surprised. 'I thought she wanted to move back in as soon as she could.'

'She did. She does,' I said. 'But she wants to go there as Mrs Parfitt.'

Everyone stared at me.

'Close your mouth, Thumper!' I said. 'You look daft.'

'Say that again,' said Gilly.

'Close your mouth, Thumper ... ' I began.

'Not that. The bit before,' said Gilly, impatiently.

'When she goes back to School Cottage she wants to go as Mrs Parfitt so she's waiting until next Saturday afternoon,' I explained.

No one understood.

'She's getting married,' I said. 'To Mr Parfitt, our gardener.'

If I had told them that she had entered the world figure skating championships they couldn't have looked more amazed.

'That's marvellous news!' said Kay, at last, when the news had finally sunk in.

'Miss Hargreaves getting married!' muttered Thumper. 'Well, I never!'

'Are we invited?' asked Gilly.

'Oh yes,' I said. 'I almost forgot.' I reached into my inside jacket pocket and took out a small bundle of white envelopes. 'She asked me to give you one of these each.'

'You ...!' cried Kay. 'How could you forget something like this!'

'Well, I don't know about the rest of you, but I'm thrilled with the news!' said Dr Brownlow.

'Absolutely delighted!' said Gilly.

'And without Mr Parfitt looking after your garden I'll stand a decent chance of winning the Show Cup next year!' Dr Brownlow said to me, rubbing his hands with glee.

I shook my head. 'Sorry to disappoint you, doctor,' I said. 'But Mr Parfitt is still going to look after the garden for us.'

Dr Brownlow tried to look disappointed but was too happy to succeed.

'Where are they holding the wedding party?' asked Kay.

'I don't know that there is going to be a wedding party,' I said.

'Oh, they've got to have a party!' said Gilly.

'Compulsory! said Thumper firmly.

I left the five of them planning the celebration party for Mr Parfitt and Miss Hargreaves. I wanted to get back to Bilbury Grange and do some more work on the book I was writing. I found that living in Bilbury was a constant inspiration.

* * *

Also Published by Chilton Designs

THE BILBURY CHRONICLES
Vernon Coleman

The first in a series of novels describing the adventures (and misadventures) of a young doctor who enters general practice as the assistant to an elderly and rather eccentric doctor in North Devon.

When he arrives in Bilbury, a small village on the edge of Exmoor, the young doctor doesn't realise how much he has to learn. And he soon discovers the true extent of his ignorance when he meets his patients.

There's Anne Thwaites who gives birth to her first baby in a field; Thumper Robinson who knows a few tricks that aren't in any textbook and Mike Trickle, a TV quiz show host who causes great excitement when he buys a house in the village.

Then there's elderly Dr Brownlow himself who lives in a house that looks like a castle, drives an old Rolls Royce and patches his stethoscope with a bicycle inner tube repair kit; Frank the inebriate landlord of the Duck and Puddle and Peter who runs the local taxi, delivers the mail and works as the local undertaker.

There's Miss Johnson, the receptionist with a look that can curdle milk; Mrs Wilson the buxom district nurse and Len her husband who is the local policeman with an embarrassing secret.

'A delightful read. I was entranced for hours.'
Miss S, Devon

'I loved this book. Please send two more copies as soon as possible.'
Mrs S, Nottingham

'Wonderful. One of the best novels I've ever read.'
Mr T, Leamington Spa

'I enjoyed "The Bilbury Chronicles" more than any other book

I've read for years. I am very much looking forward to the sequel.
Mrs G. Sunderland

ISBN 0 9503527 5 6   230 pages   £12.99

BILBURY GRANGE
Vernon Coleman

The sequel to The Bilbury Chronicles. All the books in the Bilbury series can be read and enjoyed independently.

ISBN 0 9503527 7 2   247 pages   £12.99

THE VILLAGE CRICKET TOUR
Vernon Coleman

A novel describing the adventures and mishaps of a team of cricketers who spend two weeks of their summer holidays on a cricket tour of the West Country, and who make up in enthusiasm for what they may lack in skill.

'If anyone ever manages to bottle the essence of village cricket he will very quickly scale the dizzy heights of personal fortune. In the meantime we read and write about it in the pursuit of understanding. Seminal reading here includes de Selincourt and Blunden and should now embrace Vernon Coleman's latest offering, a whimsical piece about the peregrinations of a village team on its summer tour ... all the characters are here, woven together by a raft of anecdotes and reminiscences and a travelogue of some of the most picturesque spots in the south west.'
The Cricketer

'Describes in hilarious fashion the triumphs and disasters of a Midlands team's tour of the West Country and there is not a little of Jerome K.Jerome in Mr Coleman's style.'
Worcester Evening News

'I enjoyed it immensely. He has succeeded in writing a book that will entertain, a book that will amuse and warm the cockles of tired hearts. And what a change it makes from the wearisome

cluckings of the current crop of cricket books with their grinding pomposity and, in many cases, their staggering lack of craftsmanship and originality.'
Punch

'A delightful book which also highlights some of the most spectacular scenery in Cornwall and Devon.'
The Cornishman

'Vernon Coleman is obviously a man who has enjoyed his cricket and over the years has committed to memory the many characters he has seen playing the game. He weaves them into the story as he charts the progress of his team's tour of Devon and Cornwall. The tale captures club cricket as everyone imagines it should be.'
Falmouth Packet

'Coleman is a very funny writer. It would be a pity if cricketers were the only people to read this book.'
This England

ISBN 0 9503527 3 X   173 pages   £9.95

THE MAN WHO INHERITED A GOLF COURSE
Vernon Coleman

Trevor Dukinfield, the hero of this delightful novel, is a young and not very successful journalist. Completely out of the blue, Trevor receives a letter informing him that he has inherited a golf course from an uncle he never knew he had.

You might think that this would have been welcomed by Trevor as extraordinarily good news. But then Trevor discovers the two slight snags which accompany his good fortune.

First, in order to keep the golf club under the rules of his uncle's will, Trevor has to play a round of golf in less than 100 strokes. Second, he has to find a partner to help him win a match play competition against two bankers.

Not particularly stringent conditions you might think – except that Trevor has never played a round of golf in his life, unless you count an hour spent on a crazy golf course in Weston-super-Mare.

"Another witty volume from the doctor who has successfully turned from medical topics to novel writing. The ... mix of anecdotes and moments of sheer farce make for an absorbing read"
Lancashire Evening Telegraph

"... another delightful and amusing story. I rate this one as the best of his twelve novels so far. His fans will lap it up."
Sunday Independent

ISBN 0 9503527 9 9   237 pages   £12.95.

MRS CALDICOT'S CABBAGE WAR
Vernon Coleman

Thelma Caldicot was married to her husband for thirty dull and boring years. Then, completely out of the blue, two police officers arrived at Thelma's house to break some sad news. That afternoon, while her husband was at a cricket match, she had become a widow.

Her ambitious son Derek soon appears on the scene, determined to interfere in every aspect of her mother's life. After thirty years of being dominated by her husband, it looks as though Thelma's son is about to step into his shoes and continue the good work.

But then something happens to Thelma Caldicot. After years of being pushed around and told what to do, she takes charge of her life and fights back.

Mrs Caldicot's Cabbage War is the poignant, warm and often funny story of an ordinary woman who finally decides to stand up for herself.

'... a splendid, relaxing read ...'
Sunday Independent

ISBN 0 9503527 8 0   150 pages   £9.95